Saint Peter's University Library
Withdrawn

Saint Peter's University Library
Withdrawn

ANALYTICAL TOPOLOGY

The New University Mathematics Series

Editor:
Professor E. T. DAVIES
Department of Mathematics, University of Southampton

This series is intended for readers whose main interest is in mathematics, or who need the methods of mathematics in the study of science and technology. Some of the books will provide a sound treatment of topics essential in any mathematical training, while other, more advanced, volumes will be suitable as preliminary reading for research in the field covered. New titles will be added from time to time.

BAINES and WILLIAMS: *Vector Field Theory*
BONSALL, BROWN and PAGE: *Introduction to General Analysis*
BURGESS: *Analytical Topology*
COOPER: *Functions of Real Variables*
CURLE and DAVIES: *Modern Fluid Dynamics*
PORTEOUS: *Topological Geometry*
RUND: *The Hamilton-Jacobi Theory in the Calculus of Variations*
SAMET: *Numerical Analysis*
SMITH: *Laplace Transform Theory*
SMITH: *Partial Differential Equations*
SPAIN: *Vector Analysis*

ANALYTICAL TOPOLOGY

D. C. J. BURGESS

Department of Pure Mathematics
The Queen's University, Belfast

D. VAN NOSTRAND COMPANY LTD
LONDON

TORONTO NEW YORK
PRINCETON, NEW JERSEY

D. VAN NOSTRAND COMPANY LTD.
358 Kensington High Street, London, W. 14

D. VAN NOSTRAND COMPANY INC.
120 Alexander Street, Princeton, New Jersey
24 West 40th Street, New York 18

D. VAN NOSTRAND COMPANY (CANADA) LTD.
25 Hollinger Road, Toronto 16

Library of Congress Catalogue Card No. 66-13028

Set in Monophoto and Printed by
J. W. Arrowsmith Ltd., Bristol, England

Preface

The present work, divided into three principal parts I, II and III, is intended to provide a full year's course in analytical topology for final year undergraduate honours students.

The aim of Sections 1.1 and 1.2, which deal respectively with set and function theory, is confined to giving a brief account of the terminology, notation, and results to be used in the sequel; it is assumed here that the reader already has some familiarity with the subject in question, and, for the most part, proofs are omitted or references are given. Section 1.3 treats of elementary topics in the theory of partially-ordered sets, as a preparation for the considerable use later made of these, both in facilitating general arguments and in furnishing examples.

The remaining parts, II and III, are devoted to a study of metric and topological spaces; both topics incorporate an extension to a more general context, of familiar notions of real analysis such as cluster points, continuous functions and the like. The first of these extension procedures, dealt with in Part II, is based on the idea of a **metric** on a given abstract set S; that is, a 'distance function' ρ is supposed defined on S, possessing the characteristic properties (notably the triangle-inequality: $\rho(x,z) \leqslant \rho(x,y) + \rho(y,z)$) of *distance* in ordinary two or three-dimensional space. Then S, together with such a metric ρ, is said to form a *metric space.* A *neighbourhood* of any element x of S is defined in terms of ρ; any subset X of S is then said to be *open* whenever X is a neighbourhood of each of its members. It is easily shown that the collection $\mathscr{G}$ of all these *open* sets has the properties:

I. A subset Y of S is a neighbourhood of an element x of S if, and only if, there exists a member G of $\mathscr{G}$ such that x belongs to G, and G is contained in Y.

II. (a) S itself, and the null set, both belong to $\mathscr{G}$;
(b) the union of any family of members of $\mathscr{G}$ belongs to $\mathscr{G}$;
(c) the intersection of any finite sequence of members of $\mathscr{G}$ belongs to $\mathscr{G}$.

Property I here provides a characterization of the neighbourhoods of a given element by means of $\mathscr{G}$, and with its help, a large part of the concepts introduced in the course of Part II can be defined ultimately in terms of $\mathscr{G}$ alone, *without* referring back in each case to the metric ρ. This, in turn, will enable many of those results on metric spaces which involve these ideas, to be derivable solely from the properties of $\mathscr{G}$ given in II above. In the text, such definitions and theorems (including, occasionally, parts of theorems) are distinguished from the rest by an asterisk*. Part II is actually divided into two chapters, dealing respectively with the general metric space and particular types of metric space.

The above considerations suggest that a wider generalization of real analysis than that hitherto obtained might be achieved by basing it on the idea of a given *collection* $\mathscr{G}$ *of open sets*. This is dealt with in Part III, which comprises two chapters. Given an abstract set S, it is first of all *postulated* (in the first part of Chapter 4) that there is given a collection $\mathscr{G}$ of subsets of S, which possesses properties (a), (b), (c) of II above; this yields a so-called **topological** space of which the members of $\mathscr{G}$ are said to form the 'open sets'. Result I above then suggests that a *neighbourhood* of an element x of S should in this context be *defined* as a set Y containing some member G of $\mathscr{G}$ to which x belongs. All the *starred* definitions and theorems of Part II will then necessarily be valid for any *topological* space.

Chapter 4 also contains an account of two equally general alternative procedures for the definition of a topological space, together with a comprehensive set of examples designed to show how 'unstarred' properties of metric spaces actually cease to hold in an arbitrary topological space. The following chapter deals with the *separation axioms*, which comprise a succession of progressively stronger conditions which may be imposed on a topological space in order that many of these unstarred properties (lost in the generalization from a metric to a topological space) may be recovered. Finally, in Section 5.5, conditions are established which can be imposed on a topological space in order that it may be metrizable, that is, so that the defining collection $\mathscr{G}$ of 'open sets' can be obtained (as in Part II) from some suitably chosen metric on S.

In the text, 'Ex.' stands for 'Exercise'. An asterisk* affixed to an exercise indicates that it should be treated on the lines of the *starred* theorems. A circle ° affixed to theorem, note, example, etc., indicates that, because of its comparative difficulty or specialized nature, it could be omitted on a first reading.

I am much indebted to Dr. D. B. McAlister for his invaluable help with the proofs, and to Dr. J. McGrotty and Mr. S. D. McCartan for the part they played in checking the typescript. I am grateful to Dr. Chan (of Singapore University) and to Mr. J. B. McCartney for their suggestions. Lastly, I must acknowledge my appreciation of the constant help and encouragement given by my mother in the preparation of this text.

List of Special Symbols

$\subseteq$	is contained in
$\supseteq$	contains
$\subset$	is properly contained in
$\in$	belongs to
ω	does not belong to
(x)	Set containing x only
$(x,y, \ldots w)$	Set whose members are: $x,y,z, \ldots w,$
$\varnothing$	Null (= empty) set
$[a,b]$	Set of x such that $a \leqslant x \leqslant b$
$]a,b[$	Set of x such that $a < x < b$
$[a,b[$	Set of x such that $a \leqslant x < b$
$]a,b]$	Set of x such that $a < x \leqslant b$
$[a,\rightarrow[$	Set of x such that $a \leqslant x$
$]a,\rightarrow[$	Set of x such that $a < x$
$]\leftarrow,a]$	Set of x such that $x \leqslant a$
$]\leftarrow,a[$	Set of x such that $x < a$
J	Set of integers
J^+	Set of positive integers
Q	Set of rationals
R	Set of reals
$P(S)$	Set of all subsets of S
$\{x_i\}, i \in I$	Family indexed by I
$\{x_i\}, i \geqslant 1$	Sequence
$\{x_i\}, 1 \leqslant i \leqslant n,$ *or* $\{x, \ldots x_n\}$	Finite sequence
$\bigcup, \cup$	Union
$\bigcap, \cap$	Intersection
$C_A(X)$ or $C(X)$	Complement of X (relative to A)
$X - Y$	Set of members of X not in Y

$f(X)$	Image of X under f
$f^{-1}(Y)$	Inverse image of Y under f
$f \circ g$	Composite of f,g
f_X	Restriction of f to X
$\prod_{i \in I} X_i$	Cartesian product of $\{X_i\}$, $i \in I$
$\prod_{1 \leqslant i \leqslant n} X_i$ or $X_1 \times \ldots \times X_n$	Cartesian product of $\{X_i\}$, $1 \leqslant i \leqslant n$
Y^n	$Y \times \ldots \times Y$ (to n factors)
Δ_S	Diagonal of $S \times S$
$x\mathscr{R}y$	x bears relation $\mathscr{R}$ to y
$\leqslant, \geqslant$	symbols denoting a quasi-ordering
$(E, \leqslant)$	Quasi-ordered set
$M_E(A)$ or $M(A)$	Set of upper bounds of A (in E)
$L_E(A)$ or $L(A)$	Set of lower bounds of A (in E)
$\bigvee A$	Supremum of A
$\bigwedge A$	Infimum of A
$a_1 \vee a_2 \vee \ldots \vee a_n$	Supremum of $\{a_i\}$, $1 \leqslant i \leqslant n$
$a_1 \wedge a_2 \wedge \ldots \wedge a_n$	Infimum of $\{a_i\}$, $1 \leqslant i \leqslant n$
(S,ρ)	Metric space, with metric ρ
ρ_1,ρ_2,ρ_3	Usually denote special metrics on R^n
$(R^n)_1$	Real Euclidean n-space
H^∞	Real Hilbert space
C	Space of real continuous functions on $[0,1]$
$\langle S,\rho \rangle$	Pseudo-metric space
$D(X)$	Diameter of X
$\rho(X,Y)$	Distance between X,Y
$[S,v]$	Normed vector space
$\langle x,y \rangle$	Segment joining x,y
$N_\varepsilon^\rho(x)$ or $N_\varepsilon(x)$	ε-neighbourhood of x (w.r.t.ρ)
$S_\varepsilon(x)$	Set of y with $\rho(x,y) \leqslant \varepsilon$
$\mathscr{N}_\rho(x)$ or $\mathscr{N}(x)$	Set of neighbourhoods of x (w.r.t.ρ)
$\mathscr{G}_\rho$ or $\mathscr{G}$	Set of open sets (w.r.t.ρ)
${}^\rho X'$ or X'	Derived set of X (w.r.t.ρ)
${}^\rho \overline{X}$ or $\overline{X}$	Closure of X (w.r.t.ρ)
${}^\rho X^\circ$ or X°	Interior of X (w.r.t.ρ)
$\mathscr{F}_\rho$ or $\mathscr{F}$	Set of closed sets (w.r.t.ρ)
$(\mathscr{G}_\rho)_\delta$ or $\mathscr{G}_\delta$	Set of G_δ-subsets (w.r.t.ρ)
$(\mathscr{F}_\rho)_\sigma$ or $\mathscr{F}_\sigma$	Set of F_σ-subsets (w.r.t.ρ)
${}^\rho E(X)$ or $E(X)$	Exterior of X (w.r.t.ρ)
${}^\rho \mathrm{Fr}(X)$ or $\mathrm{Fr}(X)$	Frontier of X (w.r.t.ρ)

$x_i \underset{\rho}{\to} x$ or $x_i \to x$	$\{x_i\}$, $i \geqslant 1$, converges to x (w.r.t.ρ)
$\rho \equiv \rho'$	Denotes the equivalence of metrics ρ, ρ'
$\mathscr{G}_{\rho A}$ or $\mathscr{G}_A$	Set of sets, open relative to A
${}^{\rho}X'^{A}$ or X'^{A}	Set of cluster points of X relative to A
${}^{\rho}\overline{X}^{A}$ or $\overline{X}^{A}$	Closure of X relative to A
$\mathscr{F}_{\rho A}$ or $\mathscr{F}_A$	Set of sets, closed relative to A
${}^{\rho}N(X)$ or $N(X)$	Nucleus of X (w.r.t.ρ)
$\|S,\tau\|$	Topological space, with topology τ
$\mathscr{G}^{\tau}$	Set of τ-open sets
$\mathscr{N}^{\tau}(x)$	Set of τ-neighbourhoods of x
X'^{τ}, $\overline{X}^{\tau}$, $X^{o\tau}$, ... etc.	Set of τ-cluster points, τ-closure, τ-interior, ... etc., of X
$\mathscr{F}^{\tau}$	Set of τ-closed sets
τ_I	Discrete topology
τ_0	Trivial topology
$x_i \to x$	$\{x_i\}$, $i \geqslant 1$, τ-converges to x
T_S	Set of all topologies definable on S
τ_A	Relativization of τ to A
τ^E	Intrinsic topology on E
τ^{ρ}	Topology arising from the metric ρ

Contents

Part I

PRELIMINARY THEORY

CHAPTER 1

Sets, Functions and Orderings

1.1 Set Theory

Given a set S, and subsets X,Y of S, write: $X \subseteq Y$ (or, equivalently, $Y \supseteq X$) if each member of X is a member of Y; then X is said to be **contained** in Y, and Y to **contain** X. If $X \subseteq Y$, but $X \neq Y$, write: $X \subset Y$; then X is said to be **properly** contained in Y. Given a member x of S, write: $x \in X$ if x is a member of the subset X of S; otherwise write: $x \,\omega\, X$. The subset of S whose only member is x is denoted by (x); more generally, the subset whose members (finite in number) are $x,y,z,\ldots w$ is denoted by $(x,y,z,\ldots w)$. The empty or null set is denoted by $\varnothing$. It is logically sound to regard $\varnothing$ as contained in *every* non-null subset Y of S, since, for any subset X of S, it is clear that $X \subseteq Y$ if and only if: for each member x of S, the statement: $x \,\omega\, Y$ implies the statement:

$$x \,\omega\, X. \tag{1}$$

But, if X is null, implication (1) holds for any non-null subset Y, since the statement: $x \,\omega\, X$ holds for every element x of S. The collection of all subsets of S (that is, including $\varnothing$) is denoted by $P(S)$.

If with each member i of a non-null set I (not necessarily having members in common with S) there is associated a unique subset X_i of S, then the collection of sets X_i, for i in I, forms a **family** of sets, denoted by: $\{X_i\}$, $i \in I$. Two families $\{X_i\}$, $i \in I$, and $\{Y_k\}$, $k \in K$, are identical *only* if $I = K$ and $X_i = Y_k$ for $i = k$. If $I' \subseteq I$, the family $\{X_i\}$, $i \in I'$, is said to form a **sub-family** of $\{X_i\}$, $i \in I$. If in particular $I = J^+$, the set of positive integers, a corresponding family is called a **sequence** of sets, denoted by $\{X_i\}$, $i \geqslant 1$; if I is a non-null finite subset of J^+, such a family is called a **finite** sequence; if, for example, I contains the first n

integers, this is written as: $\{X_i\}$, $1 \leqslant i \leqslant n$. The **union** of an arbitrary family $\{X_i\}$, $i \in I$, of subsets of S is denoted by $\bigcup_{i \in I} X_i$ or, more usually, by $\bigcup_i X_i$, and is defined as follows: given x in S, $x \in \bigcup_i X_i$ if and only if there exists a member i of I (dependent on the choice of x) such that $x \in X_i$. The union of a sequence $\{X_i\}$, $i \geqslant 1$, is denoted by $\bigcup_{i \geqslant 1} X_i$ and that of a finite sequence by $\bigcup_{1 \leqslant i \leqslant n} X_i$ or by: $X_1 \cup X_2 \cup \ldots \cup X_n$. The **intersection** of a family $\{X_i\}$, $i \in I$, is denoted by $\bigcap_{i \in I} X_i$ or $\bigcap_i X_i$ and is defined as follows: given x in S, $x \in \bigcap_i X_i$ if and only if $x \in X_i$ for every i in I. An obvious notation is employed to denote the intersection of a sequence or finite sequence of sets.

Given $X \subseteq A \subseteq S$, that subset of S which contains those members of A which are *not* in X is called the **complement** of X relative to A and is denoted by $C_A(X)$; where no ambiguity is likely to arise, $C_S(X)$ is written simply as $C(X)$ and is called simply the complement of X.

Properties of the union and intersection of a family of sets are collected, without proof, in:

THEOREM 1.1 For subsets of a given set S:

(a) $X \cup (Y \cup Z) = (X \cup Y) \cup Z = X \cup Y \cup Z$
$X \cap (Y \cap Z) = (X \cap Y) \cap Z = X \cap Y \cap Z$

(b) $X \cup Y = Y \cup X$; $X \cap Y = Y \cap X$

(c) $X \cup (\bigcap_i X_i) = \bigcap_i (X \cup X_i)$;

$$X \cap (\bigcup_i X_i) = \bigcup_i (X \cap X_i)$$

(d) $X \cap (X \cup Y) = X \cup (X \cap Y) = X$

(e) the following three statements are equivalent: $X \subseteq Y$; $X \cup Y = Y$; $X \cap Y = X$

(f) if $X \cup Y = X \cup Z$, and $X \cap Y = X \cap Z$, then $Y = Z$

(g) $C_A(X \cap A) = A \cap C_S(X)$

(h) for $X \subseteq A$: $X \cup C_A(X) = A$; $X \cap C_A(X) = \varnothing$

(i) for $X_i \subseteq A$: $C_A(\bigcup_i X_i) = \bigcap_i (C_A(X_i))$

$$C_A(\bigcap_i X_i) = \bigcup_i (C_A(X_i)).$$

Note 1 (I) It follows from (f), (h) above that, if $X \subseteq A$, then

$C_A(X)$ is the only subset Y of S such that $X \cup Y = A$ and $X \cap Y = \emptyset$.

(II) If X,Y are both contained in A, it follows from the above (using (g)) that $X \cap C_A(Y) = (X \cap A) \cap C_S(Y) = X \cap C_S(Y)$; that is, the expression $X \cap C_A(Y)$ is independent of the choice of A (as long as it contains X and Y), and is often denoted by $X - Y$.

DEFINITION 1 If $A \subseteq S$, then a family $\{X_i\}$, $i \in I$, of subsets of S such that $A \subseteq \bigcup_i X_i$ is said to form a **covering** of A. If $\{X_i\}$, $i \in I$, is a covering of A, any subfamily with this property is said to be a **subcovering** (of A).

DEFINITION 2 A family $\{X_i\}$, $i \in I$, of subsets of S is said to possess the **finite intersection property** if for each finite subset $(i_1, i_2, \ldots, i_n)$ of I, $\bigcap_{1 \leqslant r \leqslant n} X_{i_r} \neq \emptyset$.

Exercises for Solution

1. If X,Y,Z are subsets of S, show, from Theorem 1.1, that:
(a) $X \cap (Y - Z) = (X \cap Y) - (X \cap Z)$,
(b) $C(X - Y) = Y \cup C(X)$,
(c) $(X - Y) \cup (X - Z) = X - (Y \cap Z)$,
(d) $(X - Z) \cup (Y - Z) = (X \cup Y) - Z$,
(e) $(X - Y) \cup (Y - X) = (X \cup Y) - (X \cap Y)$,
(f) $X - (X - Y) = X \cap Y$.

2. If $A \subseteq S$, and the families $\mathscr{X} \equiv \{X_i\}$, $i \in I$, $\mathscr{Y} \equiv \{Y_k\}$, $k \in K$, of subsets of S, are coverings of A, then $\mathscr{Y}$ is said to be **finer** than $\mathscr{X}$ if, for each k in K, $\exists\, i$ in I (dependent on the choice of k) such that $Y_k \subseteq X_i$.

(i) Show that if $\mathscr{X},\mathscr{Y}$ are *partitions* of A (see Example 1.3.1 on page 11) then a necessary condition for $\mathscr{Y}$ to be finer than $\mathscr{X}$ is:
(α) for each i in I, $\exists\, k$ in K (dependent on the choice of i) such that $Y_k \subseteq X_i$.
(ii) Give an example to show that (α) is not a sufficient condition in (i).
(iii) Give an example to show that (α) need not be satisfied if $\mathscr{X},\mathscr{Y}$ are not partitions of A.

1.2 Function Theory

Given two non-null sets A,B, then, in the most general sense employed here, a **function** (or transformation or mapping) from *A into B* is a correspondence f whereby with each member x of A there is associated a non-null subset of B, called the **value** of

f at x, and denoted by $f(x)$; $f(x)$ is also said to form the **image** of x under f. A is called the **domain** of f, and f is said to be **defined** on A. If $X \subseteq A$, the union of all images $f(x)$, for x in X, is denoted by $f(X)$ and is again called the image of X under f; in particular the image $f(A)$ of the whole domain A of f is called the **range** of f. If $Y \subseteq B$, the **inverse image** of Y under f is defined to be the set of all members x of A such that $f(x) \subseteq Y$, and is denoted by $f^{-1}(Y)$; if $Y = (y)$, $f^{-1}(Y)$ is written as; $f^{-1}(y)$.

Unless otherwise stated, however, it will be assumed here that for each element x in its domain A, $f(x)$ contains *one* element y only; that is (in a simplified notation) $f(x) = y$. Such a function f is said to be **single-valued**. If $f^{-1}(y)$ is non-null for each y in B, f is said to be a function from A *onto* B. A function f from A into B is said to be **(1,1)** if, for each y in $f(A)$, $f^{-1}(y)$ contains exactly one element of A; if in addition $f(A) = B$, the sets A,B are said to be in **(1,1) correspondence** (under f). In the latter case, f^{-1} is similarly a (1,1) function, from B onto A, and is called the **inverse** of the given function f.

Given sets A,B,C, a function f from A into B, and a function g from B into C, then the function k from A into C obtained by writing $k(x) = g(f(x))$ for each x in A is called the **composite** of f,g, and is denoted by $f \circ g$. If D is a further set, and h any function from C into D, then it is easily verified that the functions from A into D denoted by $(f \circ g) \circ h$, $f \circ (g \circ h)$ are identical, and so either can be denoted by $f \circ g \circ h$.

If f is a function from A into B, and X a given non-null subset of A, then the function f_X from X into B such that $f_X(x) = f(x)$ for each x in X is called the **restriction** of f to X.

Example 1.2.1 The notion of a family of subsets of a given set S was introduced in Section 1.1. More generally, given arbitrary non-null sets A, I, a family of members of A is determined if and only if there is given a function f from I into A; the function f determines the family $\{x_i\}$, $i \in I$, where $x_i = f(i)$ for each i in I. If $I' \subseteq I$, the restriction of f to I' determines the subfamily $\{x_i\}$, $i \in I'$.

The notion of function is thus involved in the construction of the so-called **Cartesian Product** of a given family of subsets $\{X_i\}$, $i \in I$, of a non-null set S, which is defined as the set of all families $\{x_i\}$, $i \in I$, of elements of S such that $x_i \in X_i$ for each i in I; that is, the Cartesian Product, denoted by $\prod_{i \in I} X_i$, is determined by the set of all functions f from I into S such that $f(i) \in X_i$ for each i in I.

Given i in I, the function π_i from $X \equiv \prod_i X_i$ *onto* X_i, obtained by writing $\pi_i(x) = x_i$ for each $x \equiv \{x_i\}$ in X, is called the **projection** of X onto X_i. In the case (with which we shall be almost exclusively concerned in the sequel) where I contains the first n integers, the Cartesian product is denoted by $\prod_{1 \leqslant i \leqslant n} X_i$, or by $X_1 \times X_2 \times \ldots \times X_n$. If $X_i = Y$ for each i, this is often written as: Y^n.

Note 2 It is easily seen (HALMOS, Reference [3] p. 59) that the Cartesian Product of a finite sequence $\{X_i\}$, $1 \leqslant i \leqslant n$, of sets is non-null if (and only if) each X_i is non-null. It has come to be recognized however that the extension of this result to an infinite family of sets involves the making of an explicit assumption which could be formulated most simply as follows: **The Axiom of Choice.** Given an arbitrary non-null set S, and a non-empty subset $\mathscr{A}$ of $P(S) - (\varnothing)$, there exists a function f from $\mathscr{A}$ into S such that $f(X) \in X$ for each member X of $\mathscr{A}$.

A considerable amount of the reasoning appearing in the sequel (for example, the proof of part (f) of Theorem 1.5) depends on the assumption of this axiom; it will be tacitly assumed throughout.

THEOREM 1.2 Given non-null sets A,B and a function f from A into B, then:

(a) if $\{X_i\}$, $i \in I$, is a family of subsets of A:
$f(\bigcup_i X_i) = \bigcup_i f(X_i)$; $f(\bigcap_i X_i) \subseteq \bigcap_i f(X_i)$;

(b) if $\{Y_i\}$, $i \in I$, is a family of subsets of B:
$f^{-1}(\bigcup_i Y_i) = \bigcup_i f^{-1}(Y_i)$; $f^{-1}(\bigcap_i Y_i) = \bigcap_i f^{-1}(Y_i)$;

(c) if $X \subseteq A$:
$$X \subseteq f^{-1}(f(X)) \tag{1}$$
where equality holds in (1) for each $X \subseteq A$ if and only if f is (1,1);

(d) if $Y \subseteq B$:
$$f(f^{-1}(Y)) \subseteq Y \tag{2}$$
where equality holds in (2) for each $Y \subseteq B$ if and only if f is onto B;

(e) if $Y \subseteq B$: $f^{-1}(C_B(Y)) = C_A(f^{-1}(Y))$.

PROOF The conditions for equality in (1), (2) will be established; the rest of the argument will be omitted. Given that equality holds in (1), suppose $y \in f(A)$ and $x,x' \in f^{-1}(y)$; if $X = (x)$, then

$f(x') = y = f(x) \in f(X)$, i.e. $x' \in f^{-1}(f(X)) = X$. Thus $x = x'$. If, conversely, it is given that f is (1,1), let $X \subseteq A$. If $x \in f^{-1}(f(X))$, $f(x) \in f(X)$; that is, $\exists\, x'$ in X such that $f(x) = f(x')$. But the latter implies, since f is (1,1), that x,x' coincide; that is, $x \in X$ and so $f^{-1}(f(X)) \subseteq X$, giving equality. If, secondly, it is given that equality holds in (2), then, in particular, $f^{-1}(y)$ clearly cannot be null for any y in B; that is, f is onto B. If, conversely, f is given to be onto B, and $Y \subseteq B$, suppose $y \in Y$. Then, by hypothesis, $\exists\, x$ in A with $f(x) = y$; thus $x \in f^{-1}(Y)$ and so $y \in f(f^{-1}(Y))$.

THEOREM 1.3 Given non-null sets A,B, let f be a function from A into B and g a function from B into A such that: for each x in A, $g(f(x)) = x$; for each y in B, $f(g(y)) = y$. Then f is (1,1) onto B, g is (1,1) onto A, and $g = f^{-1}$.

PROOF For any y in B, $g(y) \in A$, and hence: $y = f(g(y)) \in f(A)$; thus f is onto B. Secondly, to show that f is (1,1), suppose that x,x' are elements of A such that $f(x) = f(x')$. Then: $x = g(f(x)) = g(f(x')) = x'$. Hence its inverse f^{-1} is (1,1) onto A, and the equality: $f(g(y)) = f(f^{-1}(y))$ for each y in B, implies that $g = f^{-1}$.

THEOREM 1.4 Given a finite sequence $\{S_i\}$, $1 \leqslant i \leqslant n$, of sets, if A_i and B_i are subsets of S_i for $1 \leqslant i \leqslant n$, and A is a subset of $S \equiv \prod_{1 \leqslant i \leqslant n} S_i$, then:

(a) $A \subseteq \prod_{1 \leqslant i \leqslant n} \pi_i(A)$; $\prod_{1 \leqslant i \leqslant n} A_i = \bigcap_{1 \leqslant i \leqslant n} \pi_i^{-1}(A_i)$;

(b) $(\prod_{1 \leqslant i \leqslant n} A_i) \cup (\prod_{1 \leqslant i \leqslant n} B_i) \subseteq \prod_{1 \leqslant i \leqslant n} (A_i \cup B_i)$;

(c) $(\prod_{1 \leqslant i \leqslant n} A_i) \cap (\prod_{1 \leqslant i \leqslant n} B_i) = \prod_{1 \leqslant i \leqslant n} (A_i \cap B_i)$;

(d) $C_S(\prod_{1 \leqslant i \leqslant n} A_i) = \bigcup_{1 \leqslant i \leqslant n} (S_1 \times \ldots \times S_{i-1} \times C_{S_i}(A_i) \times S_{i+1} \ldots \times S_n)$.

The proof will be left to the reader.

A set A is said to be **enumerably** (or countably) **infinite** if it is in (1,1) correspondence with the set J^+ of all positive integers; if A is either finite or enumerably infinite, it is said simply to be **enumerable**, or **countable**.

THEOREM 1.5

(a) Any subset of an enumerable set is enumerable.

(b) The union of a sequence of enumerable sets is enumerable.

(c) If A is enumerable, so is the set of all finite sequences of members of A.

(d) If the sets X_i, $1 \leqslant i \leqslant n$, are all enumerable, so is $\prod_{1 \leqslant i \leqslant n} X_i$.

(e) The set of real numbers $0 \leqslant x < 1$ is *not* enumerable.

(f) Any infinite set contains an enumerable subset.

PROOF Parts (a)–(e) are proved in, for example, NEWMAN, Reference [8] pp. 12–14. If A is an arbitrary infinite set, a sequence $\{x_n\}$, $n \geqslant 1$, of distinct members of A can be constructed as follows: Choose an element in A, and call it x_1. If, given $n > 1$, the elements $x_1, x_2, \ldots, x_{n-1}$ have been chosen in A, it is possible, since A is infinite, to choose an element x_n in $A - \bigcup_{1 \leqslant m \leqslant n-1} (x_m)$.

DEFINITION 3 Given non-null sets S, S', and a function f from S into S', the **graph** of f on S is the subset T of $S \times S'$ containing all elements of the form $\{x, f(x)\}$, where $x \in S$.

If, in particular, $S' = S$, the graph of the identity function on S is the set of all elements $\{x,x\}$ for x in S, and is called the **diagonal** of $S \times S$, denoted by Δ_S. If f is any function from S into S' (any non-null sets), the function g from S into $S \times S'$ obtained by writing $g(x) = \{x, f(x)\}$ for each x in S, is clearly a (1,1) function.

A **binary relation** is said to be defined on a non-null set S when there is given a subset $\mathscr{R}$ of $S \times S$. If x,y are elements of S, then x is said to bear the relation $\mathscr{R}$ to y when $\{x,y\} \in \mathscr{R}$; this is usually denoted by: $x \mathscr{R} y$.

Exercises for Solution

1. Show by suitable examples that (in the notation of Theorem 1.2):
(a) even if $X_1 \cap X_2 \neq \varnothing$, $f(X_1 \cap X_2)$ need not equal $f(X_1) \cap f(X_2)$;
(b) if $X \subseteq A$, neither of the relations $f(C_A(X)) \subsetneqq C_B(f(X))$ need hold.

2. Given non-null sets A,B,C, a function f from A into B, and a function g from B into C, show that:
(a) if $f \circ g$ is (1,1), then f is (1,1);
(b) if $f \circ g$ is onto C, then g is onto C;
(c) if $f \circ g$ is onto C and g is (1,1), then f is onto B;
(d) if $f \circ g$ is (1,1) and f is onto B, then g is (1,1);
(e) with $C = A$ and under the conditions of Theorem 1.3, f is (1,1) onto B (deducing this from (a) and (c) above).

3. With the notation of Exercise 2, h is a function from C into A such that $f \circ g \circ h$ and $h \circ f \circ g$ are (1,1) while $g \circ h \circ f$ is onto B. *Deduce* from Exercise 2 that f,g,h are all (1,1) and onto (resp.) B,C,A.

4. Show by suitable examples that inequalities can occur in parts (a), (b) of Theorem 1.4.

5. If $S = T^2$, where T is non-null, $X \subseteq S$, $Y \subseteq S$, $A \subseteq T$, let: $X(A)$ denote the set of those elements y of T such that $\{x,y\} \in X$ for some x in A (dependent on y), X^{-1} denote the set of those elements $\{x,y\}$ of S such that $\{y,x\} \in X$, and $Y \circ X$ denote the set of elements $\{x,z\}$ of S such that $\{x,y\} \in X$ and $\{y,z\} \in Y$ for some y in T (dependent on $\{x,z\}$). Show that:

(a) $X(A) = \pi_2(X \cap (A \times \pi_2(X))) = X(A \cap \pi_1(X))$;

(b) if $Z \subseteq S$, then $(Y \circ X) \cap Z \subseteq (Y \cap (Z \circ X^{-1})) \circ (X \cap (Y^{-1} \circ Z))$;

(c) if $X \neq \varnothing$, the following three statements are equivalent:

(i) $\exists A \subseteq T$, and a function f from A into T such that X is the graph of f on A,

(ii) for $B \subseteq T$, $C \subseteq T$: $X^{-1}(B \cap C) = X^{-1}(B) \cap X^{-1}(C)$,

(iii) $B \cap C = \varnothing$ implies: $X^{-1}(B) \cap X^{-1}(C) = \varnothing$.

(d) if $(\pi_1(X) \times \pi_2(X)) - X$ is denoted by X':

(i) $(X^{-1})' = (X')^{-1}$,

(ii) $\pi_1(X) \subseteq A$ implies: $(X^{-1})' \circ X \subseteq (\Delta_A)'$, where Δ_A denotes the diagonal of $A \times A$.

6. Show that:

(a) the set Q of all rationals in R is enumerable;

(b) if $a < b$, the open interval $]a,b[$ is not enumerable;

(c) any set of non-overlapping open intervals in R is enumerable;

(d) if f is a function from R into R such that, for some $K > 0$, $|f(x_1) + \ldots + f(x_n)| < K$ for all finite sets $(x_1, \ldots, x_n)$ of distinct members of R, then the set of points x at which $f(x) \neq 0$ is enumerable.

7. Show that the second half of Theorem 1.4, part (a) can be generalized as follows: given an arbitrary family $\{S_i\}$, $i \in I$, let I' be a non-null subset of I; then, if $A_i \subseteq S_i$ for each i in I, $\bigcap_{i \in I'} \pi_i^{-1}(A_i) = \prod_{i \in I} B_i$, where $B_i = A_i$ if $i \in I'$, and equals S_i otherwise.

1.3 Partially-Ordered Sets

DEFINITION 4 Given a non-null set E, a (binary) relation $\mathscr{R}$ defined on E is said to be a **quasi-order** on E if it satisfies the two conditions:

01: $\mathscr{R}$ is *reflexive*; that is, $x \mathscr{R} x$ for each x in E

02: $\mathscr{R}$ is *transitive*; that is, if x,y,z are elements of E such that $x \mathscr{R} y$ and $y \mathscr{R} z$, then $x \mathscr{R} z$.

When a relation $\mathscr{R}$ on E is a quasi-order, then '$x \mathscr{R} y$' is *usually* (that is, generally, except where $\mathscr{R}$ is an equivalence) written as: $x \leqslant y$ or $y \geqslant x$; if $x \neq y$, this is written as: $x < y$ or $y > x$. A set E, together with a quasi-order $\leqslant$ defined on it, is called a **quasi-ordered** set or **qoset,** denoted by $(E, \leqslant)$. Two elements x,y of E are said to be **commensurable** if either $x \leqslant y$ or $y \leqslant x$.

DEFINITION 5 A qoset $(E, \leqslant)$ is said to be a **partially-ordered** set, or a **poset**, if the quasi-order $\leqslant$ satisfies (in addition to 01, 02) a third condition:

03: $\leqslant$ is *antisymmetric*; that is, if x,y are elements of E such that $x \leqslant y$ and $y \leqslant x$, then $x = y$. Then $\leqslant$ is said to be a **partial-order** on E.

DEFINITION 6 A poset $(E, \leqslant)$ is said to be a **totally** (simply, linearly) ordered set or a **chain**, if the partial order $\leqslant$ satisfies (in addition to 01–3) a fourth condition:

04: any two elements of E are commensurable.

Then $\leqslant$ is said to be a **total** (simple, linear) order on E.

Example 1.3.1 Any equivalence $\mathscr{R}$ (that is, a reflexive, symmetric, transitive binary relation) on E is a quasi-order. It can be shown (see, for example, NEWMAN, Reference [8] p. 15) that an equivalence $\mathscr{R}$ is defined on E if and only if there is given a **partition** of E, that is, a covering $\{A_i\}$, $i \in I$, of E, by non-null subsets of E such that $A_i \cap A_j$ is null for $i \neq j$; then, given x,y in E, $x \mathscr{R} y$ if and only if x,y belong to the same member of $\{A_i\}$. The members of $\{A_i\}$ are called **$\mathscr{R}$-classes**. If one of the members of the partition contains more than one element of E, $\mathscr{R}$ is *not* a partial-order.

Example 1.3.2 If S is an arbitrary non-null set, any non-null subset E of $P(S)$ is said to be partially-ordered **by inclusion** by writing, for A,B in E, $A \leqslant B$ if and only if $A \subseteq B$ (that is, A is contained in B). If S has more than one member, it is clear that $\leqslant$ need *not* be a total order.

If $(E, \leqslant)$ is a qoset (resp. poset, chain), and A a non-null subset of E, then a binary relation $\leqslant_A$ (usually denoted again by $\leqslant$) is defined on A by writing (for x,y in A) $x \leqslant_A y$ if and only if $x \leqslant y$; then $(A, \leqslant)$ is a qoset (resp. poset, chain), denoted usually again by A if no ambiguity as to its ordering can arise.

DEFINITION 7 If $(E, \leqslant)$ is a poset, A a non-null subset of E, and a a member of A, then:

(i) a is said to be **maximum** (resp. **minimum**) in A if $x \leqslant a$ (resp. $a \leqslant x$) for each element x in A;

(ii) a is said to be **maximal** (resp. **minimal**) in A if $a \nless x$ (resp. $x \nless a$) for each element x in A.

It is clear that if a is maximum (resp. minimum) in A, then a is maximal (resp. minimal) in A, and is the only maximal (resp. minimal) element in A. If, on the other hand, A has no maximum (resp. minimum) element, then A may have 0, 1, or more maximal (resp. minimal) elements:

Example 1.3.3 If $E \equiv P(J)$ (where J is the set of all integers) is partially ordered by inclusion, then first, the subset A_1 of E containing all finite subsets of J^+ has *no* maximal member, secondly, $A_2 \equiv A_1 \cup (0)$ has *one* maximal member (but no maximum member) while, thirdly, the subset A_3 of E containing all subsets of J of not more than three members, has an infinity of maximal members.

DEFINITION 8 A poset $(E, \leqslant)$ is said to be a **well-ordered** set if $\leqslant$ satisfies a fourth condition:

05: any non-null subset of E has a minimum member.

Since 05 is clearly a stronger condition on $\leqslant$ than 04, any 'well-ordering' of a set E is necessarily a total ordering.

Example 1.3.4 The positive integers are well-ordered by magnitude.

Example 1.3.5 The real numbers are totally-, but *not* well-, ordered by magnitude; for example, an open interval $]a,b[$ of R has no minimum member.

DEFINITION 9 A poset $(E, \leqslant)$ is said to satisfy the **ascending** (resp. **descending**) **chain** condition if, given a sequence $\{x_i\}$, $i \geqslant 1$, of elements of E such that $x_i \leqslant x_{i+1}$ (resp. $x_i \geqslant x_{i+1}$) for each $i \geqslant 1$, there exists an integer j such that $x_i = x_j$ for $i \geqslant j$.

THEOREM 1.6 A poset $(E, \leqslant)$ satisfies the ascending (resp. descending) chain condition if and only if every non-null subset of E has at least one maximal (resp. minimal) member.

PROOF If $\exists$ a non-null subset A of E which has (e.g.) no minimal member, choose an element in A and call it x_1; since x_1 is not minimal in A, $\exists\, x_2$ in A such that $x_1 > x_2, \ldots$ and so on. That is, a sequence $\{x_i\}$ of elements of A can evidently be constructed so that $x_i > x_{i+1}$ for each $i \geqslant 1$. If, on the other hand, it is given that $(E, \leqslant)$ does not satisfy the descending chain condition, $\exists$ a sequence $\{x_i\}$, $i \geqslant 1$, with $x_i \geqslant x_{i+1}$ for each i and such that for each $i \geqslant 1$, $\exists j$ (dependent on the choice of i) such that $x_i > x_j$.

Clearly this means that $A \equiv \bigcup_{i \geqslant 1} (x_i)$ has no minimal element.

COROLLARY Any finite poset $(E, \leqslant)$ has at least one maximal and at least one minimal member.

Definition 10 If $(E, \leqslant)$ is a poset, and A a non-null subset of E, then an element a of E is said to be an **upper** (resp. **lower**) **bound** of A in E if $x \leqslant a$ (resp. $a \leqslant x$) for each element x in A.

The set of upper (resp. lower) bounds of A in E is denoted by $M_E(A)$ (resp. $L_E(A)$) or, where no ambiguity can arise, simply by $M(A)$ (resp. $L(A)$); if $A \equiv (x,y,z,\ldots,w)$ is finite, this is denoted by $M(x,y,z,\ldots,w)$ (resp. $L(x,y,z,\ldots,w)$). If $M(A)$ (resp. $L(A)$) is non-null, A is said to be **bounded above** (resp. **below**); if both $M(A)$, $L(A)$ are non-null, A is said simply to be **bounded.**

Definition 11. If $(E, \leqslant)$ is a poset, and A a non-null subset of E, then an element a is said to be the **supremum** (resp. **infimum**) of A in E if:

(i) $M(A)$ (resp. $L(A)$) is non-null;

(ii) a is the minimum (resp. maximum) member of $M(A)$ (resp. $L(A)$).

The supremum and infimum of A (where they exist) are, in general, denoted by $\vee A, \wedge A$ respectively; if the members of A are indexed as, say: $\{a_i\}$, $i \in I$, these are written as: $\bigvee\limits_{i \in I} a_i$, $\bigwedge\limits_{i \in I} a_i$; for a finite sequence $\{a_i\}$, $1 \leqslant i \leqslant n$, the notations: $a_1 \vee a_2 \vee \ldots \vee a_n$, $a_1 \wedge a_2 \wedge \ldots \wedge a_n$ are usually employed.

Definition 12 A poset $(E, \leqslant)$ is said to be a **lattice** if $a \vee b$ and $a \wedge b$ exist for any pair of elements a,b of E.

By induction it follows that, in a lattice, $\vee A$ and $\wedge A$ exist for any finite subset A of E. Properties of a lattice are collected without proof (see, for example, Jacobson, Reference [5], p. 190) in:

Theorem 1.7 Given a lattice $(E, \leqslant)$ and elements a,b,c of E:

(a) $a \vee (b \vee c) = (a \vee b) \vee c = a \vee b \vee c$;
$a \wedge (b \wedge c) = (a \wedge b) \wedge c = a \wedge b \wedge c$;

(b) $a \vee b = b \vee a$; $a \wedge b = b \wedge a$;

(c) $a \vee a = a = a \wedge a$;

(d) $a \vee (a \wedge b) = a \wedge (a \vee b) = a$;

(e) the following three statements are equivalent:
$a \leqslant b$; $a \vee b = b$; $a \wedge b = a$.

Definition 13 A poset $(E, \leqslant)$ is said to be a **complete lattice** if $\vee A$, $\wedge A$ exist for any non-null subset A of E.

Example 1.3.6 If $E = J^3$, and $x \equiv \{x_1,x_2,x_3\}$, $y \equiv \{y_1,y_2,y_3\}$ elements of E, write $x < y$ if and only if *either* $x_1 \leqslant y_1$ and $x_2 \leqslant y_2$ (*without* equality in both cases) *or* $x_1 = y_1$, $x_2 = y_2$, and $x_3 < y_3$. It is easily verified that $(E, \leqslant)$ is a poset such that $M(x,y)$, $L(x,y)$ are non-null for any two elements x,y of E. However, if (e.g.) $x_1 = \{0,1,0\}$, $y_1 = \{1,0,0\}$, then $M(x_1,y_1)$ is the set of all elements $z \equiv \{z_1,z_2,z_3\}$ of E where $z_1 \geqslant 1$, $z_2 \geqslant 1$, and z_3 can have any (integral) value, so that $M(x_1,y_1)$ has *no* minimum element; that is, $x_1 \vee y_1$ does not exist. Similarly, $L(x_1,y_1)$ has no maximum element.

Example 1.3.7 If $(E, \leqslant)$ denotes the set of rationals contained in the closed interval $[0,2]$ of R, (totally) ordered by magnitude, let A (resp. B) denote the set of numbers x in E such that $x^2 < 2$ (resp. $x^2 > 2$). It can be easily shown (RUDIN, Reference [10], p. 2) that A has no maximum element, and B has no minimum element. But $B = M_E(A)$. For, first, if $x \in B \cap C_E(M(A))$, $\exists x_1$ in A such that $x < x_1$, implying $x^2 < x_1^2 < 2$; conversely, if $x \in M(A) \cap C_E(B)$, then (since $x^2 \neq 2$, x being rational) $x \in A$, implying that x is the maximum element of A, and again yielding a contradiction. That is, although any complete lattice is necessarily a bounded lattice, even a bounded chain need not be complete.

Example 1.3.8 If $E = P(S)$ in Example 1.3.2, $(E, \leqslant)$ is a complete lattice where, for any family of members of E, $\bigvee_i X_i = \bigcup_i X_i$, and $\bigwedge_i X_i = \bigcap_i X_i$.

Criteria for a complete lattice are simplified by:

THEOREM 1.8 A poset $(E, \leqslant)$ is a complete lattice if:
(a) E has a maximum element (resp. minimum element);
(b) $\wedge A$ (resp. $\vee A$) exists for each non-null subset A of E.

PROOF Under the assumption that E has a maximum element I, and that $\wedge A$ everywhere exists, it will suffice to show that $\vee A$ exists. Since $I \in M(A)$, the latter is non-null, and hence has infimum a. Then $a = \vee A$. For, given x in A, $x \in L(M(A))$ and so, by choice of a, $x \leqslant a$; that is, $a \in M(A)$, and so is its minimum member.

COROLLARY A well-ordered set $(E, \leqslant)$ is complete if and only if E has a maximum member.

If $(E, \leqslant)$ is a lattice, and A is a non-null subset of E, then A is called a **sublattice** of $(E, \leqslant)$ if $a \vee b$ and $a \wedge b$ are in A for any pair of elements a,b of A. If $(E, \leqslant)$ is complete, a complete sublattice of $(E, \leqslant)$ is analogously defined.

Note 3 If $(E, \leqslant)$ is a lattice, and $\varnothing \subset A \subseteq E$, then $(A, \leqslant_A)$ may be itself a lattice without being a sublattice of $(E, \leqslant)$.

Example 1.3.9 If $S = (1,2,3)$ in Example 1.3.8, let $A = (\varnothing,(1),(2),S) \subset E$. Then $(A,\leqslant_A)$ is a lattice (with, in an obvious notation, $(1) \vee_A (2) = S$), but $(1) \vee (2) = (1,2)$, not in A.

Note 4. It is shown in HALMOS, (pp. 62–65), that a consequence of the Axiom of Choice introduced in Note 2 is:

THEOREM 1.9 ('Zorn's Lemma'). If $(E,\leqslant)$ is a poset such that $M(C)$ is non-null for each chain in E (that is, for each subset C of E such that $(C,\leqslant)$ is a totally ordered set), then E possesses at least one maximal element.

It is further shown in HALMOS, (pp. 68–69), that Theorem 1.9 implies that a well-ordering $\leqslant$ can be defined on an arbitrarily chosen non-null set E. A second consequence of Theorem 1.9 involves the notion introduced in:

DEFINITION 14 Given a non-null set E, a subset $\mathscr{S}$ of $P(E) - (\varnothing)$ is said to be of **finite character** if a given member X of $P(E) - (\varnothing)$ belongs to $\mathscr{S}$ if and only if every finite non-null subset of X belongs to $\mathscr{S}$.

THEOREM 1.10 ('Tukey's Lemma') Given a non-null set E, let $P(E)$ be partially ordered by inclusion; then if $\mathscr{S}$ is a subset of $P(E) - (\varnothing)$ of finite character, and X_0 is a given element of $\mathscr{S}$, $\mathscr{S}$ possesses a maximal member X' such that $X_0 \subseteq X'$.

PROOF It clearly suffices to show that the subset $\mathscr{S}'$ of $\mathscr{S}$ containing those members X with $X_0 \subseteq X$ has a maximal member X'. In order to apply the preceding theorem, let $\mathscr{K}$ be any chain in $\mathscr{S}'$, and let X_1 be the union of all the members of $\mathscr{K}$. Then $X_1 \in \mathscr{S}'$. For, first, clearly $X_0 \subseteq X_1$. Secondly, given any finite subset Y of X_1, $\exists$ (by choice of X_1) a finite subset $\mathscr{L}$ of $\mathscr{K}$ such that Y is contained in the union of the members of $\mathscr{L}$. Since $\mathscr{L}$ is a finite collection of sets, totally ordered by inclusion, $\exists$ a member Y_1 of $\mathscr{L}$ which contains every member of $\mathscr{L}$ and hence Y itself; hence (by Definition 14) $Y \in \mathscr{S}$. It follows that $X_1 \in \mathscr{S}$. Since X_1 is an upper bound of $\mathscr{K}$ in $\mathscr{S}'$, the required result follows.

COROLLARY ('Maximal Principle') If $(E,\leqslant)$ is a poset and C a given chain in E, then (in terms of the partial ordering of $P(E)$ by inclusion) there exists a *maximal* chain C' in E such that $C \subseteq C'$.

To prove the Corollary, it is only necessary to observe that the subset $\mathscr{S}$ of all members C of $P(E) - (\varnothing)$ such that $(C, \leqslant)$ is totally ordered, is of finite character.

Worked Exercises

1. An element a of a lattice $(E, \leqslant)$ is said to be **join irreducible** if it cannot be expressed in the form $x \vee y$, where $x < a$, $y < a$. If $(E, \leqslant)$ satisfies the descending chain condition, show that any element x of E can be expressed in the form: $a_1 \vee a_2 \vee \ldots \vee a_n$, where a_i, $1 \leqslant i \leqslant n$, is join-irreducible.

Solution: If not, the set A of those elements of E not expressible in this form is non-null and so, by Theorem 1.6, it has a minimal element a. Since $a \in A$, a is not itself join-irreducible; that is, $\exists$ elements x,y in E with $a = x \vee y$, $x < a, y < a$. But by the choice of a, neither x nor y can belong to A; that is, each can be expressed as the 'join' of a finite set of join-irreducible elements of E. But it would then follow that a itself can be so expressed, giving a contradiction.

2. If $(E, \leqslant)$ is a complete lattice, and f a function from E into E such that $f(x) \leqslant f(y)$ for any elements x,y of E with $x \leqslant y$, then $\exists$ an element a of E such that $f(a) = a$.

Solution: If A is the set of those elements x of E with $x \leqslant f(x)$, then $A \neq \varnothing$ (A contains the minimum element of E). If a denotes the supremum $\bigvee A$ of A, then $f(a) = a$. For, first, for each x in A, $x \leqslant a$, implying: $x \leqslant f(x) \leqslant f(a)$; that is, $f(a) \in M(A)$, and hence, by choice of a, $a \leqslant f(a)$. On the other hand, the last inequality implies: $f(a) \leqslant f(f(a))$; that is, $f(a) \in A$, giving: $f(a) \leqslant a$. (It incidentally follows from the proof that a is actually the maximum element of A.)

Exercises for Solution

1. A poset $(E, \leqslant)$ is said to be **directed above** (resp. **below**) if $M(x,y) \neq \varnothing$ (resp. $L(x,y) \neq \varnothing$) for any x,y in E. Show that:
   (a) if $(E, \leqslant)$ is directed above (resp. below), then any maximal (resp. minimal) element of E is a maximum (resp. minimum) element of E.
   (b) a **directed** poset (i.e., directed both above and below) need not be a lattice.

2. If $(E, \leqslant)$ is a partially-, but *not* well-, ordered set, show (by considering, for example, the union of those subsets of E each having no minimum element) that $\exists$ subsets A,B of E such that $A \cup B = E$, $A \cap B = \varnothing$, A is well-ordered if non-null, and B has no minimum element.

3. Show that part (c) of Theorem 1.7 could be deduced directly from part (d).

4. If $(E, \leqslant)$ is a lattice, and X a non-null subset of E which is bounded

above, show that the family $\{[x,y]\}$, where $x \in X$, $y \in M(X)$, possesses the finite intersection property (where $[x,y]$ denotes the set of elements z in E with $x \leqslant z \leqslant y$).

5. If $(E, \leqslant)$ is a poset, a function f from E into E is called a **closure** on E if:

(i) $x \leqslant y$ implies $f(x) \leqslant f(y)$;
(ii) $x \leqslant f(x) = f(f(x))$.

Show that:

(*a*) if f is a closure on E and F denotes the set of elements x in E with $x = f(x)$, then, for each x in E, $F \cap M(x)$ is non-null and has $f(x)$ as its minimum element.

(b) (conversely) if G is a subset of E such that, for each x in E, $G \cap M(x)$ is non-null with a minimum element (denoted by) $g(x)$, then g is a closure on E and G contains just those elements x of E with $g(x) = x$.

(c) if $(E, \leqslant)$ is a complete lattice and f, F are as in (*a*), then for any non-null subset A of F, $\wedge A \in F$.

6. Given a poset $(E, \leqslant)$ let $Q(E)$ denote the set of those non-null subsets of E which are bounded above. If $Q(E)$ is partially-ordered by inclusion and if, for each X in $Q(E)$, $f(X)$ denotes $L(M(X))$, show that f is a *closure on* $Q(E)$.

7. Given a poset $(E, \leqslant)$ let $\mathscr{E}$ denote the set of those non-null subsets X of E such that any two distinct members of X are incommensurable. Show that:

(a) if $\mathscr{E}$ is partially-ordered by inclusion, it possesses a *maximal* element;

(b) the binary relation $\preccurlyeq$ on $\mathscr{E}$ obtained by writing $X \preccurlyeq Y$ if and only if: for each x in X, $\exists\, y$ in Y (dependent on x) such that $x \leqslant y$, is a partial order on $\mathscr{E}$ such that if $(E, \leqslant)$ satisfies the condition of Theorem 1.9, then $(\mathscr{E}, \preccurlyeq)$ possesses a *maximum* element.

Part II
METRIC SPACES

CHAPTER 2

Basic Concepts for Metric Spaces

2.1 Metrics

DEFINITION 1 Given a non-empty set S of elements, a **metric** defined on S is a function ρ from $S \times S$ into R satisfying the four conditions

M1 For each $x,y \in S$, $\rho(x,y) \geqslant 0$.
M2 For each $x,y \in S$, $\rho(x,y) = \rho(y,x)$.
M3 For each $x,y,z \in S$, $\rho(x,z) \leqslant \rho(x,y) + \rho(y,z)$.
M4 Given $x,y \in S$, $\rho(x,y) = 0$ if and only if $x = y$.

A set S, together with a metric ρ defined on it, is called a **metric space**, denoted by (S,ρ).

Note 1 Given an arbitrary non-empty set S, and a positive real number k, the function ρ_0,

$$\text{where: } \rho_0(x,y) = \begin{cases} k & \text{for } x \neq y \\ 0 & \text{for } x = y \end{cases}$$

is a metric on S.

Before considering further (less trivial) examples of metric spaces, we require:

LEMMA 1 ('Cauchy's Inequality') If $a_1, \ldots, a_n$ and $b_1, \ldots, b_n$ are sequences of n real numbers,

$$(a_1b_1 + \ldots + a_nb_n)^2 \leqslant (a_1^2 + \ldots + a_n^2)(b_1^2 + \ldots + b_n^2)$$

PROOF Write $A = \sum_{i=1}^{n} a_i^2, \quad B = \sum_{i=1}^{n} a_ib_i, \quad C = \sum_{i=1}^{n} b_i^2.$

The quadratic expression $Q(\lambda,\mu) \equiv A\lambda^2 + 2B\lambda\mu + C\mu^2 = \sum_{i=1}^{n} (\lambda a_i + \mu b_i)^2 \geqslant 0$ for all real λ,μ.
Hence its discriminant is non-positive,

i.e.
$$B^2 \leqslant AC.$$

LEMMA 2 If $x_1, \ldots, x_n$, $y_1, \ldots, y_n$, and $z_1, \ldots, z_n$ are three sequences of n real numbers, then:

$$\left[\sum_{i=1}^{n} (x_i - z_i)^2\right]^{\frac{1}{2}} \leqslant \left[\sum_{i=1}^{n} (x_i - y_i)^2\right]^{\frac{1}{2}} + \left[\sum_{i=1}^{n} (y_i - z_i)^2\right]^{\frac{1}{2}}$$

PROOF
$$\left\{\left[\sum_{i=1}^{n} (x_i - y_i)^2\right]^{\frac{1}{2}} + \left[\sum_{i=1}^{n} (y_i - z_i)^2\right]^{\frac{1}{2}}\right\}^2$$

$$= \sum_{i=1}^{n} (x_i - y_i)^2 + \sum_{i=1}^{n} (y_i - z_i)^2 + 2\left[\sum_{i=1}^{n} (x_i - y_i)^2\right]^{\frac{1}{2}} \left[\sum_{i=1}^{n} (y_i - z_i)^2\right]^{\frac{1}{2}}$$

$$\geqslant \sum_{i=1}^{n} (x_i - y_i)^2 + \sum_{i=1}^{n} (y_i - z_i)^2 + 2\sum_{i=1}^{n} (x_i - y_i)(y_i - z_i)$$

by Lemma 1

$$= \sum_{i=1}^{n} [(x_i - y_i) + (y_i - z_i)]^2 = \sum_{i=1}^{n} (x_i - z_i)^2.$$

Example 2.1.1 $S = R^n$. Given $x \equiv \{x_1, \ldots, x_n\}$ and $y \equiv \{y_1, \ldots, y_n\}$ in S, write:

$$\rho_1(x,y) = \left[\sum_{i=1}^{n} (x_i - y_i)^2\right]^{\frac{1}{2}}.$$

Conditions M1, 2, 4 for a metric are clearly satisfied, while M3 reiterates Lemma 2. The space (S,ρ_1) so formed is called **real Euclidean *n*-space,** often denoted briefly by $(R^n)_1$.

Other metrics on S are:

$$\rho_2(x,y) = \sum_{i=1}^{n} |x_i - y_i|$$

$$\rho_3(x,y) = \max_{1 \leqslant i \leqslant n} |x_i - y_i|$$

$\rho_1, \ldots, \rho_3$ clearly coincide for $n = 1$.

Example 2.1.2 Let S be the set of infinite sequences $\{x_i\}$, $i \geqslant 1$, of real numbers with Σx_i^2 convergent. Given $x \equiv \{x_i\}$, and $y \equiv \{y_i\}$, in S,† write:

$$\rho_1(x,y) = \left[\sum_{i=1}^{\infty} (x_i - y_i)^2\right]^{\frac{1}{2}}.$$

† Since $(x_i - y_i)^2 \leqslant 2(x_i^2 + y_i^2)$ for $i \geqslant 1$, the series clearly converges.

Again, conditions M1, 2, and 4 are satisfied; to verify M3, note that, for any three elements $x \equiv \{x_i\}$, $y \equiv \{y_i\}$, and $z \equiv \{z_i\}$, and any positive integer n:

$$\left[\sum_{i=1}^{n} (x_i - z_i)^2\right]^{\frac{1}{2}} \leqslant \left[\sum_{i=1}^{n} (x_i - y_i)^2\right]^{\frac{1}{2}} + \left[\sum_{i=1}^{n} (y_i - z_i)^2\right]^{\frac{1}{2}}$$
$$\leqslant \rho_1(x,y) + \rho_1(y,z)$$

hence:

$$\rho_1(x,z) \leqslant \rho_1(x,y) + \rho_1(y,z).$$

(S,ρ_1) is called **real Hilbert Space** (or ***H*-space**), denoted usually by H^∞.

Example 2.1.3 Let S be the set of continuous functions f from the unit interval [0,1] into R. For f, g in S, write:

$$\rho_1(f,g) = \max_{0 \leqslant x \leqslant 1} |f(x) - g(x)|$$

$$\rho_2(f,g) = \int_0^1 |f(x) - g(x)|\, dx$$

ρ_1 is clearly a metric on S; the space (S,ρ_1) is often denoted by C. Conditions M1–3 are clearly satisfied by ρ_2; to verify M4, let f be a member of S such that

$$\int_0^1 |f(x)|\, dx = 0; \text{ write } F(y) = \int_0^y |f(x)|\, dx$$

Then, since f is continuous,

$$|f(x)| = F'(x)$$
$$= 0 \quad \text{for } 0 \leqslant x \leqslant 1.$$

Example 2.1.4 Let S be the set of Riemann-integrable functions f from [0,1] into R. If ρ_1, ρ_2 are defined as:

$$\rho_1(f,g) = \sup_{0 \leqslant x \leqslant 1} |f(x) - g(x)|; \qquad \rho_2(f,g) = \int_0^1 |f(x) - g(x)|\, dx,$$

ρ_1 is a metric on S, but ρ_2 does *not* satisfy M4.

For example, if:

$$f(x) = \begin{cases} 1 & \text{for } x = 0 \\ 0 & \text{for } 0 < x \leqslant 1 \end{cases}$$

$$\int_0^1 |f(x)|\, dx = 0,$$

but f is not the zero function.

Example 2.1.5 Let S be the set of bounded functions f from $[0,1]$ into R; if ρ_1 is defined as in Example 2.1.4, ρ_1 is a metric on S.

Note 2 A function ρ such as ρ_2 in Example 2.1.4 (i.e., a function ρ from $S \times S$ into R satisfying M1–M4, but with $\rho(x,y) = 0$ only a *necessary* condition that $x = y$) is called a **pseudo-metric** or 'écart' on S, and S, ρ together form a pseudo-metric space, denoted by $\langle S,\rho \rangle$. With an arbitrary such space $\langle S,\rho \rangle$, we can associate a metric space $(\tilde{S},\tilde{\rho})$ by considering the (binary) relation $\mathscr{R}$ on S, where, given x,y in S, $x \mathscr{R} y$ if and only if $\rho(x,y) = 0$. $\mathscr{R}$ is clearly an equivalence relation on S. On the set $\tilde{S}$ of $\mathscr{R}$-classes, we write, for each pair $\tilde{x},\tilde{y} \in \tilde{S}$, $\tilde{\rho}(\tilde{x},\tilde{y}) = \rho(x,y)$, where x,y are arbitrary members of $\tilde{x},\tilde{y}$ respectively. The function $\tilde{\rho}$ is unambiguously defined on $\tilde{S} \times \tilde{S}$, for, given x,x' in $\tilde{x}$ and y,y' in $\tilde{y}$:

$$\rho(x',y') \leqslant \rho(x',x) + \rho(x,y) + \rho(y,y') = \rho(x,y)$$

Similarly:

$$\rho(x,y) \leqslant \rho(x',y')$$

$\tilde{\rho}$ is easily seen to satisfy M1–M4.

DEFINITION 2 Given a metric space (S,ρ), a non-null subset X of S is said to be **bounded** if there exists $K > 0$ such that $\rho(x,y) < K$, for all x,y in X.

Given a bounded subset X of S, its **diameter** is defined as: $\sup_{x,y \in X} \rho(x,y)$ and is denoted by $D(X)$.

Given two non-null subsets X,Y of S, the **distance** between X,Y is defined as: $\inf_{\substack{x \in X \\ y \in Y}} \rho(x,y)$ and is denoted again by $\rho(X,Y)$. In particular, if $Y = (y)$, this is written as: $\rho(X,y)$

Example 2.1.6 $S = R$, $\rho = \rho_1$ (see Example 2.1.1)

$$X = \bigcup_{n \geqslant 1} (n^{-1});\ y = 0$$

$$\rho(X,y) = \inf_{n \geqslant 1} |n^{-1} - 0| = 0, \qquad \text{but } y \,\omega\, X.$$

If, for a given metric space, S itself is bounded (according to Definition 2), ρ is said to be bounded (on S).

Note 3 Given an arbitrary metric ρ defined on a set S, a bounded metric ρ' on S can be obtained by, for example, writing:

$$\rho'(x,y) = \frac{\rho(x,y)}{1 + \rho(x,y)} \quad \text{for } x,y \text{ in } S.$$

To verify that M3 is satisfied by ρ', note that, if a,b,c are any non-negative numbers:

$$\frac{c}{1+c} \leqslant \frac{a}{1+a} + \frac{b}{1+b}$$

if:

$$c \leqslant a + b + 2ab + abc$$

and hence if:

$$c \leqslant a + b. \tag{1}$$

But (1) holds with $a = \rho(x,y)$, $b = \rho(y,z)$, $c = \rho(x,z)$ and any three elements x,y,z of S; hence

$$\rho'(x,z) \leqslant \rho'(x,y) + \rho'(y,z).$$

Note 4 Given a sequence of n arbitrary sets S_i, $1 \leqslant i \leqslant n$, on each of which a metric ρ_i is defined, let S be (the Cartesian product) $\prod_{1 \leqslant i \leqslant n} S_i$. Given $x \equiv \{x_1, \ldots, x_n\}$, and $y \equiv \{y_1, \ldots, y_n\}$ in S, write:

$$\rho^{(1)}(x,y) = \left[\sum_{i=1}^{n} \{\rho_i(x_i,y_i)\}^2\right]^{\frac{1}{2}}$$

$$\rho^{(2)}(x,y) = \sum_{i=1}^{n} \rho_i(x_i,y_i)$$

$$\rho^{(3)}(x,y) = \max_{1 \leqslant i \leqslant n} \rho_i(x_i,y_i)$$

$\rho^{(1)}, \ldots, \rho^{(3)}$ are immediate generalizations of the functions $\rho_1, \ldots, \rho_3$ appearing in Example 2.1.1 above, and, by analogous methods, can be shown to satisfy conditions M1–4.

Given a real vector space† S (that is, a vector space over the field R) with zero 0, a **norm** ν defined on S is a function from S into R such that for x,y in S and a in R:

N1 $\quad \nu(a \,.\, x) = |a|\nu(x)$

N2 $\quad$ If $x \neq 0$, $\nu(x) \neq 0$

N3 $\quad \nu(x + y) \leqslant \nu(x) + \nu(y)$.

† See, for example, NEWMAN, p. 19.

A vector space S, together with a norm v defined on it, is called a **normed** (vector) **space**, denoted by $[S,v]$.

It is easily seen (e.g. NEWMAN, p. 19) that the function ρ_v from $S \times S$ into R where: for x,y in S, $p_v(x,y) = v(x - y)$, is a metric on S; that is, any normed space $[S,v]$ gives rise to a metric space (S,ρ_v). However, if, conversely, ρ is an arbitrary metric given on a vector space S, there does not necessarily exist a norm v definable on S such that $v(x - y) = \rho(x,y)$ throughout S. For example, the function: ρ', where $\rho'(x,y) = |x - y|/(1 + |x - y|)$, is, by Note 3, a metric on R. However, if $v(x) = |x|/(1 + |x|)$ for x in S, $v(2) \neq 2 . v(1)$.

If x,y are distinct points of a real vector space S, the subset of S of all points of the form: $(1 - t)x + ty$, where $0 \leqslant t \leqslant 1$, is called the **segment** of S joining x,y, and is denoted by $\langle x,y \rangle$.

A subset A of a real vector space S is said to be **convex** when $\langle x,y \rangle \subseteq A$ for any two points x,y in A.

Worked Exercises

1. Given two metrics ρ_i on an arbitrary non-null set S, show that $\exists$ a metric ρ on S such that:

$$\rho(x,y) \geqslant \rho_i(x,y) \text{ for all } x,y \text{ in } S \text{ and } i = 1,2. \tag{1}$$

Show that this result does not however hold if the inequality in (1) is reversed.

Solution: For each x,y in S, write $\rho(x,y) = \rho_1(x,y) + \rho_2(x,y)$; clearly ρ is a metric on S satisfying (1). On the other hand, take $S = R$, define $\rho_1(x,y) = |x - y|$, and $\rho_2(x,y) = |f(x) - f(y)|$, where f is the function from R into R such that: $f(0) = 1$, $f(1) = 0$, $f(x) = x$ otherwise. Since f is (1,1), clearly ρ_2 is a metric on S. If $\exists$ a metric ρ on S such that $\rho(x,y) \leqslant \rho_i(x,y)$, then for any integer $n > 1$: $\rho(1,0) \leqslant \rho_2(1,n^{-1}) + \rho_1(n^{-1},0) = 2n^{-1}$; that is, $\rho(1,0) = 0$, contradicting M4.

2. Show in the usual notation that if X,Y,Z are any non-null subsets of S such that Z is bounded, then:

$$\rho(X,Y) \leqslant \rho(X,Z) + \rho(Y,Z) + D(Z) \tag{2}$$

hence, in particular, for any elements y,z of S: $|\rho(X,y) - \rho(X,z)| \leqslant \rho(y,z)$.

Solution: For any elements x in X, y in Y and z,z' in Z:

$$\rho(x,z') \geqslant \rho(x,z) - \rho(z,z') \geqslant (\rho(x,y) - \rho(y,z)) - D(Z)$$
$$\geqslant \rho(X,Y) - \rho(y,z) - D(Z).$$

Hence:

$$\rho(X,Z) \geqslant \rho(X,Y) - \rho(y,z) - D(Z);$$

that is, $\rho(y,z) \geqslant \rho(X,Y) - \rho(X,Z) - D(Z)$, implying immediately the required result (2).

Exercises for Solution

1. Show that neither of the functions given by: $\rho(x,y) = (x - y)^2$, $\rho'(x,y) = |x - y|^2$ is a metric on R.

2. (By using the identity: $(a + b - 2c)^2 = 2(a - c)^2 + 2(b - c)^2 - (a - b)^2$), show that if x,y are any two points of H^∞, $\exists$ exactly one point z in H such that: $\rho_1(x,z) = \rho_1(z,y) = \frac{1}{2}\rho_1(x,y)$.

3. A metric ρ on a non-null set S is said to be an **ultra-metric** on S if: $\rho(x,y) \leqslant \max\{\rho(x,z),\rho(y,z)\}$ for any elements x,y,z in S. Show that:

(a) if ρ is an ultra-metric on S, and $\rho(x,z) \neq \rho(y,z)$, then: $\rho(x,y) = \max\{\rho(x,z),\rho(y,z)\}$;

(b) if, given an arbitrary metric space (S,ρ), and x,y in S, $\rho'(x,y)$ denotes the greatest lower bound of the set of real numbers ε such that $\exists$ an 'ε-chain' between x,y, (i.e., $\exists$ a finite sequence $\{x_i\}$, $0 \leqslant i \leqslant n + 1$, of elements of S such that: $x = x_0$, $y = x_{n+1}$, and $\rho(x_i,x_{i+1}) < \varepsilon$ for $0 \leqslant i \leqslant n$), then ρ' is a pseudo-metric on S and the associate metric $\tilde{\rho}'$ is an ultra-metric on $\tilde{S}$;

(c) if S denotes the Cartesian Product of an infinite sequence of arbitrary sets S_i, and if, for any pair of elements $x \equiv \{x_i\}$, $y \equiv \{y_i\}$ of S:

$$\rho(x,y) = \begin{cases} i_0^{-1} & \text{where } i_0 \text{ is the least integer } i \text{ with } x_i \neq y_i \\ 0 & \text{if } x = y, \end{cases}$$

then ρ is an ultra-metric on S.

4. Show, by means of an example, that the term $D(Z)$ cannot be omitted from the right-hand side of inequality (2) of Worked Example 2.

5. Show in the usual notation that if X,Y are any bounded subsets of a set S, then $D(X \cup Y) \leqslant D(X) + D(Y) + \rho(X,Y)$; hence, in particular, $D(X \cup Y) \leqslant D(X) + D(Y)$ if $X \cap Y \neq \varnothing$.

6. If S' denotes the set of all sequences of real numbers, write, for any two elements $x' \equiv \{x_i\}$, $y' \equiv \{y_i\}$ of S':

$$\rho'(x',y') = \sum_{i=1}^{\infty} i^{-2}\{\min(|x_i - y_i|,1)\}.$$

Show that ρ' is a metric on S'.

2.2 Neighbourhoods and Open Sets

Given space (S,ρ), $x \in S$, and $\varepsilon > 0$, the set of all elements y in S

such that $\rho(x,y) < \varepsilon$ is denoted by $N_\varepsilon^\rho(x)$ or, if no ambiguity is possible, simply by $N_\varepsilon(x)$.

Example 2.2.1 For arbitrary non-null S and ρ_0 defined as in Note 1,

$$N_\varepsilon(x) = \begin{cases} (x) & \text{for } 0 < \varepsilon \leqslant k \\ S & \text{for } k < \varepsilon. \end{cases}$$

Example 2.2.2 For space $(R^3)_1$, given $x \equiv \{x_1,x_2,x_3\}$, $N_\varepsilon(x)$ is interior of the sphere, centre with coordinates x_1,x_2,x_3 and radius ε.

Example 2.2.3 For space (R^2,ρ_3), given $x \equiv \{x_1,x_2\}$, $N_\varepsilon(x)$ is interior of the square, centre with coordinates x_1,x_2 and side 2ε. i.e., $N_\varepsilon(x)$ is set of $y \equiv \{y_1,y_2\}$ such that:

$$x_i - \varepsilon < y_i < x_i + \varepsilon \quad \text{for } i = 1,2.$$

DEFINITION 4 Given space (S,ρ), and $x \in S$, a subset X of S is said to be a **neighbourhood of x** w.r.t.ρ if there exists $\varepsilon > 0$ s.t.: $N_\varepsilon(x) \subseteq X$; if no ambiguity is possible, it is called simply a **neighbourhood** of x. The set of all neighbourhoods of x is denoted by $\mathcal{N}_\rho(x)$ or $\mathcal{N}(x)$.
(For any $\varepsilon > 0$, $N_\varepsilon(x)$ is itself a neighbourhood of x, called the 'ε-neighbourhood of x'.)

DEFINITION 5 Given space (S,ρ), a subset X of S is said to be **open (in S)** w.r.t.ρ if, for each x in X, there exists $\varepsilon > 0$ (depending on choice of x in X) such that $N_\varepsilon(x) \subseteq X$, i.e., if, for each x in X, $X \in \mathcal{N}(x)$. If no ambiguity is possible, X is said simply to be **open**. The set of all open subsets of S is denoted by $\mathcal{G}_\rho$ or $\mathcal{G}$; the members of $\mathcal{G}_\rho$ are sometimes said to be 'ρ-open'.

Example 2.2.4 Given a space (S,ρ): for each $x \in S$ and $\varepsilon > 0$, $N_\varepsilon(x)$ is open. To see this, let $y \in N_\varepsilon(x)$, and write $\varepsilon' = \varepsilon - \rho(x,y) > 0$. Then, if z is an arbitrary element in $N_{\varepsilon'}(y)$,

$$\rho(x,z) \leqslant \rho(x,y) + \rho(y,z) < \rho(x,y) + \varepsilon' = \varepsilon$$

Thus: $N_{\varepsilon'}(y) \subseteq N_\varepsilon(x)$.

Example 2.2.5 Given a space (S,ρ): S, and the null set $\varnothing$ are open.
To see that $\varnothing$ is open, note that, by Definition 5, a subset X of S is open if and only if the following implication holds:

$$\text{'**if** } x \text{ in } S \text{ is such that } X\ \omega\ \mathcal{N}(x), \text{ **then** } x\ \omega\ X\text{'} \qquad (1)$$

But, if X is null, the statement '$x\ \omega\ X$' is true for every x in S; hence (1) holds.

Note 5 In Definition 5, a subset X of S was defined to be open if and only if $X \in \mathcal{N}(x)$ for each x in X; that is, by Definition 5, $\mathcal{G}$ is given in terms of the sets $\mathcal{N}(x)$. Theorem 2.1 below shows how, conversely, the sets $\mathcal{N}(x)$ can be given in terms of $\mathcal{G}$.

THEOREM 2.1 Given a space (S,ρ), $x \in S$, and $X \subseteq S$, then $X \in \mathcal{N}(x)$ if and only if there exists G in $\mathcal{G}$ such that

$$x \in G \subseteq X \tag{1}$$

PROOF Since any ε-neighbourhood of x is open, we need only consider the sufficiency of condition (1). Given G in $\mathcal{G}$ such that $x \in G \subseteq X$, there exists (by Definition 5) $\varepsilon > 0$ such that $N_\varepsilon(x) \subseteq G$, implying: $N_\varepsilon(x) \subseteq X$, i.e., $X \in \mathcal{N}(x)$.

Note 6 A neighbourhood of an element is not necessarily itself open.

Example 2.2.6 For space $(R^2)_1$, let $x = \{0,0\}$; then the set X of those elements y in R such that $\rho_1(x,y) \leqslant 1$ contains $N_1(x)$ as a subset and hence is a neighbourhood of x. However, X is not open; for if $y = \{1,0\} \in X$ and $z = \{1 + \varepsilon/2, 0\}$ where $\varepsilon > 0$, $z \in N_\varepsilon(y)$ but $z \,\omega\, X$.

The basic properties of the set $\mathcal{G}$ of open sets of a space are given by:

THEOREM 2.2 For any space (S,ρ):
(a) S and the null set belong to $\mathcal{G}$.
(b) The union of any family of members of $\mathcal{G}$ belongs to $\mathcal{G}$.
(c) The intersection of any finite sequence of members of $\mathcal{G}$ belongs to $\mathcal{G}$.

PROOF (a) This has been already observed.

(b) Let $\{G_i\}_{i \in I}$ be any family of members of $\mathcal{G}$, let $G = \bigcup_i G_i$ and x any member of G. Then $\exists\, i' \in I$ such that $x \in G_{i'}$ and hence, since $G_{i'} \in \mathcal{G}$, $\exists\, \varepsilon > 0$ (dependent on choice of x, i') such that $N_\varepsilon(x) \subseteq G_{i'}$; hence $N_\varepsilon(x) \subseteq G$.

(c) Let $\{G_i\}$, $1 \leqslant i \leqslant n$, be a finite sequence of members of $\mathcal{G}$, and $H = \bigcap_{1 \leqslant i \leqslant n} G_i$. If H is null, result follows from (a). If not, let $x \in H$; then, corresponding to each i with $1 \leqslant i \leqslant n$, $\exists\, \varepsilon_i > 0$ (dependent on choice of x) such that $N_{\varepsilon_i}(x) \subseteq G_i$. If $\varepsilon = \min_{1 \leqslant i \leqslant n} \varepsilon_i > 0$, $N_\varepsilon(x) \subseteq N_{\varepsilon_i}(x) \subseteq G_i$ for $1 \leqslant i \leqslant n$,

i.e., $$N_\varepsilon(x) \subseteq H.$$

Note 7 Theorem 2.2(c) does not hold for an infinite family of members of $\mathscr{G}$.

Example 2.2.7 For space $(R^n)_1$, let $x = \{0, \ldots, 0\}$; for each $i = 1,2, \ldots, G_i \equiv N_{i^{-1}}(x)$ is open; let $H = \bigcap_{i \geq 1} G_i$. Then $H = (x)$, for, given any y in H, $\rho_1(x,y) < i^{-1}$ for every i, i.e., $\rho_1(x,y) = 0$. Since, however, $N_\varepsilon(x)$ contains the element $\{\varepsilon/2,0, \ldots, 0\}$ ω H for each $\varepsilon > 0$, H is not open.

Note 8 As indicated in the Introduction, we pay special attention to those results in a metric space which can be derived (often with the help of Theorem 2.1) from the properties of $\mathscr{G}$ established in Theorem 2.2. For example, in the proof of Theorem 2.3 below, use of Theorem 2.1 enables us to deduce from Theorem 2.2 basic properties of the sets $\mathscr{N}(x)$.

THEOREM 2.3* For any space (S,ρ), $x \in S$ and $X,Y \subseteq S$:

(a) $X \in \mathscr{G}$ if and only if $X \in \mathscr{N}(x)$ for each x in X.

(b) If $X \in \mathscr{N}(x)$ and $X \subseteq Y$, then $Y \in \mathscr{N}(x)$.

(c) The intersection of any finite sequence of members of $\mathscr{N}(x)$ belongs to $\mathscr{N}(x)$.

(d) If $X \in \mathscr{N}(x)$, there exists a member Z of $\mathscr{N}(x)$ (dependent on the choice of X) such that $X \in \mathscr{N}(y)$ for each $y \in Z$.

PROOF (a) If $X \in \mathscr{G}$, then result follows immediately from Theorem 2.1 by taking $G = X$. Conversely, suppose $X \in \mathscr{N}(x)$ for each x in X. Then, by Theorem 2.1 there corresponds to each x in X a member G_x (dependent on the choice of x) of $\mathscr{G}$ such that: $x \in G_x \subseteq X$; let

$$G = \bigcup_{x \in X} G_x.$$

Clearly $X = G$, a member of $\mathscr{G}$ by Theorem 2.2.

(b) This is immediate from Theorem 2.1.

(c) For $x \in S$, let X_i, $1 \leq i \leq n$, be members of $\mathscr{N}(x)$; for each i with $1 \leq i \leq n$, there corresponds (by Theorem 2.1) an open set G_i such that $x \in G_i \subseteq X_i$. If $H = \bigcap_{1 \leq i \leq n} G_i$, $x \in H \subseteq \bigcap_{1 \leq i \leq n} X_i$ and $H \in \mathscr{G}$ by Theorem 2.2. That is, by Theorem 2.1, $\bigcap_{1 \leq i \leq n} X_i \in \mathscr{N}(x)$.

(d) By Theorem 2.1, $\exists$ open set G with $x \in G \subseteq X$; if $Z = G$, $Z \in \mathscr{N}(x)$, by Theorem 2.1, and, by part (a), $Z \in \mathscr{N}(y)$ for each y in Z; by part (b), $X \in \mathscr{N}(y)$.

Note 9 Part (a) of Theorem 2.3 is of course actually a restatement of Definition 5, which is here derived from Theorems 2.1 and 2.2 above. Part (d) could be interpreted roughly as follows: 'a neighbourhood of x is also a neighbourhood of any element y sufficiently close to x'.

Again (see Introduction) we emphasize those concepts which are ultimately definable in terms of $\mathscr{G}$, as, for example, in Definition 6 below:

DEFINITION 6* If $\mathscr{G}$ is the set of open sets of the space (S,ρ), a subset $\mathscr{G}'$ of $\mathscr{G}$ is said to be a **base for** $\mathscr{G}$ if each non-null member of $\mathscr{G}$ is the union of some family of members of $\mathscr{G}'$.

THEOREM 2.4* If $\mathscr{G}$ is the set of open sets of the space (S,ρ), a subset $\mathscr{G}'$ of $\mathscr{G}$ is a base for $\mathscr{G}$ if and only if: for each x in S, and $X \in \mathscr{N}(x)$, there exists G' in $\mathscr{G}'$ (dependent on the choice of x,X) with

$$x \in G' \subseteq X \tag{1}$$

PROOF To prove necessity of the condition (1), let $\mathscr{G}'$ be a base for $\mathscr{G}$, x an element of S, and $X \in \mathscr{N}(x)$; then, by Theorem 2.1, $\exists\, G \in \mathscr{G}$ such that $x \in G \subseteq X$. By definition, $G = \bigcup_{i \in I} G_i'$ for some family of members of $\mathscr{G}'$; then $\exists\, i'$ in I such that $x \in G_{i'}'$, and it is immediate that (1) holds.

Suppose conversely that $\mathscr{G}'$ satisfies (1); given non-null G in $\mathscr{G}$, to show that G is the union of members of G'. For each $x \in G$, $G \in \mathscr{N}(x)$ (Theorem 2.3); hence, by (1), $\exists\, G_x'$ in $\mathscr{G}'$ (dependent on choice of x) such that $x \in G_x' \subseteq G$. Clearly $G = \bigcup_{x \in G} G_x'$.

COROLLARY The set of all subsets of S of the form $N_\varepsilon(x)$, for $x \in S$ and $\varepsilon > 0$, is a base for $\mathscr{G}$.

DEFINITION 7* If $\mathscr{G}$ is the set of open sets of the space (S,ρ), a subset $\mathscr{G}''$ of $\mathscr{G}$ is said to be a **subbase for** $\mathscr{G}$ if the set $\mathscr{G}'$ of all finite intersections of members of $\mathscr{G}''$ is a base for $\mathscr{G}$. (By Theorem 2.2, $\mathscr{G}' \subseteq \mathscr{G}$.)

Example 2.2.8 For $(R^2)_1$, the set $\mathscr{G}''$ of all half-planes of any of the (four) forms $x_1 \gtrless a$, $x_2 \gtrless a$, is a subbase for $\mathscr{G}$.

Denote above sets by ${}_aX^1$, X_a^1, ${}_aX^2$, X_a^2 respectively. Then, first, each member of $\mathscr{G}''$ is open. Consider, for example, a set ${}_aX^2$. Given $x \equiv \{x_1,x_2\}$ in ${}_aX^2$, write $\varepsilon = (x_2 - a) > 0$. Then for any $y \equiv \{y_1,y_2\}$ in $N_\varepsilon(x)$, $|y_2 - x_2| \leqslant \rho_1(x,y) < \varepsilon$, implying:

$-\varepsilon < (y_2 - x_2)$, so that : $y_2 - a = (x_2 - a) + (y_2 - x_2) > \varepsilon - \varepsilon = 0$. i.e., $y \in {}_aX^2$. Thus $N_\varepsilon(x) \subseteq {}_aX^2$.

Secondly, the set $\mathscr{G}'$ of all finite intersections of members of $\mathscr{G}''$ satisfies condition (1). Given $x \equiv \{x_1,x_2\} \in R^2$, and $X \in \mathscr{N}(x)$, $\exists\, \varepsilon > 0$ such that: $N_\varepsilon(x) \subseteq X$. Let Y be the set of those elements $y \equiv \{y_1,y_2\}$ in R^2 such that

$$x_i - \varepsilon/2 < y_i < x_i + \varepsilon/2 \quad \text{for } i = 1,2.$$

Then $x \in Y = {}_{a_1}X^1 \cap X^1_{b_1} \cap {}_{a_2}X^2 \cap X^2_{b_2}$ (where $a_i = x_i - \varepsilon/2$, $b_i = x_i + \varepsilon/2$), a member of $\mathscr{G}'$.

Further, if $y \in Y$, $\rho_1(x,y) < \{(\varepsilon/2)^2 + (\varepsilon/2)^2\}^{\frac{1}{2}} < \varepsilon$ so that: $x \in Y \subseteq N_\varepsilon(x) \subseteq X$, from above. That is, $\mathscr{G}'$ satisfies condition (1).

2.3 Cluster Points, Closed Sets, Sequences

DEFINITION 8* Given space (S,ρ) and $X \subseteq S$, an element x of S is said to be a **cluster point** (limit point, point of accumulation) **of X** w.r.t. ρ, if

$$(Y - (x)) \cap X \neq \varnothing \text{ for each } Y \in \mathscr{N}(x). \tag{1}$$

Interpreted metrically, (1) is equivalent to: 'if, for each $\varepsilon > 0$, $\exists$ a member y of X (dependent on the choice of ε) such that

$$0 < \rho(x,y) < \varepsilon\text{'}. \tag{1'}$$

The set of all cluster points of X is called the (first) **derived set** of X, denoted by ${}^\rho X'$ or, usually, simply by X'.

Note 10 If, for some x in S, the one-element set (x) belongs to $\mathscr{N}(x)$, that is, if $\exists\, \varepsilon > 0$ such that $N_\varepsilon(x) = (x)$, then clearly x cannot be a cluster point of S (and hence of any subset X of S). (See Example 2.2.1.) Indeed we can prove:

THEOREM 2.5 If, for the space (S,ρ), the element x is a cluster point of the subset X of S, then, for any Y in $\mathscr{N}(x)$, $Y \cap X$ is an infinite set.

PROOF If not, $\exists\, \varepsilon > 0$ such that $N_\varepsilon(x) \cap X$ is only a finite set. If $(N_\varepsilon(x) - (x)) \cap X$ is empty, there is nothing more to prove. If not, let $x_1,x_2,\ldots,x_n$, for some positive integer n, denote its members, and let $\varepsilon' = \min\limits_{1 \leqslant i \leqslant n} \rho(x,x_i) > 0$. Then again, $(N_{\varepsilon'}(x) - (x)) \cap X$ is empty, and a contradiction to the hypothesis is once more obtained.

COROLLARY If X is finite, X' is empty.

As the examples below show, a cluster point of a set X may or may not be a member of X itself; indeed $X \cap X'$ may be null (as in Example 2.3.1 below).

Example 2.3.1 For space $(R^2)_1$, let X denote the set of all elements of R^2 of the form:

$$x_{m,n} = \left\{\frac{m}{n}, 1 - \frac{1}{n}\right\} \quad \text{where } m,n \in J \text{ and } n \geqslant 1.$$

We shall show that X' is the set Y of those elements $x \equiv \{x_1,x_2\}$ of R^2 such that $x_2 = 1$. We prove this in stages (a) and (b):

(a) $Y \subseteq X'$. Given $x \equiv \{x_1,1\} \in Y$, and $\varepsilon > 0$, $\exists$ a rational number $r = p/q$ (where $p,q \in J$) such that $x_1 < r < x_1 + \varepsilon/2^{\frac{1}{2}}$ and positive integer n such that $n > 2^{\frac{1}{2}}/\varepsilon$. Then if $y = \{p/q, 1 - (1/nq)\}$ clearly $y \in X$ and $\rho_1(x,y) = \{(x_1 - r)^2 + 1/(nq)^2\}^{\frac{1}{2}}$ which, by the choice of r and n, is less than $(\varepsilon^2/2 + \varepsilon^2/2)^{\frac{1}{2}} = \varepsilon$.

Thus, for any $\varepsilon > 0$, $(N_\varepsilon(x) - (x)) \cap X \neq \varnothing$.

(b) $X' \subseteq Y$. Suppose $x \equiv \{x_1,x_2\}\ \omega\ Y$; let $2\delta = |x_2 - 1| > 0$. Then:

$$\rho_1(x_{m,n},x) \geqslant \left|x_2 - \left(1 - \frac{1}{n}\right)\right|$$

$$\geqslant |x_2 - 1| - \frac{1}{n} \geqslant \delta \quad \text{for } n \geqslant \delta^{-1}$$

i.e.,

$$x_{m,n}\ \omega\ N_\delta(x) \quad \text{for } n \geqslant \delta^{-1}. \tag{1}$$

Again,

$$\rho_1(x_{m,n},x) \geqslant \left| x_1 - \frac{m}{n}\right| \geqslant \frac{|m|}{n} - |x_1|$$

$$\geqslant \delta \quad \text{for } |m| \geqslant n(|x_1| + \delta)$$

i.e.,

$$x_{m,n}\ \omega\ N_\delta(x) \quad \text{for } |m| \geqslant n(|x_1| + \delta). \tag{2}$$

(1), (2) imply that $N_\delta(x)$ contains at most those members $x_{m,n}$ of X which satisfy simultaneously the two conditions:

$$n < \delta^{-1} \quad \text{and } |m| < n(|x_1| + \delta)$$

i.e., $N_\delta(x)$ contains only a finite number of elements of X.

So, by Theorem 2.5, $x\ \omega\ X'$.

Example 2.3.2 For space $(R)_1$, let X be the set Q of all rational points. Since, given x in R, and $\varepsilon > 0$, $\exists r$ in X such that $x < r < x + \varepsilon$, every member of R is a cluster point of X; that is, $X' = R$ itself. Similarly, $(C(X))' = R$.

Thus, a given cluster point of X may or may not be a member of X itself.

DEFINITION 9* Given space (S,ρ) and $X \subseteq S$, an element x of S is said to be a **point of condensation** of X w.r.t.ρ if, for each Y in $\mathcal{N}(x)$: $(Y - (x)) \cap X$ is non-enumerable.

Example 2.3.3 In Example 2.3.2 above, $]x,x + \varepsilon[\cap C(X)$ is non-enumerable for each x in R and $\varepsilon > 0$.

DEFINITION 10* Given space (S,ρ) and $X \subseteq S$, the **closure** of X w.r.t. ρ is defined as $X \cup X'$, and is denoted by ${}^{\rho}\overline{X}$ or $\overline{X}$.

Thus, for a finite set X, $\overline{X} = X$, while, in Examples 2.3.1 and 2.3.2 above, $\overline{X} = X \cup Y$, R respectively.

THEOREM 2.6 Given space (S,ρ), $X \subseteq S$ and x in S, then $x \in \overline{X}$ if and only if one of the following conditions is satisfied:

(a)* for each Y in $\mathcal{N}(x)$, $Y \cap X \neq \varnothing$;
(b) for each $\varepsilon > 0$, $N_\varepsilon(x) \cap X \neq \varnothing$;
(c) $\rho(x,X) = 0$.

The proof is left to the reader.

The basic properties of the notion of closure are given in:

THEOREM 2.7* For any space (S,ρ) and $X,Y \subseteq S$:

(a) The closure of the null set is the null set;
(b) $X \subseteq \overline{X}$;
(c) $\overline{\overline{X}} = \overline{X}$;
(d) $\overline{X \cup Y} = \overline{X} \cup \overline{Y}$.

PROOF (a), (b) are immediate.

(c) From (b), it suffices to show: $\overline{\overline{X}} \subseteq \overline{X}$. Let $x \in \overline{\overline{X}}$ and Y an arbitrary member of $\mathcal{N}(x)$; then, by Theorem 2.3, part (d), $\exists$ a member Z of $\mathcal{N}(x)$ such that Y is a neighbourhood of every member of Z. But, by Theorem 2.6, $Z \cap \overline{X} \neq \varnothing$; that is, $\exists$ an element y in Z such that $y \in \overline{X}$. But, again, the latter statement means that each neighbourhood of y has an element in common with X; hence, in particular, $Y \cap X \neq \varnothing$. Since Y was chosen arbitrarily in $\mathcal{N}(x)$, it follows that $x \in \overline{X}$.

(d) If $x \in \overline{X} \cup \overline{Y}$, then, for any Z in $\mathcal{N}(x)$, $Z \cap (X \cup Y) = (Z \cap X) \cup (Z \cap Y)$, clearly non-empty; that is, $x \in \overline{X \cup Y}$.

On the other hand, suppose $x\,\omega\,\overline{X} \cup \overline{Y}$; then $\exists\, Z,Z'$ in $\mathcal{N}(x)$ such that $Z \cap X$, and $Z' \cap Y$ are both null. If $W = Z \cap Z'$, W belongs to $\mathcal{N}(x)$, by Theorem 2.3, and clearly

$$W \cap (X \cup Y) = (W \cap X) \cup (W \cap Y) = \varnothing; \text{ that is, } x\,\omega\,\overline{X \cup Y}.$$

COROLLARY

(a) If $X \subseteq Y \subseteq S$, $\quad \overline{X} \subseteq \overline{Y}$;

(b) For any family $\{X_i\}$, $i \in I$, of subsets of S

$$\bigcup_i \overline{X}_i \subseteq \overline{\bigcup_i X_i}; \qquad \overline{\bigcap_i X_i} \subseteq \bigcap_i \overline{X}_i;$$

(c) For a finite sequence $\{X_i\}$, $1 \leqslant i \leqslant n$, of subsets of S, $\overline{\bigcup_{1 \leqslant i \leqslant n} X_i} = \bigcup_{1 \leqslant i \leqslant n} \overline{X}_i$.

Note 11 In the Corollary above, equality need not hold in the second part of (b) (even for two sets X_1, X_2 with non-null intersection) and it need not hold in the first part for an infinite family.

Example 2.3.4 For space $(R)_1$, let Y be the open interval $]0,1[$, $X_1 = Y \cup (\bigcup_{n \geqslant 1} (2 + n^{-1}))$, $\quad X_2 = Y \cup (\bigcup_{n \geqslant 1} (2 - n^{-1}))$. Then:

$$\overline{X_1 \cap X_2} = \overline{Y} = [0,1] \subset [0,1] \cup (2) = \overline{X}_1 \cap \overline{X}_2.$$

Example 2.3.5 For space (R_1), take $X_i = (i^{-1})$ for all positive integers i. Clearly: $\overline{\bigcup_{i \geqslant 1} X_i}$ contains 0, while $\bigcup_{i \geqslant 1} \overline{X}_i = \bigcup_{i \geqslant 1} X_i$.

THEOREM 2.8 Given space (S,ρ), let X be a bounded subset of S; then $\overline{X}$ is bounded and $D(\overline{X}) = D(X)$.

The proof is left to the reader.

DEFINITION 11* Given space (S,ρ), a member x of a subset X of S is said to be an **interior point** of X w.r.t. ρ if $X \in \mathcal{N}_\rho(x)$.

The set of all interior points of X is called the **interior** of X, denoted by ${}^{\rho}X^{\circ}$ or, usually, by X°. Clearly X is open if and only if $X^{\circ} = X$.

Note 12 X° can very well be null, even if X is non-enumerable.

Example 2.3.6 For space $(R)_1$, let X be set of all irrational points. For any $\varepsilon > 0$, the ε-neighbourhood of any member x of X contains rational points, and so x is *not* an interior point of X. That is, X° is null.

THEOREM 2.9* For any space (S,ρ) and $X \subseteq S$:

(a) $C(X^\circ) = \overline{C(X)}$; $C(\overline{X}) = (C(X))^\circ$;
(b) X° is the maximum open set contained in X;
(c) $X^{\circ\circ} = X^\circ$;
(d) For any family $\{X_i\}$, $i \in I$, of subsets of S: $\bigcup_i X_i^\circ \subseteq (\bigcup_i X_i)^\circ$, $(\bigcap_i X_i)^\circ \subseteq \bigcap_i X_i^\circ$;
(e) For a finite sequence $\{X_i\}$, $1 \leqslant i \leqslant n$, of subsets of S, $(\bigcap_{1\leqslant i\leqslant n} X_i)^\circ = \bigcap_{1\leqslant i\leqslant n} X_i^\circ$.

The proof (depending for parts (d), (e) on Theorem 2.7, Corollary) is left to the reader.

Example 2.3.7 If, in any space (S,ρ), with x in S and $\varepsilon > 0$, $S_\varepsilon(x)$ denotes the set of those elements y in S such that $\rho(x,y) \leqslant \varepsilon$, then: $N_\varepsilon(x) \subseteq (S_\varepsilon(x))^\circ$ (Cf. Note 14, below).

DEFINITION 12* Given space (S,ρ), a subset X of S is said to be **closed** (in S) w.r.t. ρ if $X = {}^\rho\overline{X}$. If no ambiguity can arise, X is said simply to be **closed**. The set of all closed subsets of S is denoted by $\mathscr{F}_\rho$ or $\mathscr{F}$.

Clearly $\overline{X}$ is closed for arbitrary $X \subseteq S$.

THEOREM 2.10* Given space (S,ρ), let X be closed and $X' \subseteq Y \subseteq X$. Then Y is closed.

The proof is left to the reader.

THEOREM 2.11 For any space (S,ρ) and $X \subseteq S$, X' is closed.

PROOF If X is null, the result is immediate. If not, let $x \in (\overline{X'})$, and Y be an arbitrary member of $\mathscr{N}(x)$; then (as in the proof of Theorem 2.7(c)) $\exists$ a member Z of $\mathscr{N}(x)$ such that Y is a neighbourhood of every member of Z. Then $Z \cap X' \neq \varnothing$; that is, $\exists$ an element y in Z such that $y \in X'$. But, by Theorem 2.5, the latter implies that each neighbourhood of y has an infinity of elements in common with X; so, in particular, Y has *a fortiori more than one* element in common with X; hence $(Y - (x)) \cap X \neq \varnothing$. Thus $x \in X'$.

Note 13 Although the proof of Theorem 2.11 has much in common with that of Theorem 2.7(c), the former result cannot (in contrast to the latter) be deduced from Theorem 2.2. To see why an appeal to Theorem 2.5 is essential here, let Y,Z,y be chosen as above. Then, without the support of Theorem 2.5, all that we can deduce from the assertion: '$y \in X'$' is that, for an arbitrary member W of $\mathscr{N}(y)$, $(W - (y)) \cap X$ contains at least one element; hence, in particular (since Y is a neighbourhood of every member of Z) $(Y - (y)) \cap X$ contains at least one element; that is, $\exists$ at least one member z of $Y \cap X$ such that $z \neq y$. Since, without the support of Theorem 2.5, we cannot assert that the number of such elements z is necessarily greater than one, it cannot be deduced that $\exists$ a member z of $Y \cap X$ such that z does not coincide with x itself; that is, that $(Y - (x)) \cap X$ is non-null.

THEOREM 2.12* Given a space (S,ρ) and $X \subseteq S$:
(a) $X \in \mathscr{F}$ if and only if $C(X) \in \mathscr{G}$;
(b) $X \in \mathscr{G}$ if and only if $C(X) \in \mathscr{F}$.

PROOF (a) $X \in \mathscr{F}$ if and only if $X = \overline{X}$, that is, $C(X) = C(\overline{X}) = (C(X))^{\circ}$.
(b) Write $Y = C(X)$, so that $X = C(Y)$. Then: $X \in \mathscr{G}$ if and only if $C(Y) \in \mathscr{G}$, i.e., $Y \in \mathscr{F}$, by part (a).

The next theorem is an analogue of Theorem 2.2:

THEOREM 2.13* For any space (S,ρ):
(a) S and the null set belong to $\mathscr{F}$.
(b) The intersection of any family of members of $\mathscr{F}$ belongs to $\mathscr{F}$.
(c) The union of any finite sequence of members of $\mathscr{F}$ belongs to $\mathscr{F}$.

PROOF (a) This is immediate from Theorems 2.2 and 2.12.
(b) Let $\{F_i\}$, $i \in I$, be any family of members of $\mathscr{F}$; let $F = \bigcap_i F_i$. Then $C(F) = \bigcup_i C(F_i)$ where each $C(F_i) \in \mathscr{G}$. By Theorem 2.2, $C(F)$ hence belongs to $\mathscr{G}$. That is, $F \in \mathscr{F}$.
(c) This is a similar deduction from Theorems 2.2 and 2.12.

Example 2.3.8 If, in any space, $S_\varepsilon(x)$ is defined as in Example 2.3.7 above, then $S_\varepsilon(x)$ is closed and hence:

$$\overline{N_\varepsilon(x)} \subseteq S_\varepsilon(x) \tag{1}$$

Given y in $C(S_\varepsilon(x))$, write $\varepsilon' = \rho(x,y) - \varepsilon > 0$; then (Cf. Example 2.2.4) it is seen that: $N_{\varepsilon'}(y) \subseteq C(S_\varepsilon(x))$, so that $C(S_\varepsilon(x))$ is open.
(1) follows from Theorem 2.7, Corollary, part (a).

Example 2.3.9 In any space, the set X of those elements y in S such that $\rho(x,y) = \varepsilon > 0$, is closed, for:

$$X = S_\varepsilon(x) \cap C(N_\varepsilon(x)), \qquad \text{where } C(N_\varepsilon(x)) \text{ is closed.}$$

Example 2.3.10 For the space $(R)_1$, any closed set X, bounded above (resp. below) contains its supremum (resp. infimum). Indeed, for an arbitrary set X, bounded above (resp. below), sup X (resp. inf X) is a member of $\overline{X}$. For if, for example, $x = \sup X$, and ε is positive, then $x - \varepsilon$ is not an upper bound of X; that is, $x - \varepsilon < y$, for some member y of X. Since $y \leqslant x \leqslant x + \varepsilon$, $y \in N_\varepsilon(x) \cap X$.

Note 14 Equality need not hold either in Example 2.3.7 or in Example 2.3.8(1);

Example 2.3.11 If S is an arbitrary set with more than one member, and k is positive, define the metric ρ_0 on S as in Note 1. For any x in S: $N_k(x) = (x)$, implying $\overline{N_k(x)} = (x)$, while $S_k(x) = S$ itself. Thus $N_k(x) \subset S = (S_k(x))^\circ$ and $\overline{N_k(x)} \subset S_k(x)$.

However we can prove:

THEOREM 2.14 Given the space (S,ρ), then for each x in S and positive ε: $N_\varepsilon(x) = (S_\varepsilon(x))^\circ$ (resp. $\overline{N_\varepsilon(x)} = S_\varepsilon(x)$) if, given y in $S - (x)$ and δ positive, there exists an element y' of $N_\delta(y)$ such that:

$$\rho(x,y') > \rho(x,y) \text{ (resp. } \rho(x,y') < \rho(x,y)).$$

The proof is left to the reader.

Example 2.3.12 Both conditions of Theorem 2.14 are easily verified for (R^n,ρ_i), $n \geqslant 1$, $i = 1,2,3$ (see Example 2.1.1).

In particular then, for $n = 1$ and real numbers a,b with $a < b$:

$$[a,b]^\circ =]a,b[\quad \text{and} \quad \overline{]a,b[} = [a,b]$$

If then $X = Q \cap [a,b]$ and $Y =]a,b[\cup (c)$, $b < c$, clearly (Cf. Example 2.3.2) $\overline{X} = [a,b]$, giving $(\overline{X})^\circ =]a,b[$ while: $Y^\circ =]a,b[$, giving $\overline{Y^\circ} = [a,b]$.

That is, provided that at least one of a, b is rational, neither of the pairs $(X,(\overline{X})^\circ)$, $(Y,\overline{Y^\circ})$ is comparable set-theoretically.

The following is an analogue of Theorem 2.9, part (b):

THEOREM 2.15* For any space (S,ρ) and $X \subseteq S$, $\overline{X}$ is the intersection (that is, the minimum) of all closed sets containing X.

The proof is immediate.

THEOREM 2.16 For any space (S,ρ):

(a) any closed set is the intersection of some sequence of open sets;

(b) any open set is the union of some sequence of closed sets.

PROOF (a) Given $F \in \mathscr{F}$, let $G_i = \bigcup_{x \in F} N_{i^{-1}}(x)$ for each $i = 1,2,\ldots$ Each $G_i \in \mathscr{G}$, and clearly $F \subseteq \bigcap_{i \geqslant 1} G_i$. On the other hand, given $x \in \bigcap_{i \geqslant 1} G_i$, choose $\varepsilon > 0$ and integer $i_0 \geqslant \varepsilon^{-1}$; then, in particular, $x \in G_{i_0}$; that is, $\exists$ y in F such that $x \in N_{i_0^{-1}}(y)$, thus

$$y \in N_{i_0^{-1}}(x) \subseteq N_\varepsilon(x).$$

Thus $N_\varepsilon(x) \cap F \neq \varnothing$ for any $\varepsilon > 0$. Hence $x \in \bar{F} = F$.

(b) This is immediate from part (a) and Theorem 2.12.

The subset of $P(S)$ of all members expressible as the intersection of a sequence of open sets is denoted by $(\mathscr{G}_\rho)_\delta$ or, more usually, merely by $\mathscr{G}_\delta$, and any member is called a **G_δ-subset of S**, (w.r.t. ρ). The notations: '$(\mathscr{F}_\rho)_\sigma$ or $\mathscr{F}_\sigma$', and 'F_σ-subset' have an analogous significance.

THEOREM 2.17 Given a space (S,ρ), X a closed proper subset of S, and member x of $C(X)$, there exist open sets G_i, $i = 1,2$, such that: $G_1 \cap G_2 = \varnothing$, $X \subseteq G_1$, and $x \in G_2$.

PROOF We first show that it suffices to verify the assertion: 'if G is any open set containing x, $\exists$ an open set G' (dependent on the choice of G) containing x and such that $\overline{G'} \subseteq G$' (1)

For, supposing the truth of (1), let X be a closed set not containing x; then $x \in C(X)$, which is open, by Theorem 2.12. By taking $G = C(X)$ in (1) it follows that $\exists$ an open set G' containing x such that $\overline{G'} \subseteq C(X)$, implying: $X \subseteq C(\overline{G'})$, which is open by Theorem 2.12. $C(\overline{G'})$ and G' satisfy the requirements enunciated above.

To show, finally, that assertion (1) actually holds for any space (S,ρ), choose positive ε so that $N_\varepsilon(x) \subseteq G$ and let $G' = N_{\frac{1}{2}\varepsilon}(x)$. Then, from Example 2.3.8 above, $\overline{G'} \subseteq S_{\frac{1}{2}\varepsilon}(x) \subseteq N_\varepsilon(x) \subseteq G$.

COROLLARY Given a space (S,ρ), and the distinct elements x_i $(i = 1,2)$, of S, there exist open sets G_i, $i = 1,2$, such that $G_1 \cap G_2 = \varnothing$ and $x_i \in G_i$, $i = 1,2$.

DEFINITION 13* Given space (S,ρ), a member x of a subset X of S is said to be an **isolated point** of X (w.r.t. ρ) if x is *not* a member of ${}^\rho X'$.

A subset X is called an **isolated set** when all its members are isolated points of X; that is, when $X \cap X'$ is null.

A subset X is said to be **discrete** if X' itself is null.

A discrete set is necessarily isolated, but (Cf. Example 2.3.1) an isolated set need not be discrete.

A metric ρ on a set S such that S (and hence each subset X of S) is discrete is said to be a **discrete metric**, and the space (S,ρ) is itself said to be discrete. (For example, the space (S,ρ_0) of Note 1.) There, every subset X of S is both open and closed.

DEFINITION 14* Given the space (S,ρ), and $X \subseteq S$, an element x of S is said to be an **exterior point** to X (w.r.t. ρ) if x is in ${}^{\rho}(C(X))^{\circ}$.

The set of all elements exterior to X is called the **exterior** of X, denoted by ${}^{\rho}E(X)$ or $E(X)$.

DEFINITION 15* Given the space (S,ρ) and $X \subseteq S$, an element x of S is said to be a **frontier** (or boundary) **point** of X (w.r.t. ρ) if, for each Y in $\mathcal{N}(x)$, neither $Y \cap X$ nor $Y \cap C(X)$ is null.

The set of frontier points of X is called the **frontier** of X, denoted by ${}^{\rho}\mathrm{Fr}(X)$ or $\mathrm{Fr}(X)$.

Clearly: $\mathrm{Fr}(X) = \overline{X} \cap \overline{C(X)} = \overline{X} \cap C(X^{\circ})$, $\mathrm{Fr}(X)$ is closed, and $\mathrm{Fr}(X) = \mathrm{Fr}(C(X))$.

Also, for any $X \subseteq S$, S can be expressed as the union of the mutually disjointed sets: X°, $E(X)$, $\mathrm{Fr}(X)$.

Example 2.3.13 For space (R^n,ρ_i), $i = 1,2,3$, it follows from Theorem 2.14 that $\mathrm{Fr}(N_\varepsilon(x)) = \mathrm{Fr}(S_\varepsilon(x))$, which is the set of those elements y of S with $\rho(x,y) = \varepsilon$.

Example 2.3.14 For $(R)_1$, $\mathrm{Fr}(Q) = R$ itself (See Example 2.3.2).

Example 2.3.15 If (S,ρ) is discrete, $\mathrm{Fr}(X)$ is null for every subset X of S. This could have been deduced from part (a) of Theorem 2.18 below:

THEOREM 2.18* For any space (S,ρ) and $X, Y \subseteq S$:

(a) $\mathrm{Fr}(X)$ is null if and only if X is both open and closed;

(b) If $\mathrm{Fr}(X) \cap \mathrm{Fr}(Y)$ is null,

$$\text{(I)}\quad (X \cup Y)^{\circ} = X^{\circ} \cup Y^{\circ}; \qquad \text{(II)}\quad \overline{X \cap Y} = \overline{X} \cap \overline{Y}.$$

PROOF (a) Clearly $X \in \mathcal{G} \cap \mathcal{F}$ if and only if $\overline{X} \subseteq X^{\circ}$; that is, $\overline{X} \cap C(X^{\circ}) = \varnothing$.

(b) (I) By Theorem 2.9, it suffices to show that $(X \cup Y)^{\circ} \subseteq X^{\circ} \cup Y^{\circ}$. Suppose not; that is, $\exists x$ in $(X \cup Y)^{\circ}$ such that

$x \,\omega\, X^\circ \cup Y^\circ$. Let Z be an arbitrary member of $\mathcal{N}(x)$, and write:

$$W = Z \cap (X \cup Y) = (Z \cap X) \cup (Z \cap Y) \tag{1}$$

Since $X \cup Y \in \mathcal{N}(x)$, $W \in \mathcal{N}(x)$, and so, since $x \,\omega\, X^\circ$, $W \cap C(X) \neq \varnothing$; similarly $W \cap C(Y) \neq \varnothing$ (2)

Now $W \cap X = Z \cap ((X \cup Y) \cap X) = Z \cap X$, so, if $W \cap X$ were null, W would equal $Z \cap Y$ (by (1)) which would imply: $W \subseteq Y$, contradicting (2). Hence $W \cap X \neq \varnothing$; similarly $W \cap Y \neq \varnothing$. *A fortiori*, Z must meet X, and $C(X)$; that is, $x \in \mathrm{Fr}(X)$; similarly, $x \in \mathrm{Fr}(Y)$, giving a contradiction to hypothesis.

(II) This is a straightforward deduction from Theorem 2.9(a), and part (I) above, where $\overline{X \cap Y} = C((C(X) \cup C(Y))^\circ)$.

Note 15 Where $\mathrm{Fr}(X) \cap \mathrm{Fr}(Y)$ is not null, equality will hold in Theorem 2.18(a) (I) clearly only where $\overline{C(X)} \cap \overline{C(Y)}$ equals $\overline{C(X) \cap C(Y)}$; in Example 2.3.4, it was seen that this need not be the case.

DEFINITION 16* If $\mathcal{F}$ is the set of closed sets of the space (S,ρ), a subset $\mathcal{F}'$ of $\mathcal{F}$ is said to be a **base for** $\mathcal{F}$ if each member of $\mathcal{F}$ (with the possible exception of S itself), is the intersection of some family of members of $\mathcal{F}'$.

It is clear from Definition 6 and Theorem 2.12 that a given subset $\mathcal{F}'$ of $\mathcal{F}$ is a base for $\mathcal{F}$ if and only if the set $\mathcal{G}'$ of the complements (w.r.t. S) of the members of $\mathcal{F}'$ is a base for $\mathcal{G}$, the set of open sets of the space.

Again, analogously to Definition 7, we have:

DEFINITION 17* If $\mathcal{F}$ is the set of closed sets of the space (S,ρ), a subset $\mathcal{F}''$ of $\mathcal{F}$ is said to be a **subbase for** $\mathcal{F}$ if the set $\mathcal{F}'$ of all finite unions of members of $\mathcal{F}''$ is a base for $\mathcal{F}$.

(By Theorem 2.13, $\mathcal{F}' \subseteq \mathcal{F}$.)

Again, a given subset $\mathcal{F}''$ of $\mathcal{F}$ is clearly a subbase for $\mathcal{F}$ if and only if the set $\mathcal{G}''$ of the complements of the members of $\mathcal{F}''$ is a subbase for $\mathcal{G}$.

Example 2.3.16 By Example 2.2.8, it is clear that the set $\mathcal{F}''$ of all half-planes of any of the forms $x_1 \gtreqless a$, $x_2 \gtreqless a$, is a subbase for the set $\mathcal{F}$ of all closed sets of the space $(R^2)_1$.

DEFINITION 18 Given a space (S,ρ), a sequence $\{x_i\}$, $i \geqslant 1$, of elements of S is said to be **fundamental** (w.r.t. ρ) if, given $\varepsilon > 0$, there exists i_0 (dependent on the choice of ε) such that $\rho(x_i,x_j) < \varepsilon$ whenever $j > i \geqslant i_0$.

Clearly any fundamental sequence is bounded, in the sense that $X \equiv \bigcup_{i \geqslant 1} (x_i)$ is bounded in the sense of Definition 2.

DEFINITION 19* Given a space (S,ρ), a sequence $\{x_i\}$, $i \geqslant 1$, of elements of S is said to **converge** to an element x of S (w.r.t. ρ) if, given Y in $\mathcal{N}(x)$, there exists i_0 (dependent on the choice of Y) such that $x_i \in Y$ for $i \geqslant i_0$.

Such a sequence is said to be **convergent** (to x), and we write: $x_i \underset{\rho}{\rightarrow} x$ or, usually, $x_i \rightarrow x$. Thus $x_i \rightarrow x$ if and only if $\lim_i \rho(x_i,x) = 0$.

THEOREM 2.19 Given a space (S,ρ), let $\{x_i\}$, $i \geqslant 1$, be a sequence of elements of S converging to the element x of S. Then:

(a) $\{x_i\}$ is a fundamental sequence;
(b) $\{x_i\}$ is bounded;
(c) $\{x_i\}$ cannot converge to any element of S distinct from x;
(d)*Every subsequence of $\{x_i\}$ converges to x.

PROOF We shall confine ourselves to proving (c).

If $\exists$ an element y in S, distinct from x, such that $x_i \rightarrow y$, denote the (positive) number $\rho(x,y)$ by $2k$. By definition, $\exists$ integers i_0, i'_0 such that $\rho(x_i,x) < k$ for $i \geqslant i_0$ and: $\rho(x_i,y) < k$ for $i \geqslant i'_0$. If i''_0 denotes the greater of i_0,i'_0, clearly: $2k \leqslant \rho(x_{i''_0},x) + \rho(x_{i''_0},y) < 2k$.

THEOREM 2.20 Given a space (S,ρ), let $\{x_i\}$, $i \geqslant 1$, be a fundamental sequence of elements of S such that some subsequence $\{x_{i_r}\}$, $r \geqslant 1$, converges to x. Then $\{x_i\}$ itself converges to x.

PROOF Given $\varepsilon > 0$, $\exists$ integer i_0 (dependent on ε) such that $\rho(x_i,x_j) < \varepsilon/2$ for $j > i \geqslant i_0$; further, since $x_{i_r} \rightarrow x$, $\exists$ integer r_0 such that $\rho(x_{i_r},x) < \varepsilon/2$ for $r \geqslant r_0$. If integer r' is chosen so that $r' \geqslant r_0$ *and* $i_{r'} \geqslant i_0$, then for $i \geqslant i_{r'}$:

$$\rho(x_i,x) \leqslant \rho(x_i,x_{i_{r'}}) + \rho(x_{i_{r'}},x) < \varepsilon.$$

THEOREM 2.21 Given a space (S,ρ), let $A \subseteq S$ and x be an element of S. Then:

(a) x is a cluster point of A if* and only if $A - (x)$ contains a sequence of distinct elements converging to x;
(b) A is open if and only if* for each x in A, and sequence $\{x_i\}$ such that $x_i \rightarrow x$, there exists i_0 such that $x_i \in A$ for $i \geqslant i_0$;

(c) if $\{x_i\}$ is any sequence of elements such that x is a cluster point of $\bigcup_{i \geqslant 1} (x_i)$, there exists a subsequence $\{x_{i_r}\}$, $r \geqslant 1$, converging to x.

PROOF (a) If $x \in A'$, then, corresponding to each $i = 1,2,\ldots$, $\exists$ an element x_i of A with $x_i \in N_{i^{-1}}(x) - (x)$; that is, $x_i \in A - (x)$ and $\rho(x_i,x) < i^{-1}$. It is clear from Theorem 2.5 that the x_i can be chosen to be distinct. The converse is immediate.

(b) If A is open, and $x \in A$, $A \in \mathcal{N}(x)$; it is immediate from Definition 19 that an integer i_0 exists as required. Conversely, if A is not open, $C(A)$ is not closed; that is, some member x of A is a cluster point of $C(A)$, implying, by part (a), that $C(A)$ contains some sequence $\{x_i\}$ converging to x; that is, $x_i \to x$ although $x_i \,\omega\, A$ for every i.

(c) A strictly increasing sequence $\{i_r\}$, $r \geqslant 1$, of positive integers can be constructed as follows:

Choose i so that $x_i \in N_1(x)$; call it i_1. If, given $r > 1$, the terms $i_1, i_2, \ldots, i_{r-1}$ have been chosen, there exists (by Theorem 2.5) an integer $i > i_{r-1}$ such that $x_i \in N_{r^{-1}}(x)$; let i_r denote the least of these. Since $x_{i_r} \in N_{r^{-1}}(x)$ for each $r = 1,2,\ldots$, clearly $x_{i_r} \to x$.

COROLLARY $x \in \bar{A}$ if* and only if A contains a sequence of elements converging to x.

Worked Exercises (on Section 2.3)

(a)* Given a space (S,ρ), $X \subseteq S$, and Y in $\mathcal{G}$, show that:

$$\bar{X} \cap Y \subseteq \overline{X \cap Y}.$$

Solution: Given x in $\bar{X} \cap Y$, and any Z in $\mathcal{N}(x)$, it is clear from Theorem 2.3 that $Z \cap Y \in \mathcal{N}(x)$. Hence (since $x \in \bar{X}$),

$$Z \cap (X \cap Y) = (Z \cap Y) \cap X \neq \varnothing; \text{ and so } x \in \overline{X \cap Y}.$$

(b) Given a space (S,ρ), let $\mathcal{K} \equiv \{F_i\}$, $i \in I$, be a non-enumerable chain in $\mathcal{F}$ (when partially-ordered by inclusion); if $F = \bigcup_i F_i$, show that $F \in \mathcal{F}_\sigma$.

Solution: If $\exists$ a sequence of members of $\mathcal{K}$ whose union is F, the result is immediate. If not, there will clearly correspond to each sequence $\{F_{i_r}\}$, $r \geqslant 1$, of members of $\mathcal{K}$, a member i' of I such that $F_{i'} - F_{i_r} \neq \varnothing$ for $r \geqslant 1$. But, for each r, either $F_{i'} \subseteq F_{i_r}$ or $F_{i_r} \subseteq F_{i'}$; hence, by above:

$$F_{i_r} \subset F_{i'} \quad \text{for all } r \geqslant 1 \tag{1}$$

Then, if $x \in \bar{F}$, $\exists$ (by Theorem 2.21, Corollary) a sequence $\{x_j\}$, $j \geqslant 1$, of elements of F such that $x_j \underset{\rho}{\rightarrow} x$. For each $j \geqslant 1$, $\exists$ i_j in I with $x_j \in F_{i_j}$; application of (1) above to the sequence $\{F_{i_j}\}$, $j \geqslant 1$, yields an i' in I such that: $F_{i_j} \subset F_{i'}$, all j, implying that each member of $\{x_j\}$ lies in $F_{i'}$. Hence $x \in \bar{F}_{i'} = F_{i'} \subseteq F$. Thus $F \in \mathscr{F} \subseteq \mathscr{F}_\sigma$.

Exercises for Solution (on Sections 2.2–2.3)

1. (a)* Given a space (S,ρ), show that a given subset $\mathscr{G}''$ of $\mathscr{G}$ is a subbase for $\mathscr{G}$ if and only if $\exists$ a subbase $\mathscr{G}_1''$ for $\mathscr{G}$ such that: for each x in S and member G_1 of $\mathscr{G}_1''$ containing x, $\exists$ G in $\mathscr{G}''$ such that

$$x \in G \subseteq G_1. \tag{1}$$

(b) Deduce from (a) (and Example 2.2.8) that $\exists$ an enumerable base for the open sets of $(R^2)_1$.

(c) If $\mathscr{G}''$ is a subbase for $\mathscr{G}$ in a space (S,ρ), must (1) hold for *every* subbase $\mathscr{G}_1''$? If not, justify answer by means of an example.

2.* Given a space (S,ρ), and $X \subseteq S$, write: $\alpha(X) = (\bar{X})^\circ$, $\beta(X) = \overline{X^\circ}$. (Cf. Example 2.3.12.) Show that:

(a) if $X \in \mathscr{G}$, $X \subseteq \alpha(X)$; if $X \in \mathscr{F}$, $\beta(X) \subseteq X$;
(b) $\alpha(\alpha(X)) = \alpha(X)$; $\beta(\beta(X)) = \beta(X)$;
(c) if G, G' are open, and $G \cap G' = \varnothing$, then: $\alpha(G) \cap \alpha(G') = \varnothing$.

3.* Given a space (S,ρ) and $X \subseteq S$, write $\gamma(X) = X \cap \overline{C(X)}$. If X is called a **border set** when $X = \gamma(X)$, show that:

(a) X is a border set if and only if $X^\circ = \varnothing$;
(b) if X is a border set, and $Y \subseteq X$, so is Y;
(c) for any $X \subseteq S$, $\gamma(\gamma(X)) = \gamma(X)$.

4. Show that (with reference to Theorem 2.16) $\mathscr{F}_\rho = (\mathscr{G}_\rho)_\delta$ only when (S,ρ) is discrete.

5.* For any space (S,ρ) and subsets X,Y of S, show that:

(a) $\mathrm{Fr}(\bar{X}) \subseteq \mathrm{Fr}(X)$; $\mathrm{Fr}(X^\circ) \subseteq \mathrm{Fr}(X)$;
(b) $\mathrm{Fr}(X \cup Y) \subseteq \mathrm{Fr}(X) \cup \mathrm{Fr}(Y)$, equality holding if $\bar{X} \cap \bar{Y} = \varnothing$;
(c) $\mathrm{Fr}(X \cap Y) \subseteq (\bar{X} \cap \mathrm{Fr}(Y)) \cup (\bar{Y} \cap \mathrm{Fr}(X))$
$= (X \cap \mathrm{Fr}(Y)) \cup (Y \cap \mathrm{Fr}(X)) \cup (\mathrm{Fr}(X) \cap \mathrm{Fr}(Y))$;
(d) if X,Y are open: $(X \cap \mathrm{Fr}(Y)) \cup (Y \cap \mathrm{Fr}(X)) \subseteq \mathrm{Fr}(X \cap Y)$.

6. If ρ is an ultra-metric (see Ex. 3 on p. 27) on S, show that:

(a) for each x in S, and $\varepsilon > 0$: $N_\varepsilon(x)$ and $S_\varepsilon(x)$ are both open and closed;
(b) if $y \in N_\varepsilon(x)$, then $N_\varepsilon(y) = N_\varepsilon(x)$;
(c) if $S_\varepsilon(X)$, $S_\eta(x)$ are such that $S_\varepsilon(x) \cap S_\eta(x) \neq \varnothing$, then one of them is contained in the other;
(d) a sequence $\{x_i\}$, $i \geqslant 1$, of elements of S is a fundamental sequence if and only if $\lim_i \rho(x_i, x_{i+1}) = 0$.

7. If ρ is a metric on S, and $\{x_i\}$, $\{y_i\}$, $i \geqslant 1$, are fundamental sequences of elements of S, show that: $\lim_i \rho(x_i, y_i)$ exists.

8. If $\{x_i\}$, $i \geqslant 1$, is a convergent sequence in a space (S,ρ), show that the set $\bigcup_{i \geqslant 1} (x_i)$ cannot have more than one cluster point.

9. For the space (S',ρ') constructed in Ex. 6 p. 27, show that if $\{x'^{(n)}\}$, $n \geqslant 1$, is a sequence of elements of S', with $x'^{(n)} = \{x_i^{(n)}\}$, $i \geqslant 1$, for each n, then $x'^{(n)} \underset{\rho'}{\rightarrow} x' \equiv \{x_i\}$ if (and only if) $x_i^{(n)} \underset{\rho_1}{\rightarrow} x_i$ for each i, where ρ_1 denotes the usual metric on R. Show that such a result does *not* however hold for Hilbert Space H^∞.

2.4 Comparison of Metrics; Product Spaces

DEFINITION 20 If ρ and ρ' are metrics defined on a given non-null set S, then ρ' is said to be **finer** than ρ if $\mathscr{G}_\rho \subseteq \mathscr{G}_{\rho'}$.

When ρ' is finer than ρ, we write: $\rho \leqslant \rho'$, and clearly obtain a quasi-ordering of the metrics definable on S. Since, if S has more than one element, two distinct discrete metrics can be defined on S (by, for example, taking two distinct values for k in Note 1), the above quasi-ordering is not a partial-ordering.

THEOREM 2.22 If ρ and ρ' are metrics defined on a given non-null set S, then ρ' is finer than ρ if and only if one of the following (equivalent) conditions is satisfied:

(a) for each x in S, $\mathscr{N}_\rho(x) \subseteq \mathscr{N}_{\rho'}(x)$;

(b) for each subset X of S, ${}^{\rho'}\overline{X} \subseteq {}^{\rho}\overline{X}$.

PROOF Suppose $\rho \leqslant \rho'$, and let x be an element of S. If $Y \in \mathscr{N}_\rho(x)$ then $\exists\, G$ in $\mathscr{G}_\rho$ (and hence in $\mathscr{G}_{\rho'}$, by hypothesis) such that $x \in G \subseteq Y$. That is, $Y \in \mathscr{N}_{\rho'}(x)$.

Secondly, suppose (a) holds, and let X be any subset of S; let $x \in {}^{\rho'}\overline{X}$. If $Y \in \mathscr{N}_\rho(x)$, $Y \in \mathscr{N}_{\rho'}(x)$, by hypothesis; hence, $Y \cap X$ is non-null; that is, $x \in {}^{\rho}\overline{X}$.

Thirdly, suppose (b) holds, and let G be any member of $\mathscr{G}_\rho$. Then:

$$
\begin{aligned}
{}^{\rho'}\overline{C(G)} &\subseteq {}^{\rho}\overline{C(G)}, && \text{by hypothesis} \\
&= C(G), && \text{since} \quad C(G) \in \mathscr{F}_\rho. \text{ That is, } C(G) \in \mathscr{F}_{\rho'}.
\end{aligned}
$$

DEFINITION 21 Two metrics ρ,ρ' defined on a given non-null set S are said to be **equivalent** if: $\rho \leqslant \rho'$ and $\rho' \leqslant \rho$.

We write $\rho \equiv \rho'$ if this is the case.

THEOREM 2.23 If ρ, ρ' are metrics defined on a given non-null set S, then $\rho \leqslant \rho'$ if and only if:

given $\varepsilon > 0$, x in S, there exists $\delta > 0$ (dependent on ε,x) such that $\rho(x,y) < \varepsilon$ for any element y in S with $\rho'(x,y) < \delta$.

PROOF The condition above has clearly the alternative form: 'given $\varepsilon > 0$, x in S, $\exists\, \delta > 0$ (dependent on ε,x) such that

$$N_\delta^{\rho'}(x) \subseteq N_\varepsilon^\rho(x)\text{'}. \tag{1}$$

Suppose that $\rho \leqslant \rho'$; let $x \in S$, ε be positive. Then, $N_\varepsilon^\rho(x) \in \mathscr{G}_{\rho'}$ (by hypothesis); that is (by Definition 5), since $x \in N_\varepsilon^\rho(x)$, $\exists\, \delta > 0$ (dependent on x,ε) such that $N_\delta^{\rho'}(x) \subseteq N_\varepsilon^\rho(x)$, giving (1).

Conversely, suppose that (1) holds; let G be a non-null member of $\mathscr{G}_\rho$. If x is any member of G, $\exists\, \varepsilon > 0$ such that $N_\varepsilon^\rho(x) \subseteq G$; hence, by (1), for some $\delta > 0$, $N_\delta^{\rho'}(x) \subseteq G$; that is, $G \in \mathscr{G}_{\rho'}$.

COROLLARY I: Two metrics ρ, ρ' on S are equivalent if and only if given x in S, and $\varepsilon > 0$, there exist numbers δ, δ' (both dependent on x,ε) such that:

(a) $\rho(x,y) < \varepsilon$ for any element y in S with $\rho'(x,y) < \delta$;
(b) $\rho'(x,y) < \varepsilon$ for any element y in S with $\rho(x,y) < \delta'$.

COROLLARY II: If ρ is a metric on S, an equivalent bounded metric ρ' can be defined on S.

PROOF By Note 3, the function:

$$\rho'(x,y) = \frac{\rho(x,y)}{1 + \rho(x,y)}$$

for x,y in S, is a bounded metric on S. Since $\rho'(x,y) \leqslant \rho(x,y)$, condition (b) of I holds. To verify condition (a), note that, if x,y are elements of S with $\rho'(x,y) < \frac{1}{2}$, then:

$$\rho(x,y) = \frac{\rho'(x,y)}{1 - \rho'(x,y)} \leqslant 2\rho'(x,y)$$

Example 2.4.1 Let S,ρ_1,ρ_2 be defined as in Example 2.1.3. Since $\rho_2(f,g) \leqslant \rho_1(f,g)$, $\rho_2 \leqslant \rho_1$. However ρ_1,ρ_2 are *not* equivalent, since condition (a) of Corollary I (to Theorem 2.23) is not satisfied with $\rho = \rho_1$,$\rho' = \rho_2$; indeed it will be seen that, given arbitrary positive numbers ε, δ, $\exists\, f$ in S with $\rho_2(f,0) < \delta$ but $\rho_1(f,0) = \varepsilon$.

For, if $\eta = \min(\delta,\varepsilon)$, define f as follows:

$$f(x) = \begin{cases} 2\varepsilon^2\eta^{-1}x & \text{for } 0 \leqslant x \leqslant \tfrac{1}{2}\eta\varepsilon^{-1} \\ 2\varepsilon(1 - \varepsilon\eta^{-1}x) & \text{for } \tfrac{1}{2}\eta\varepsilon^{-1} < x < \eta\varepsilon^{-1} \\ 0 & \text{for } \eta\varepsilon^{-1} \leqslant x \leqslant 1. \end{cases}$$

Clearly, $f \in S$, $\rho_1(f,0) = \varepsilon$, $\rho_2(f,0) = \frac{1}{2}\eta < \delta$.

Note 16 Given any finite sequence $\{(S_i,\rho_i)\}$, $1 \leqslant i \leqslant n$, of metric spaces, the three metrics $\rho^{(1)}$, $\rho^{(2)}$, $\rho^{(3)}$ defined (as in Note 4) on $S \equiv \prod_{1 \leqslant i \leqslant n} S_i$ are equivalent.

For, given $x \equiv \{x_1, \ldots, x_n\}$, $y \equiv \{y_1, \ldots, y_n\}$ in S, and $1 \leqslant i \leqslant n$: $\rho_i(x_i,y_i) \leqslant \rho^{(1)}(x,y) \leqslant \rho^{(2)}(x,y)$ and hence:

$$\rho^{(3)}(x,y) \leqslant \rho^{(1)}(x,y) \leqslant \rho^{(2)}(x,y) \leqslant n \,.\, \rho^{(3)}(x,y).$$

If, given $\{(S_i,\rho_i)\}$, $1 \leqslant i \leqslant n$, any metric ρ defined on $S \equiv \prod_{1 \leqslant i \leqslant n} S_i$ which is equivalent to $\rho^{(1)}$ is said to be a **product metric** on S, we establish in the next theorem a relation connecting $\mathscr{G}_\rho$ (the set of subsets of S open w.r.t. ρ) with the sets $\mathscr{G}_{\rho_i}$ (the set of subsets of S_i open w.r.t. ρ_i) where $1 \leqslant i \leqslant n$.

THEOREM 2.24 Given the spaces (S_i,ρ_i), $1 \leqslant i \leqslant n$, let $\mathscr{G}_i'$ be a base for $\mathscr{G}_{\rho_i}$. If ρ is a product metric on $S \equiv \prod_{1 \leqslant i \leqslant n} S_i$, the set $\mathscr{G}'$ of all subsets of S of the form: $\prod_{1 \leqslant i \leqslant n} G_i$, where $G_i \in \mathscr{G}_i'$, forms a base for $\mathscr{G}_\rho$.

PROOF It is sufficient to take the case: $\rho = \rho^{(3)}$. Then we prove: (I) $\mathscr{G}' \subseteq \mathscr{G}_\rho$. Given $G \equiv \prod_{1 \leqslant i \leqslant n} G_i$, where $G_i \in \mathscr{G}_i'$, $1 \leqslant i \leqslant n$, and $x \equiv \{x_1, \ldots, x_n\}$ in G, $\exists$ for each i (since $G_i \in \mathscr{G}_{\rho_i}$) positive ε_i such that $N_{\varepsilon_i}^{\rho_i}(x_i) \subseteq G_i$. Let $\varepsilon = \min_{1 \leqslant i \leqslant n} \varepsilon_i$. Then for any $y \equiv \{y_1, \ldots, y_n\}$ in $N_\varepsilon^\rho(x)$ and $1 \leqslant i \leqslant n$:

$$\rho_i(x_i,y_i) \leqslant \rho(x,y) < \varepsilon \leqslant \varepsilon_i$$

that is: $y_i \in N_{\varepsilon_i}^{\rho_i}(x_i) \subseteq G_i$. So: $N_\varepsilon^\rho(x) \subseteq G$.
(II) If $X \in \mathscr{N}_\rho(x)$, $\exists\, G$ in $\mathscr{G}'$ such that $x \in G \subseteq X$. Given positive ε such that $N_\varepsilon^\rho(x) \subseteq X$, $\exists$ for each i (since $\mathscr{G}_i'$ is a base for $\mathscr{G}_{\rho_i}$) a member G_i of $\mathscr{G}_i'$ such that $x_i \in G_i \subseteq N_\varepsilon^{\rho_i}(x_i)$. If $G = \prod_{1 \leqslant i \leqslant n} G_i$, then:

$$x \in G \subseteq N_\varepsilon^{\rho_1}(x_1) \times \ldots \times N_\varepsilon^{\rho_n}(x_n) \tag{1}$$

But, for each $y \equiv \{y_1, \ldots, y_n\}$ in the r.h.s. of (1), and each i,

$\rho_i(x_i, y_i) < \varepsilon$. Hence: $\rho(x,y) < \varepsilon$; that is, $N_\varepsilon^\rho(x)$ contains y. Thus: $G \subseteq X$, as required.

Example 2.4.2 If R has the usual metric, then, for each positive integer n, each of the metrics ρ_1, ρ_2, ρ_3 introduced in Example 2.1.1, is a product metric on R^n. It follows by Theorem 2.24, that, for $1 \leqslant j \leqslant 3$, the set $\mathscr{G}'$ of all 'generalized open rectangular parallelepipeds' of the form:

$$G \equiv \prod_{1 \leqslant i \leqslant n}]x_i - \varepsilon, x_i + \varepsilon[, \text{ for } \varepsilon > 0 \text{ and } x_i \in R, \text{ is a base for } \mathscr{G}_{\rho_j}.$$

Theorem 2.24 suggests the following:

DEFINITION 22* A space (S,ρ) is said to be a **product space** of the spaces (S_i, ρ_i), $1 \leqslant i \leqslant n$, if:

(i) $S = \prod_{1 \leqslant i \leqslant n} S_i$;

(ii) for each $1 \leqslant i \leqslant n$, there exists a base $\mathscr{G}_i'$ for $\mathscr{G}_{\rho_i}$ such that the set $\mathscr{G}'$ of all subsets of S of the form $\prod_{1 \leqslant i \leqslant n} G_i$, where $G_i \in \mathscr{G}_i'$, forms a base for $\mathscr{G}_\rho$.

For, by Theorem 2.24:
first, condition (ii) of this Definition is independent of the choice of the base $\mathscr{G}_i'$ in each S_i; *secondly*, if condition (i) holds, then (S,ρ) is a product space of the (S_i, ρ_i) if and only if ρ is a product metric on S.

THEOREM 2.25* If (S,ρ) is a product space of the spaces (S_i, ρ_i), $1 \leqslant i \leqslant n$, let $X_i \subseteq S_i$, $1 \leqslant i \leqslant n$; then

$$^{\rho}\overline{\prod_{1 \leqslant i \leqslant n} X_i} = \prod_{1 \leqslant i \leqslant n} {}^{\rho_i}\overline{X_i}.$$

COROLLARY If $X = \prod_{1 \leqslant i \leqslant n} X_i$, then:

$X \in \mathscr{F}_\rho$ if and only if $X_i \in \mathscr{F}_{\rho_i}$, $1 \leqslant i \leqslant n$.

The proof is left to the reader.

*Worked Exercise

Let (S'', ρ'') be a product space of the given spaces (S,ρ), (S',ρ'). Given subsets A, X of S'', S respectively, let $A(X)$ denote the set of those elements y of S' such that $\{x,y\} \in A$ for some x in X (dependent on y). If $x \in S$, $\mathscr{N}_\rho(x)$ constitutes the family $\{X_i\}$, $i \in I$, and $A \in \mathscr{F}_{\rho''}$, show that $\bigcap_{i \in I} {}^{\rho'}\overline{A(X_i)} = A((x))$.

Solution: Clearly $A((x)) \subseteq {}^{\rho'}\overline{A(X_i)}$ if $x \in X_i$. Conversely, suppose $y \in {}^{\rho'}\overline{A(X_i)}$ for each i in I, and let G,G' be arbitrary members of $\mathcal{G}_\rho$, $\mathcal{G}_{\rho'}$ respectively, such that $x \in G$, $y \in G'$. Then, in particular, $y \in {}^{\rho'}\overline{A(G)}$; hence (since $G' \in \mathcal{N}_{\rho'}(y)$), $G' \cap A(G)$ contains an element y' of S'; that is, $\exists$ an element $\{x',y'\}$ of A such that $x' \in G$ *and* $y' \in G'$; in other words:

$$(G \times G') \cap A \neq \emptyset. \tag{1}$$

Since the set of all subsets of S'' of the form $G \times G'$, where $G \in \mathcal{G}_\rho$, $G' \in \mathcal{G}_{\rho'}$, forms a base for $\mathcal{G}_{\rho''}$ it follows from (1) that: $\{x,y\} \in {}^{\rho''}\overline{A} = A$; i.e., $y \in A((x))$.

Exercises for Solution

1. Verify that the function defined by writing $\rho(x,y)$ equal to $|x - y| + 1$ if just one of the x,y is positive, and equal to $|x - y|$ otherwise, is a metric on R. How is it related to the usual metric ρ_1 on R (in terms of the quasi-order introduced after Definition 20)?

2. With the notation of the Worked Exercise above, obtain an example of spaces (S,ρ), (S',ρ') and a member G of $\mathcal{G}_{\rho''}$ such that:

$$\bigcap_{i \in I} G(X_i) \neq {}^{\rho'}\overline{G((x))}.$$

3.* If (S_1,ρ_1) is a product space of (S,ρ), (S',ρ'), and (S_2,ρ_2) is a product space of (S',ρ'), (S'',ρ''), let $G_1 \in \mathcal{G}_{\rho_1}$, $G_2 \in \mathcal{G}_{\rho_2}$. If (S_3,ρ_3) is a product space of (S,ρ), (S'',ρ''), and $G_2 \circ G_1$ denotes the set of those elements $\{x,z\}$ of S_3 such that $\{x,y\} \in G_1$, $\{y,z\} \in G_2$ for some y in S' (dependent on $\{x,z\}$), show that $G_2 \circ G_1 \in \mathcal{G}_{\rho_3}$.

4.* If (S'',ρ'') is a product space of (S,ρ), (S',ρ'), and $A \subseteq S$, $B \subseteq S'$, show that:

(a) ${}^{\rho''}(A \times B)^\circ = {}^{\rho}A^\circ \times {}^{\rho'}B^\circ$;

(b) ${}^{\rho''}\mathrm{Fr}(A \times B) = ({}^{\rho}\mathrm{Fr}(A) \times {}^{\rho'}\overline{B}) \cup ({}^{\rho}\overline{A} \times {}^{\rho'}\mathrm{Fr}(B))$.

2.5 Subspaces; Dense Sets

Given a space (S,ρ), and an arbitrary non-null subset A of S, let ρ_A be the restriction of ρ to $A \times A$; ρ_A is a metric on A, giving rise to the space (A,ρ_A). If x is a member of A and ε is positive, the set of all elements y in A with $\rho(x,y) < \varepsilon$ (that is, the ε-neighbourhood of x, regarded as a member of A) is $N_\varepsilon^\rho(x) \cap A$ ($\equiv N_\varepsilon(x) \cap A$), and is called the ε-neighbourhood of x **in** $\boldsymbol{A}$. Thus a given subset X of A is open (in A) w.r.t. ρ_A if and only if: for each x in X, $\exists\, \varepsilon > 0$ (depending on x) such that

$$N_\varepsilon(x) \cap A \subseteq X. \tag{1}$$

The following theorem provides a criterion, in terms of the set $\mathscr{G}_\rho$ of open sets of the original space (S,ρ), for a given subset of A to be open (in A) w.r.t. ρ_A:

THEOREM 2.26 Given a space (S,ρ) and $X \subseteq A \subseteq S$, X is open (in A) w.r.t. ρ_A if and only if there exists a member G of $\mathscr{G}_\rho$ such that $X = G \cap A$.

PROOF If X is open (in A) w.r.t. ρ_A, then, by (1) above, there corresponds to each member x of X a positive ε_x (depending on the choice of x) such that $N_{\varepsilon_x}(x) \cap A \subseteq X$. If $G = \bigcup_{x \in X} N_{\varepsilon_x}(x)$, then $G \in \mathscr{G}_\rho$ and:

$$G \cap A = \bigcup_{x \in X} (N_{\varepsilon_x}(x) \cap A) = X.$$

Conversely, if $\exists\, G$ in $\mathscr{G}_\rho$ with $X = G \cap A$, then, for each x in X, x belongs to G; hence $\exists\, \varepsilon > 0$ such that $N_\varepsilon(x) \subseteq G$; hence: $N_\varepsilon(x) \cap A \subseteq X$, and result again follows from (1) above.

Theorem 2.26 suggests the following:

DEFINITION 23* A space (A,ρ') is said to be a **subspace** of a space (S,ρ) if:
(i) A is a subset of S;
(ii) a subset X of A belongs to $\mathscr{G}_{\rho'}$ (that is, X is open (in A) w.r.t. ρ') if and only if there exists a member G of $\mathscr{G}_\rho$ such that $X = G \cap A$.

For, by Theorem 2.26, if condition (i) holds, then (A,ρ') is a subspace of (S,ρ) if and only if ρ' and ρ_A are equivalent metrics on A. In particular, if ρ' is identical with ρ_A, (A,ρ') is called a **restricted** subspace of (S,ρ).

Since, under the conditions of the definition, the set $\mathscr{G}_{\rho'}$ of open sets of (A,ρ') depends only on A and $\mathscr{G}_\rho(\equiv \mathscr{G})$, we denote the former in future by $\mathscr{G}_{\rho A}$ or, more usually, by $\mathscr{G}_A$; any member of $\mathscr{G}_A$ is said to be **open relative to A**. From Definition 23, there follows immediately:

THEOREM 2.27* Given a space (S,ρ) and $A \subseteq S$:
(a) If X is a subset of A belonging to $\mathscr{G}$, X belongs to $\mathscr{G}_A$;
(b) if A belongs to $\mathscr{G}$, $\mathscr{G}_A \subseteq \mathscr{G}$.

Note 17 The proviso '$A \in \mathscr{G}$' cannot be omitted from Theorem 2.27:

Example 2.5.1 For space $(R)_1$, take $A = [0,1]$, $X =]0,1]$, $G =]0,2[$. Then $G \in \mathscr{G}$, and $X = G \cap A$ so that $X \in \mathscr{G}_A$. However, since $1 \,\omega\, X^\circ$, $X \,\omega\, \mathscr{G}$.

By Theorem 2.1, if (A,ρ') is a subspace of (S,ρ), and x is a member of A, a given subset X of A is a neighbourhood of x w.r.t. ρ' (that is, in respect of the space (A,ρ')) if and only if $\exists$ a member G' of $\mathscr{G}_A$ such that $x \in G' \subseteq X$; that is, $\exists$ a member G of $\mathscr{G}$ such that

$$x \in G \cap A \subseteq X. \tag{2}$$

The set of such neighbourhoods of x thus again depends only on A and $\mathscr{G}_\rho(\equiv \mathscr{G})$, and is denoted by $\mathscr{N}_{\rho A}(x)$ or $\mathscr{N}_A(x)$; a member of the latter is called a neighbourhood of x in A.

THEOREM 2.28* Given a space (S,ρ), $A \subseteq S$, and a member x of A, a subset X of A belongs to $\mathscr{N}_A(x)$ if and only if there exists Y in $\mathscr{N}(x)$ such that $X = Y \cap A$.

PROOF If $X \in \mathscr{N}_A(x)$, it follows by (2) that $\exists G$ in $\mathscr{G}$ with $x \in G \cap A \subseteq X$. If $Y = G \cup X$, clearly $Y \in \mathscr{N}(x)$ and $Y \cap A = (G \cap A) \cup (X \cap A) = X$. The converse is immediate from (2).

By Definition 8, if (A,ρ') is a subspace of (S,ρ), and if $X \subseteq A$, then a given member x of A is a cluster point of X w.r.t. ρ' if and only if:

$$(Y - (x)) \cap X \neq \varnothing \quad \text{for each } Y \text{ in } \mathscr{N}_A(x)$$

that is:

$$((Y \cap A) - (x)) \cap X \neq \varnothing \quad \text{for each } Y \text{ in } \mathscr{N}(x).$$

But:

$$\begin{aligned} ((Y \cap A) - (x)) \cap X &= ((Y \cap A) \cap C(x)) \cap X \\ &= (Y \cap C(x)) \cap (A \cap X) \\ &= (Y - (x)) \cap X. \end{aligned}$$

Thus, given x in A, x is a cluster point of X w.r.t. ρ' if and only if it is a cluster point w.r.t. ρ; that is, the set of cluster points of X in respect of the space (A,ρ') is ${}^\rho X' \cap A$ or $X' \cap A$. The latter set is denoted by ${}^\rho X'^A$ or X'^A; each member is called a cluster point of X **relative to** A. Hence the closure of X w.r.t. ρ' is:

$$X \cup ({}^\rho X' \cap A) = {}^\rho\overline{X} \cap (X \cup A) = {}^\rho\overline{X} \cap A;$$

it is denoted by ${}^\rho\overline{X}^A$ or $\overline{X}^A$ and is called the closure of X **relative to** A. Then X will be closed (in A) w.r.t. ρ' when $X = \overline{X} \cap A$ or

$X' \cap A \subseteq X$. X is said to be **closed relative to** A. The set of such subsets of X is denoted by $\mathscr{F}_{\rho A}$ or $\mathscr{F}_A$.

THEOREM 2.29* Given a space (S,ρ) and $X \subseteq A \subseteq S$, X belongs to $\mathscr{F}_A$ if and only if there exists a member F of $\mathscr{F}$ such that $X = F \cap A$.

The proof is left to the reader.

COROLLARY (a) If $X \subseteq A$ and $X \in \mathscr{F}$, then $X \in \mathscr{F}_A$;
(b) If $A \in \mathscr{F}$, then $\mathscr{F}_A \subseteq \mathscr{F}$.

THEOREM 2.30* Given space (S,ρ), $X \subseteq S$:

(a) if $\{A_i\}$, $i \in I$, is an arbitrary family of subsets of S such that $X \subseteq A_i$ and $X \in \mathscr{F}_{A_i}$ for each i in I, then, if $A = \bigcup_i A_i$, $X \in \mathscr{F}_A$;

(b) if $\{A_i\}$, $1 \leqslant i \leqslant n$, is a finite sequence of subsets of S such that $X \subseteq A_i$ and $X \in \mathscr{G}_{A_i}$ for each i with $1 \leqslant i \leqslant n$, then, if $A = \bigcup_{1 \leqslant i \leqslant n} A_i$, $X \in \mathscr{G}_A$.

PROOF (a) For each i in I; $X = \overline{X} \cap A_i$; hence

$$\overline{X} \cap A = \bigcup_i (\overline{X} \cap A_i) = X.$$

(b) To each i with $1 \leqslant i \leqslant n$, there corresponds a member G_i of $\mathscr{G}$ such that $X = G_i \cap A_i$; write $G = \bigcap_{1 \leqslant i \leqslant n} G_i$. Then $G \in \mathscr{G}$ and, clearly, $X \subseteq G \cap A$. On the other hand, $G \cap A = \bigcup_{1 \leqslant i \leqslant n} (G \cap A_i)$ where, for each i, $G \cap A_i \subseteq G_i \cap A_i = X$.

Thus $X = G \cap A$ and $X \in \mathscr{G}_A$.

Note 18 Theorem 2.30(b) does not hold for an arbitrary infinite sequence $\{A_i\}$, $i \geqslant 1$.

Example 2.5.2 For space $(R)_1$, let $X = (0)$, $A_i = (0, i^{-1})$ for $i \geqslant 1$. Then $C_{A_i}(X) = (i^{-1}) \in \mathscr{F}_{A_i}$; thus $X \in \mathscr{G}_{A_i}$, all i.

However, if $A = \bigcup_{i \geqslant 1} A_i$, clearly: $0 \in (C_A(X))' \cap A$, which is hence not a subset of $C_A(X)$; that is, $C_A(X)\, \omega\, \mathscr{F}_A$ and so $X\, \omega\, \mathscr{G}_A$.

Again, if (A,ρ') is a subspace of (S,ρ), the interior, exterior and frontier w.r.t. ρ' of any subset X of A depend on A and $\mathscr{G}_\rho (\equiv \mathscr{G})$ only; these are denoted respectively by ${}^{\rho}X^{\circ A}$ (or $X^{\circ A}$), ${}^{\rho}E_A(X)$ (or $E_A(X)$) and ${}^{\rho}\mathrm{Fr}_A(X)$ (or $\mathrm{Fr}_A(X)$). Since $X^\circ \subseteq X \subseteq A$, it follows from Theorems 2.9 and 2.27 that $X^\circ \subseteq X^{\circ A}$. If (S,ρ) is not discrete, and A is a non-empty set, not belonging to G_ρ, then clearly

$A^\circ \subset A = A^{\circ A}$; that is, the sets X°, $X^{\circ A}$ above need not coincide.

DEFINITION 24* Given a space (S,ρ) and $X \subseteq A \subseteq S$, X is said to be **dense in** A (w.r.t. ρ) if $\overline{X}^A = A$.

If $A = S$, X is usually simply said to be **dense**.

THEOREM 2.31* Given a space (S,ρ), then:

(a) if $X \subseteq A \subseteq B \subseteq S$, with X dense in A, and A dense in B, then X is dense in B;

(b) if (S,ρ) is a product space of the spaces (S_i,ρ_i), $1 \leqslant i \leqslant n$, and $X_i \subseteq S_i$, $1 \leqslant i \leqslant n$, then each X_i is dense (in S_i) if and only if $X \equiv \prod_{1 \leqslant i \leqslant n} X_i$ is dense (in S).

The proof is left to the reader.

According to definition, any subset X of S is dense in X; however, the term 'dense-in-itself' is reserved for a different property:

DEFINITION 25* Given a space (S,ρ), a subset X of S is said to be **dense-in-itself** (w.r.t. ρ) if $X \subseteq X'$.

If in addition, X is closed, X is said to be **perfect**.

DEFINITION 26* Given a space (S,ρ) and $X \subseteq A \subseteq S$, X is said to be **nowhere dense** in A (w.r.t. ρ) if $C_A(\overline{X}^A)$ is dense in A.

That is, X is nowhere dense in A if and only if: $C_A\{\overline{C_A(\overline{X}^A)}^A\}$ is null; that is, from Theorem 2.9, when: $(\overline{X}^A)^{\circ A}$ is null. If $A = S$, X is said simply to be **nowhere dense.** Clearly a subset of A cannot be both dense and nowhere dense in A.

Example 2.5.3 For space $(R)_1$, take $X = \bigcup_{i \geqslant 1} (i^{-1})$, $A = X \cup (0)$. Then X is dense in A (indeed $\overline{X} = A$), but, since $X \cap X'$ is null, X is not dense-in-itself. Although (as remarked above) X cannot be nowhere-dense in A, it is nowhere-dense (in S). For $(\overline{X})^\circ$ could only be non-null if A contained the whole of some open interval of real numbers.

Example 2.5.4. For space $(R)_1$, set Q (of all rational points) is both dense-in-itself and dense.

THEOREM 2.32* Given a space (S,ρ), and $X \subseteq S$:

(a) if X is dense-in-itself, so is $\overline{X}$;

(b) if X is dense-in-itself and $X \subseteq Y \subseteq X'$, Y is dense-in-itself;

(c) the union of any family of subsets of S, each of which is dense-in-itself, is again dense-in-itself.

The proof is left to the reader.

By Theorem 2.32, there is a maximum dense-in-itself subset of any given subset X of S; this is called the **nucleus** of X (w.r.t. ρ), denoted by ${}^{\rho}N(X)$ or $N(X)$. If $N(X)$ is null, X is said to be **scattered** (w.r.t. ρ). For arbitrary X, $X - N(X)$ is clearly scattered.

THEOREM 2.33* For a space (S,ρ), and $X \subseteq S$, $N(X)$ is closed relative to X.

PROOF We have:

$$N(X) \subseteq (N(X))' \cap X \subseteq (N(X))' \tag{1}$$

But, by Theorem 2.32, $(N(X))'$ is dense-in-itself; hence, by (1), $(N(X))' \cap X$ is dense-in-itself; hence: $(N(X))' \cap X \subseteq N(X)$; that is, $N(X) \in \mathscr{F}_X$.

THEOREM 2.34* Given a space (S,ρ) and $X \subseteq A \subseteq S$, then X is nowhere dense in A if and only if:

given a non-null set G, open relative to A, there exists a non-null set G', open relative to A, with $G' \subseteq G$ and $G' \cap X$ null. (1)

PROOF There is clearly no loss of generality suffered if A is taken to be S itself, so that $\mathscr{G}_A$ becomes $\mathscr{G}$.

If G is an arbitrary non-null member of $\mathscr{G}$, then $G \nsubseteq \overline{X}$, if X is nowhere dense; clearly the set $G' \equiv G \cap C(\overline{X})$ satisfies condition (1). Conversely, with G as before, choose G' as in (1). Then, since $X \subseteq C(G')$, a member of $\mathscr{F}$, it follows that $\overline{X} \subseteq C(G')$; that is, $G' \subseteq C(\overline{X})$. Since $G' \subseteq G$, $G \nsubseteq \overline{X}$. So $(\overline{X})^\circ$ is null.

THEOREM 2.35* Given a space (S,ρ) and $X \subseteq A \subseteq S$:

(a) if X is nowhere-dense in A, so is $\overline{X}$;

(b) if X is nowhere-dense in A and $Y \subseteq X$, Y is nowhere-dense in A;

(c) The union of a finite sequence of subsets of A, each nowhere-dense in A, is again nowhere-dense in A.

PROOF We shall prove only (c). There is again no loss of generality if A is taken to be S, and only two subsets X,Y of A are considered, since induction can then immediately be applied.

Thus, by hypothesis,

$$S = \overline{C(\overline{X})} = \overline{C(\overline{Y})} \tag{1}$$

$$C(\overline{X}) \subseteq C(\overline{X}) \cup \overline{Y} = (C(\overline{X} \cup \overline{Y})) \cup \overline{Y} = (C(\overline{X \cup Y})) \cup \overline{Y}$$

hence, by (1):

$$S = \overline{(C(\overline{X \cup Y})) \cup \overline{Y}} = \overline{C(\overline{X \cup Y})} \cup \overline{Y},$$

implying:

$$C(\overline{Y}) \subseteq \overline{C(\overline{X \cup Y})}.$$

Hence, again from (1):

$$S = \overline{C(\overline{X \cup Y})}.$$

Note 19 Theorem 2.35(c) does not hold for an arbitrary infinite sequence of nowhere-dense sets.

Example 2.5.5 For space $(R)_1$, let the set Q of rationals be enumerated as: $\{r_i\}$, $i \geqslant 1$. If $X_i = (r_i)$, for each i, X_i is nowhere-dense, but $\bigcup_{i \geqslant 1} X_i = Q$, where Q is dense.

A property P applicable to a space is said to be a **hereditary** property if when it is possessed by a space (S,ρ), it is possessed also by any subspace of (S,ρ).

Example 2.5.6 The property of being discrete is clearly a hereditary property.

Example 2.5.7 The property P_1: 'S is dense-in-itself (w.r.t. ρ)' is a property (applicable to a space (S,ρ)) which is not hereditary. For example, the space $(R)_1$ possesses P_1 (since $R = Q' \subseteq R'$), but the subspace $(J,(\rho_1)_J)$ does not; indeed the latter is discrete.

*Worked Exercise

A space (S,ρ) is said to be **resolvable** if S contains a subset A such that A and $C_S(A)$ are both dense (in S). If so, show that S is dense-in-itself and that, if G is a non-null open subset of S, then any subspace (G,ρ') of (S,ρ) is resolvable. Conversely, if $\exists$ a set $\mathscr{B}$ of non-null open subsets of S such that:

(a) some subspace (G,ρ') is resolvable, for each member G of $\mathscr{B}$;

(b) for each non-null open subset G' of S, $\exists$ a member G of $\mathscr{B}$ such that $G \subseteq G'$;

then show that (S,ρ) is itself resolvable.

Solution: Given x in S, suppose $x \in A$. Then $x \in \overline{C(A)} - C(A) \subseteq (C(A))' \subseteq S'$. A similar argument holds if $x \in C(A)$. Secondly, since $\overline{A} = S$, $G = \overline{A} \cap G \subseteq \overline{A \cap G}$, by Worked Exercise (a), on page 43; hence $A \cap G$ is dense in G. Also, $C_G(A \cap G) = C_S(A) \cap G$, which is similarly seen to be dense in G.

Conversely, let $\mathscr{S}$ denote the subset of $P(\mathscr{B})$ containing all non-null members $\mathscr{B}'$ of $P(\mathscr{B})$ such that any two distinct members of $\mathscr{B}'$ are *disjoint*. Since, given $\mathscr{B}'$ in $P(\mathscr{B})$, it is clear that $\mathscr{B}' \in \mathscr{S}$ if and only if any two-member subset of $\mathscr{B}'$ belongs to $\mathscr{S}$, $\mathscr{S}$ is of finite character. Hence, by Tukey's Lemma, (i.e., taking $E = \mathscr{B}$ in Theorem 1.10) $\mathscr{S}$ has a maximal member $\mathscr{B}_1$, i.e., $\mathscr{B}$ contains a maximal subset $\mathscr{B}_1$, any two members of which are disjoint. If then the members of $\mathscr{B}_1$ comprise the family $\{G_i\}$, $i \in I$, $\exists$ (by (a)) corresponding to each i in I, subsets A_i, B_i of G_i such that $\bar{A}_i^{G_i} = G_i = \bar{B}_i^{G_i}$ and $B_i = C_{G_i}(A_i)$. Write $A = \bigcup_i A_i$, $B = \bigcup_i B_i$. It is clear from the definition of $\mathscr{B}_1$ that $A_i \cap B_j = \varnothing$ for distinct i,j in I (supposing $G_i \neq G_j$), so that $A \cap B = \varnothing$. (1)

Then $\bar{A} = S$, for if $\exists x$ in $C_S(\bar{A})$, then $\exists G'$ in $\mathscr{G}_\rho$ with x in G' and $G' \cap A = \varnothing$; hence, by (b), $\exists\, G$ in $\mathscr{B}$ such that $G \cap A = \varnothing$; that is, $A \subseteq C_S(G)$, which implies: $\bar{A} \subseteq \overline{C_S(G)} = C_S(G)$, by Theorem 2.12. Hence, for each i in I, $G_i \subseteq \bar{A}_i \subseteq C_S(G)$; that is, $\mathscr{B}_2 \equiv \mathscr{B}_1 \cup (G) \in \mathscr{S}$. But since $\mathscr{B}_1 \subset \mathscr{B}_2$, this contradicts the maximality of $\mathscr{B}_1$ in $\mathscr{S}$. Similarly, $\bar{B} = S$, and hence it is immediate from (1) that $\overline{C_S(A)} = S$.

Exercises for Solution

1.* Given a space (S,ρ) and $A \subseteq S$, show that:

(a) for any $X \subseteq S$, $\overline{X \cap A}^A \subseteq \bar{X} \cap A$, giving an example of inequality;
(b) for any $X \subseteq S$, $\mathrm{Fr}_A(X \cap A) \subseteq \mathrm{Fr}(X) \cap A$, giving an example of inequality;
(c) $A^\circ \neq \varnothing$ if and only if $A \cap X \neq \varnothing$ for each dense subset X of S;
(d) if A is dense (in S), $x \in A$ and $X \in \mathscr{N}_A(x)$, then $\bar{X} \in \mathscr{N}(x)$;
(e) $(\mathrm{Fr}(A))^\circ$ is dense-in-itself.

2.* Given a space (S,ρ), a subset X of S is said to be **locally closed** (w.r.t. ρ) if, corresponding to each x in X, $\exists$ a member Z_x of $\mathscr{N}(x)$ such that $X \cap Z_x$ is closed relative to Z_x. Show that X is locally closed if and only if $\exists$ members F, G of $\mathscr{F}_\rho$, $\mathscr{G}_\rho$ respectively such that $X = F \cap G$.

3.* If (S'',ρ'') is a product space of (S,ρ), (S',ρ'), and $X \subseteq S$, $Y \subseteq S'$, show that $X \times Y$ is dense-in-itself (w.r.t. ρ'') if and only if at least one of X, Y is dense-in-itself.

4.* Given a space (S,ρ), show that a subset X of S is nowhere-dense if and only if $\exists$ *no* non-null open subset G of S with $G \subseteq \overline{G \cap X}$.

5.* Given a space (S,ρ), and $X \subseteq A \subseteq S$, show that if X is nowhere-dense in A, then X is nowhere-dense (in S).

6.* Given a space (S,ρ), a subset X of S is said to be **meagre** if $\exists$ a sequence $\{A_i\}$, $i \geqslant 1$, of nowhere-dense subsets of S such that $X = \bigcup_{i \geqslant 1} A_i$. If, for a given subset X of S, $\delta(X)$ denotes the set of those elements x

of S such that, for each Z in $\mathcal{N}(x)$, $Z \cap X$ is *not* meagre, show that:

(a) $\delta(X) \subseteq \bar{X}$;
(b) $\delta(X \cup Y) = \delta(X) \cup \delta(Y)$;
(c) $\delta(X)$ is closed;
(d) if $G \in \mathcal{G}$, $G \cap \delta(X) = G \cap \delta(X \cap G)$.

7.* If $\mathcal{G}'$ is a base for the open sets of the space (S,ρ), and (A,ρ_1) is a subspace of (S,ρ), show that the set of all subsets of A of the form $G \cap A$, where $G \in \mathcal{G}'$, forms a base for the open sets of (A,ρ_1). Hence show that if (B,ρ'_1) is a subspace of a second space (S',ρ'), then any product space of (A,ρ_1), (B,ρ'_1) is a subspace of any product space of (S,ρ), (S',ρ').

2.6 Continuous Functions

It will be recalled that, in real variable theory, if A is a subset of R, then a function f from A into R is said to be continuous in A at a given point x of A if, given positive ε, there exists $\delta > 0$ (dependent on x,ε) such that $|f(x) - f(y)| < \varepsilon$ for each point y of A with $|x - y| < \delta$. Such a condition could be extended to a more general context as follows: Given arbitrary metric spaces (S,ρ), (S',ρ'), and A a subset of S, a function f from A into S' could be said to be **(ρ,ρ′)-continuous**, in A at a given element x of A if, given $\varepsilon > 0$, there exists $\delta > 0$ (dependent on x,ε) such that $\rho'(f(x), f(y)) < \varepsilon$ for each element y in A with $\rho(x,y) < \delta$; that is, such that:

$$f(N_\delta^\rho(x) \cap A) \subseteq N_\varepsilon^{\rho'}(f(x)) \quad \text{or:} \quad N_\delta^\rho(x) \cap A \subseteq f^{-1}(N_\varepsilon^{\rho'}(f(x)))$$

Thus, expressed in terms of the neighbourhood systems in the spaces in question, we have:

DEFINITION 27* Given spaces (S,ρ), (S',ρ'), $A \subseteq S$, a function f from A into S' is said to be (ρ,ρ')-continuous in A at an element x of A if, for each Y in $\mathcal{N}_{\rho'}(f(x))$, $f^{-1}(Y) \in \mathcal{N}_{\rho A}(x)$.

If no ambiguity is likely to arise, f is said simply to be 'continuous in A at x'. If $A = S$, f is said to be 'continuous at x'.

Note 20 (I) If, in the notation of Definition 27, (T,ρ'') is a subspace of (S',ρ') such that $f(A) \subseteq T$, then it is seen that f is (ρ,ρ')-continuous at x *if and only if* f, regarded as a function from A *into* T, is (ρ,ρ'')-continuous at x. For, if for convenience of notation the latter function is denoted by g, and if Y,Y' are subsets of S',T respectively such that $Y' = Y \cap T$, then: $g^{-1}(Y') = f^{-1}(Y) \cap f^{-1}(T) = f^{-1}(Y) \cap A = f^{-1}(Y)$, since

$f(A) \subseteq T$. The result then follows immediately from Theorem 2.28. An important consequence is that in establishing a property of a function f from A into S' which relates to its (ρ,ρ')-continuity we often can, without loss of generality, not only take A to be S itself but also assume that f is a function *onto* S'. Such a procedure occurs a number of times, particularly in the following chapter.

(II) If, again, (S,ρ), (S',ρ') are given spaces, and f a function from S into S' which is (ρ,ρ')-continuous at an element x of S, it is clear that the restriction f_A of f to a subset A of S (where $x \in A$) will necessarily be continuous in A at x; the following example shows that the converse does not hold:

Example 2.6.1 $S = S' = R$; $\rho = \rho' = \rho_1$; $A = Q$; $f(x) = 1$ for x in A; $f(x) = 0$ for x in $S - A$. For x in A, and $0 < \varepsilon < 1$, $N_\varepsilon(f(x)) =]1 - \varepsilon, 1 + \varepsilon[$; hence: $f^{-1}(N_\varepsilon(f(x))) = A$. But, for any $\delta > 0$, $\exists$ an element y of $S - A$ with $x - \delta < y < x + \delta$ hence: $N_\delta(x) \nsubseteq f^{-1}(N_\varepsilon(f(x)))$; that is, f is not continuous at x.

Since, however, $N_\delta(x) \cap A \subseteq A = f_A^{-1}(N_\varepsilon(f_A(x)))$, for x in A, f_A is continuous in A at x.

(III) If x is an isolated point of a subset A of S, then any function f defined on A is necessarily continuous in A at x. For, since $x \,\omega\, A'$, $\exists$ a member X of $\mathcal{N}_\rho(x)$ such that $X \cap A = (x)$. Then, for any Y in $\mathcal{N}_{\rho'}(f(x))$: $X \cap A \subseteq f^{-1}(Y)$.

DEFINITION 28* Given spaces (S,ρ), (S',ρ'), $A \subseteq S$, a function f from A into S' is said to be **(ρ, ρ′)-continuous on** A if it is continuous in A at each element of A.

The most important criteria for determining the continuity of a function appear in:

THEOREM 2.36* Given spaces (S,ρ), (S',ρ'), $A \subseteq S$, a function f from A into S' is (ρ,ρ')-continuous on A if and only if one of the following conditions is satisfied:

(a) for each G' in $\mathcal{G}_{\rho'}$, $f^{-1}(G')$ is in $\mathcal{G}_{\rho A}$;
(b) for each F' in $\mathcal{F}_{\rho'}$, $f^{-1}(F')$ is in $\mathcal{F}_{\rho A}$.

PROOF Again, we can take $A = S$. Given that f is continuous on A, let G' be a member of $\mathcal{G}_{\rho'}$ such that $f^{-1}(G')$ is non-null (otherwise the case is trivial); if $x \in f^{-1}(G')$, $f(x) \in G'$, so that $G' \in \mathcal{N}_{\rho'}(f(x))$; hence by definition of continuity at x, $f^{-1}(G') \in \mathcal{N}_\rho(x)$. Since the latter is true for every member x of $f^{-1}(G')$, $f^{-1}(G') \in \mathcal{G}_\rho$. Conversely, given that (a) holds, given x in S, and Y in $\mathcal{N}_{\rho'}(f(x))$, $\exists\, G'$

in $\mathscr{G}_{\rho'}$ with $f(x) \in G' \subseteq Y$, implying: $x \in f^{-1}(G') \subseteq f^{-1}(Y)$. By (a), $f^{-1}(G') \in \mathscr{G}_\rho$; that is, $f^{-1}(Y) \in \mathscr{N}_\rho(x)$ and so f is continuous at x.

It remains to verify the equivalence of (a) and (b). It need only be noted that (a) holds if and only if:

$$f^{-1}(C_{S'}(F')) \in \mathscr{G}_\rho, \text{ that is: } C_S(f^{-1}(C_{S'}(F'))) \in \mathscr{F}_\rho, \text{ if } F' \in \mathscr{F}_{\rho'}.$$

$$\text{But } C_S(f^{-1}(C_{S'}(F'))) = C_S(C_S(f^{-1}(F'))) = f^{-1}(F').$$

Theorem 2.37* Given spaces (S,ρ), (S',ρ'), (S'',ρ''), $A \subseteq S$, let f be a function from A into S' which is (ρ,ρ')-continuous on A, and g a function from S' into S'' which is (ρ',ρ'')-continuous; then $f \circ g$ is (ρ,ρ'')-continuous on A.

The proof is immediate.

Note 21 In applications of Theorem 2.36 it is often convenient to express conditions (a) and (b) in the form:

(a′) $\exists$ a subbase $\mathscr{G}''$ of $\mathscr{G}_{\rho'}$ such that, for each member G'' of $\mathscr{G}''$, $f^{-1}(G'')$ is in $\mathscr{G}_{\rho A}$;

(b′) $\exists$ a subbase $\mathscr{F}''$ of $\mathscr{F}_{\rho'}$ such that, for each member F'' of $\mathscr{F}''$, $f^{-1}(F'')$ is in $\mathscr{F}_{\rho A}$.

To show (for example) that (b′) implies (b), let F' be an arbitrary member of $\mathscr{F}_{\rho'}$. Since, by Definition 17, the set $\mathscr{F}'$ of all finite unions of members of $\mathscr{F}''$ forms a base for $\mathscr{F}_{\rho'}$, $\exists$ a family $\{F'_i\}$, $i \in I$, of members of $\mathscr{F}'$ such that $F' = \bigcap_i F'_i$; but since, in turn, each member F'_i of the family can be expressed as the union of a certain finite sequence $\{F''_{i,j}\}$, $1 \leqslant j \leqslant n_i$, of members of $\mathscr{F}''$:

$$f^{-1}(F') = f^{-1}\{\bigcap_{i \in I}(\bigcup_{1 \leqslant j \leqslant n_i} F''_{i,j})\} = \bigcap_{i \in I}\{\bigcup_{1 \leqslant j \leqslant n_i} f^{-1}(F''_{i,j})\}$$

which, by (b′) and Theorem 2.13, belongs to $\mathscr{F}_{\rho A}$.

Example 2.6.2 If ρ,ρ' are metrics defined on a given non-null set S, then the identity function f on S is (ρ,ρ')-continuous if and only if $\rho' \leqslant \rho$. For, by Theorem 2.36, f is (ρ,ρ')-continuous if and only if $f^{-1}(G') \in \mathscr{G}_\rho$ for each member G' of $\mathscr{G}_{\rho'}$; since, however, G', $f^{-1}(G')$ coincide, the latter condition is simply that $\mathscr{G}_{\rho'} \subseteq \mathscr{G}_\rho$.

Example 2.6.3 Given a space (S,ρ), and $A \subseteq S$, let f be a function from A into R; if ρ_1 is the usual metric on R, f is (ρ,ρ_1)-continuous on A if and only if for each member a of R: $f^{-1}\{]a,\rightarrow[\}$ and $f^{-1}\{]\leftarrow,a[\}$ belong to $\mathscr{G}_A$.

Since the set of all subsets of R which are of the form $]a,\rightarrow[$ or $]\leftarrow,a[$ forms a subbase for $\mathscr{G}_{\rho_1}$, this follows immediately from Note 21.

THEOREM 2.38 If (S,ρ) is a product space of the spaces (S_i,ρ_i), $1 \leqslant i \leqslant n$, then:

(a)* for $1 \leqslant i \leqslant n$, the projection π_i (of S onto S_i) is (ρ,ρ_i)-continuous;

(b) if ρ' is an arbitrary metric on S such that π_i is (ρ',ρ_i)-continuous for $1 \leqslant i \leqslant n$, then $\rho \leqslant \rho'$.

PROOF (a) Given $1 \leqslant i \leqslant n$, and a member G_i of $\mathscr{G}_{\rho_i}$, then: $\pi_i^{-1}(G_i) = S_1 \times S_2 \times \ldots \times S_{i-1} \times G_i \times S_{i+1} \times \ldots \times S_n$. But the right-hand side is a subset of S which is a member of $\mathscr{G}_\rho$, since (by remarks following Definition 22) each $\mathscr{G}_i'$ can be taken equal to $\mathscr{G}_{\rho_i}$ itself in part (ii) of the definition. So the required result follows from Theorem 2.36.

(b) By Definition 22, $\exists$ for each i a base $\mathscr{G}_i'$ for $\mathscr{G}_{\rho_i}$ such that the set $\mathscr{G}'$, as defined there, forms a base for $\mathscr{G}_\rho$. It suffices to show that if π_i is (ρ',ρ_i)-continuous for each i, then $\mathscr{G}' \subseteq \mathscr{G}_{\rho'}$. Given G' in $\mathscr{G}'$, and G_i in $\mathscr{G}_i'$, $1 \leqslant i \leqslant n$, such that $G' = \prod_{1 \leqslant i \leqslant n} G_i$, then $G' = \bigcap_{1 \leqslant i \leqslant n} \pi_i^{-1}(G_i)$, (by Theorem 1.4) where, by assumption on ρ' and Theorem 2.36, each $\pi_i^{-1}(G_i) \in \mathscr{G}_{\rho'}$. Hence $G' \in \mathscr{G}_{\rho'}$.

Further sets of criteria for the continuity of a function appear in the next theorem and corollary:

THEOREM 2.39 Given spaces (S,ρ), (S',ρ'), $A \subseteq S$, a function f from A into S' is (ρ,ρ')-continuous on A if and only if one of the following conditions is satisfied:

(a)* for each subset X of A, $f({}^\rho\overline{X}^A) \subseteq {}^{\rho'}\overline{f(X)}$;

(b) if $x \in A$ and $\{x_i\}$, $i \geqslant 1$, is a sequence of members of A such that $x_i \underset{\rho}{\rightarrow} x$, then $f(x_i) \underset{\rho'}{\rightarrow} f(x)$.

PROOF Take again $A = S$.

(a) Given that f is continuous on A, and given $X \subseteq A$, ${}^{\rho'}\overline{f(X)} \in \mathscr{F}_{\rho'}$; hence, by Theorem 2.36, $f^{-1}({}^{\rho'}\overline{f(X)}) \in \mathscr{F}_\rho$. Since $X \subseteq f^{-1}({}^{\rho'}\overline{f(X)})$, it follows that ${}^\rho\overline{X} \subseteq f^{-1}({}^{\rho'}\overline{f(X)})$. Conversely, given that (a) holds, and F' in $\mathscr{F}_{\rho'}$, write $X = f^{-1}(F')$. Then clearly ${}^{\rho'}\overline{f(X)} \subseteq {}^{\rho'}\overline{F'} = F'$, implying that $f({}^\rho\overline{X}) \subseteq F'$, or that ${}^\rho\overline{X} \subseteq X$; the continuity of f follows immediately from Theorem 2.36.

(b) We shall supply a proof only of the fact that condition (b) is sufficient for the continuity of f. If $\exists$ an element x_0 in S at which f is not continuous, then, for some member Y_0 of $\mathscr{N}_{\rho'}(f(x_0))$:

$$f(X) \cap C_{S'}(Y_0) \neq \varnothing \text{ for any } X \text{ in } \mathscr{N}_\rho(x_0) \qquad (1)$$

In particular, for each $i = 1,2,\ldots$, (taking $X = N^{\rho}_{i^{-1}}(x_0)$ in (1)) $\exists$ member x_i of $N^{\rho}_{i^{-1}}(x_0)$ such that $f(x_i)\,\omega\,Y_0$. Then, although $x_i \underset{\rho}{\rightarrow} x_0$, it is *not* true that $f(x_i) \underset{\rho'}{\rightarrow} f(x_0)$.

COROLLARY* f is (ρ,ρ')-continuous on A if and only if for each subset X of A, and member x of ${}^{\rho}X'^{A}$, $f(x) \in f(X) \cup {}^{\rho'}(f(X))'$.

The condition appearing in the Corollary is used by some authors (e.g., HOCKING and YOUNG, Reference [4] p. 4) to *define* the concept of continuity.

Note 22 In conditions (a), (b) of Theorem 2.36, inverse images under f cannot be replaced by direct images; indeed the three following statements are logically independent:

(I) f is continuous on A;
(II) for each G in $\mathscr{G}_{\rho A}$, $f(G)$ is in $\mathscr{G}_{\rho'}$;
(III) for each F in $\mathscr{F}_{\rho A}$, $f(F)$ is in $\mathscr{F}_{\rho'}$.

This is shown by the following:

Example 2.6.4 $S = R^2$, $S' = R$, with usual metrics. A: set of $x \equiv \{x_1,x_2\}$ in S with $x_1x_2 = 0$. f: the restriction to A of π_1. By Theorem 2.38, π_1 is continuous (on S); hence f is continuous on A. If G denotes the set of points x in A with $x_1 = 0$ and $0 < x_2 < 1$, $G \in \mathscr{G}_A$ (since $G = G' \cap A$, where G' is the subset: $0 < x_2 < 1$ of R^2); however, since $f(G) = (0)$, (II) does not hold. On the other hand, for any member F of $\mathscr{F}_A$, $f(F) = f(F_1)$ *or* $f(F_1) \cup (0)$ where F_1 is the subset of F contained by the x_1-axis; since clearly $f(F_1) \in \mathscr{F}_{\rho'}$, $f(F) \in \mathscr{F}_{\rho'}$, and so (III) holds. That is, (II) is *not* a consequence of (I) and (III) together.

Example 2.6.5 S,S' as in 2.6.4, with usual metrics; $A = S$, $f = \pi_1$. By Theorem 2.38 and Theorem 2.40 (below), f satisfies (I) and (II); however, if F denotes the set of points $x \equiv \{x_1,x_2\}$ in A with $x_1x_2 = 1$, it is easily seen that $F \in \mathscr{F}_A$, while $f(F) = S' - (0)$, *not* a member of $\mathscr{F}_{\rho'}$. Thus, (III) is *not* a consequence of (I) and (II).

Example 2.6.6 $S = R$, $\rho = \rho_1$; $S' = (0,1)$ with any metric; $A = S$. The function f from S onto S' such that $f(x) = 1$ at each rational point and $f(x) = 0$ elsewhere is (as in Example 2.6.1) not continuous; however (II), (III) clearly hold. Thus (I) is *not* a consequence of (II) and (III).

DEFINITION 29* Given spaces (S,ρ), (S',ρ'), $A \subseteq S$, a function f from A into S' is said to be **(ρ, ρ′)-open** on A if, for each G in $\mathscr{G}_{\rho A}$, $f(G)$ is in $\mathscr{G}_{\rho'}$.

The notion of being '**(ρ, ρ')-closed** on A' is analogously defined.

It is easily seen that, in Definition 29, it is sufficient to postulate that $f(G)$ be in $\mathscr{G}_{\rho'}$ for each member G of some base for $\mathscr{G}_{\rho A}$. Hence there follows immediately:

THEOREM 2.40* If (S,ρ) is a product space of the spaces (S_i,ρ_i), $1 \leqslant i \leqslant n$, then, for each i, the projection π_i is (ρ,ρ_i)-open.

The proof is left to the reader.

Analogues of Theorem 2.39, part (a) appear in:

THEOREM 2.41* Given spaces (S,ρ), (S',ρ'), $A \subseteq S$, a function f from A into S' is:

(a) (ρ,ρ')-open on A if and only if for each subset X of A, $f({}^{\rho}X^{\circ A}) \subseteq {}^{\rho'}(f(X))^{\circ}$;

(b) (ρ,ρ')-closed on A if and only if for each subset X of A, ${}^{\rho'}\overline{f(X)} \subseteq f({}^{\rho}\overline{X}^{A})$.

PROOF Take again $A = S$.

(a) Given that f is open on A, and given $X \subseteq A$, $f({}^{\rho}X^{\circ}) \in \mathscr{G}_{\rho'}$; that is

$$f({}^{\rho}X^{\circ}) = {}^{\rho'}(f({}^{\rho}X^{\circ}))^{\circ} \subseteq {}^{\rho'}(f(X))^{\circ}.$$

Conversely, given that (a) holds and given G in $\mathscr{G}_{\rho}$, $f(G) = f({}^{\rho}G^{\circ}) \subseteq {}^{\rho'}(f(G))^{\circ}$; that is, $f(G) \in \mathscr{G}_{\rho'}$.

(b) This is left to the reader.

THEOREM 2.42* Given spaces (S,ρ), (S',ρ'), if f is a (1,1) function from S onto S', the following three statements are equivalent:

(a) f is (ρ,ρ')-continuous (on S);
(b) f^{-1} is (ρ',ρ)-open (on S');
(c) f^{-1} is (ρ',ρ)-closed (on S').

DEFINITION 30* Given spaces (S,ρ), (S',ρ'), a (1,1) function f from S onto S' is said to be a **(ρ, ρ')-homeomorphism** if: (a) f is (ρ,ρ')-continuous (on S) and: (b) f^{-1} is (ρ',ρ)-continuous (on S') *or* (equivalently) f is (ρ,ρ')-open or closed (on S).

Two spaces (S,ρ), (S',ρ') are said to be **homeomorphic** (images of one another) if such a homeomorphism exists. Such a relation between two spaces is an equivalence on the set of all metric spaces.

More generally, if, given spaces (S,ρ), (S',ρ'), A, B are subsets of S,S' respectively, then a function f from A onto B is said to be a (ρ,ρ')-homeomorphism from A onto B if it is a (ρ_A,ρ'_B)-homeomorphism (where ρ_A, ρ'_B are respectively the restrictions of ρ, ρ' to A, B), that is, the statements: '(A, ρ_1) is a subspace of (S, ρ)' and '(B, ρ'_1) is a subspace of (S', ρ')' together imply the statement: 'f is a (ρ_1, ρ'_1)-homeomorphism'. Then, again, the subsets A, B are said to be (ρ, ρ')-homeomorphic. Clearly such a condition depends only on A, B themselves and on $\mathscr{G}_\rho, \mathscr{G}_{\rho'}$.

Note 23 Condition (b) could not be omitted from Definition 30.

Example 2.6.7 Let (S', ρ') be an arbitrary non-discrete space, $S = S'$, and ρ any discrete metric on S. Since $\mathscr{G}_{\rho'} \subset \mathscr{G}_\rho$, it follows from Example 2.6.2 that the identity function f is (ρ, ρ')-continuous, while $f^{-1}(= f)$ is *not* (ρ', ρ)-continuous.

THEOREM 2.43* Given spaces (S, ρ), (S', ρ'), if f is a (1,1) function from S onto S', the following statements are equivalent:

(a) f is a (ρ, ρ')-homeomorphism;
(b) for each $X \subseteq S$, $X \in \mathscr{G}_\rho$ if and only if $f(X) \in \mathscr{G}_{\rho'}$;
(c) for each $X \subseteq S$, $X \in \mathscr{F}_\rho$ if and only if $f(X) \in \mathscr{F}_{\rho'}$;
(d) for each $X \subseteq S$, ${}^{\rho'}\overline{f(X)} = f^{\rho}(\overline{X})$;
(e) for each x in S, and $X \subseteq S$: $X \in \mathscr{N}_\rho(x)$ if and only if $f(X) \in \mathscr{N}_{\rho'}(f(x))$.

Example 2.6.8 If (S, ρ), (S', ρ') are both discrete, then any (1,1) function f from S onto S' is a (ρ, ρ')-homeomorphism.

Example 2.6.9 If ρ, ρ' are metrics defined on a non-null set S, the identity function on S is a (ρ, ρ')-homeomorphism if and only if ρ, ρ' are equivalent. Thus, for example, any two product spaces of a given finite sequence of spaces are homeomorphic.

THEOREM 2.44* Given spaces (S_i, ρ_i), $1 \leqslant i \leqslant 3$, let (S, ρ) be a product space of (S_1, ρ_1), (S_2, ρ_2), let (S', ρ') be a product space of (S_2, ρ_2), (S_1, ρ_1) and (S'', ρ'') a product space of (S_2, ρ_2) and (S_3, ρ_3). Then:

(a) *Commutative Property*: (S, ρ) and (S', ρ') are homeomorphic;
(b) *Associative Property*: A product space of (S, ρ), (S_3, ρ_3) and a product space of (S_1, ρ_1) and (S'', ρ'') are homeomorphic.

Note 24 Given spaces (S, ρ), (S', ρ'), define functions σ from S into $P(P(S))$ and χ from $P(S)$ into $P(S)$:

for each x in S, $\sigma(x) = \mathscr{N}_\rho(x)$
for each $X \subseteq S$, $\chi(X) = {}^{\rho}\overline{X}$
and similar functions σ', χ' for (S', ρ').

Then, if f is a (ρ,ρ')-homeomorphism, it follows from Theorem 2.43 that:

(I) for $X \subseteq S$, $X \in \mathscr{G}_\rho$ if and only if $f(X) \in \mathscr{G}_{\rho'}$;

(II) for x in S, and $X \subseteq S$:
$X \in \sigma(x)$ if and only if $f(X) \in \sigma'(f(x))$

(III) for $X \subseteq S$, $\chi'(f(X)) = f(\chi(X))$.

Hence, if $\{X_i\}$, $i \in I$, is a family of subsets of S, these satisfy a given relation $\mathscr{R}$ expressible (ultimately) in terms of $\mathscr{G}_\rho,\chi,\sigma$ and the operations and relations of set theory if and only if the corresponding family $\{f(X_i)\}$ of subsets of S' satisfy the relation $\mathscr{R}'$ obtained from $\mathscr{R}$ by replacing $\mathscr{G}_\rho$ by $\mathscr{G}_{\rho'}$, χ by χ', σ by σ'. That is, any such relation $\mathscr{R}$ holding among the members of a family of subsets of S has its exact counterpart $\mathscr{R}'$ for the family of corresponding subsets of S', and vice versa; it follows that from a point of view where we are concerned only with relations of this kind holding among the subsets and neither with the intrinsic nature of the elements themselves nor with the particular metrics ρ,ρ' which happen to be defined on S,S' respectively, the spaces in question cannot be distinguished one from another. In such a case we often find it natural and convenient to agree to identify each member x of S with its image $f(x)$ in S', so that S becomes coincidental with S'. This procedure is particularly adopted where (S',ρ') is a subspace (in the sense of Definition 23) of a third space (S'',ρ''). Then, when each member of S has been identified with its image in S', ρ becomes a metric on S', while f becomes the identity function on S'. Since f remains a (ρ,ρ')-homeomorphism, it follows that $\mathscr{G}_\rho$ and $\mathscr{G}_{\rho'}$ will coincide; that is, (S,ρ) becomes a subspace of (S'',ρ''). Then (S,ρ) is said to be **homeomorphically imbedded** in (S'',ρ''); if $S' \subset S''$, such an imbedding is said to be proper.

DEFINITION 31 Given spaces (S,ρ), (S',ρ'), a (1,1) function f from S onto S' is said to be a **(ρ, ρ')-isometry** if, for each x,y in S: $\rho(x,y) = \rho'\{f(x), f(y)\}$. Then the spaces are said to be **isometric.**

Clearly any isometry is necessarily a homeomorphism, but not conversely; for example, if $S = S'$, the identity function is an isometry only if ρ,ρ' are identical, contrasting with Example 2.6.9.

Two isometric spaces (S,ρ), (S',ρ') are thus indistinguishable not only as regards such relations $\mathscr{R}$ as decribed in Note 24, but also as regards their respective metrics. If (S',ρ') is a restricted subspace of a space (S'',ρ'') (in the sense that ρ' is identical with the restriction of ρ'' to S') the metric ρ on S will, on the identification as before of each member of S with its image under f in S', become coincidental with the metric ρ' on S' so that (S,ρ) becomes itself a restricted subspace of (S'',ρ''). (S,ρ) is then said to be **isometrically** imbedded in (S'',ρ'').

Example 2.6.10 $S = R$, $\rho = \rho_1$; $S' =]0,1[$, ρ' the restriction of ρ_1 to S'. It will be seen that (S,ρ) is homeomorphic to (S',ρ'); that is, (S,ρ) can be properly homeomorphically imbedded in (S,ρ) itself. To this end, define a function g from S' into S: for $y \in S'$, $g(y) = (1 - y)^{-1} - y^{-1}$. Then:

(I) g is (1,1) onto S. That is, to each x in S, there corresponds just one y in S' with $g(y) = x$, that is, such that $h(x,y) \equiv xy^2 + (2 - x)y - 1 = 0$. For, given x in S, $h(x,y)$ is a linear or quadratic polynomial in y such that $h(x,0) = -1$ and $h(x,1) = 1$; hence, by the continuity of h, the equation in y above has just one root in $]0,1[$. Thus $f \equiv g^{-1}$ is a (1,1) function from S onto S'.

(II) g is (ρ',ρ)-continuous. This follows from the existence of the derivative of g throughout $]0,1[$.

(III) g is (ρ',ρ)-open. Since its derivative is positive throughout $]0,1[$ g is strictly increasing; hence, the image under g of any interval $]a,b[$ contained in S' will either be some open interval in S or S itself. Since these subintervals of S' form a base for $\mathscr{G}_{\rho'}$, it follows immediately that g is (ρ',ρ)-open.

It is perhaps worth noting that (S,ρ), (S',ρ') cannot be isometric, since the latter is a bounded space, while the former is not.

The same could be proved if S' were an arbitrary open interval in R.

It might be suspected—from Example 2.6.10 for instance—that a space could not be (properly) isometrically imbedded in itself. However the following example shows that, on the contrary, a space (S,ρ) can be imbedded in itself in such a way that the subset S' of S containing those elements with which the members of S are identified in the imbedding process, is actually nowhere dense (in S).

Example 2.6.11 $(S,\rho) =$ Hilbert Space H^∞; S': the set of those elements $\{x_i\}$ of S with $x_1 = 0$. Then:

(I) (S,ρ) and its restricted subspace $(S',\rho_{S'})$ are isometric.

(II) S' is nowhere dense.

First, given $x \equiv \{x_i\}$ in S, write $f(x) = \{0,x_1,x_2,\ldots\}$; f is clearly (1,1) onto S' and, for x,y in S: $\rho_{S'}(f(x),f(y)) = \rho(x,y)$.

Secondly, given an arbitrary non-null member G of $\mathscr{G}_\rho$, choose $x \equiv \{x_i\}$ in G, and $\varepsilon > 0$ such that $N_\varepsilon(x) \subseteq G$; choose further a non-zero number a in $]x_1,x_1 + \frac{1}{2}\varepsilon[$. If $x' = \{a,x_1,x_2,\ldots\}$ in S, $\rho(x',x) < \frac{1}{2}\varepsilon$ and so, for any y in $N_{\frac{1}{2}\varepsilon}(x')$, $\rho(x,y) < \varepsilon$; hence, if $\eta = \min(|a|,\frac{1}{2}\varepsilon)$,

$$N_\eta(x') \subseteq N_\varepsilon(x) \tag{1}$$

But if $z \equiv \{z_i\}$ is a member of $N_\eta(x')$, $|a - z_1| \leqslant \rho(x',z) < \eta \leqslant |a|$, implying that $z_1 \neq 0$; that is, $z \,\omega\, S'$; hence, by (1), G contains a non-null open set $G'(= N_\eta(x'))$ such that $G' \cap S' = \varnothing$; hence, by Theorem 2.34, S' is nowhere dense.

Example 2.6.12 Given an arbitrary family $\{(S_i,\rho_i)\}$, $i \in I$, of spaces, a space (S,ρ) can be constructed in which each member of the family can be isometrically imbedded. For each i in I, choose a member $x_i^{(o)}$ of S_i. If S denotes the set of all pairs (x_i,S_i), where x_i is a member of S_i, and $i \in I$, define a function ρ from $S \times S$ into R:

given $z \equiv (x_i,S_i)$, $z' \equiv (x_j,S_j)$ in S:

$$\rho(z,z') = \begin{cases} \rho_i(x_i,y_i) & \text{if } i = j \\ \\ \rho_i(x_i,x_i^{(o)}) + \rho_j(x_j,x_j^{(o)}) + 1 & \text{if } i \neq j \end{cases}$$

It can be shown that ρ is a metric on S such that, for each i in I, (S_i,ρ_i) is isometric to the restricted subspace (T_i,ρ_{T_i}) of (S,ρ), where T_i is the subset of S of all elements (x_i,S_i).

DEFINITION 32* A property P applicable to a space is said to be a **homeomorphic** property if when it is possessed by a space (S,ρ), it is possessed also by any space homeomorphic to it.

The notion of 'isometric property' is analogous.

DEFINITION 33* A property P' applicable to a subset of a space is said to be a **homeomorphic** property if when it is possessed by a subset A of a space (S,ρ), it is possessed also by any subset B of a space (S',ρ') such that A,B are (ρ,ρ')-homeomorphic.

Note 25 (I) From Note 24 it is evident that a property P applicable to a space (S,ρ) is a homeomorphic property if it is expressible (ultimately) in terms of $\mathscr{G},\chi,\sigma$, and the operations and relations of set theory. For example, the property P_1:

'given non-null G in $\mathscr{G}$, $\exists\, X \subset G$ such that: $X \nsubseteq (\overline{X})^\circ \nsubseteq X$'

(which is, incidentally, possessed by, for example, the space $(R)_1$

(See Example 2.3.12) and not by any discrete space) is a homeomorphic property, since $(\bar{X})^\circ = C(\chi(C(X)))$. On the other hand, the property of being bounded is not a homeomorphic property of a space; for even if (S,ρ) is an unbounded space, a bounded metric ρ' can be defined on S (as seen in Theorem 2.23, Corollary II) such that ρ' is equivalent to ρ; that is, the identity function on S is a (ρ,ρ')-homeomorphism.

(II) From Definitions 32, 33, it is clear that a property P' applicable to a subset A of a space (S,ρ) is a homeomorphic property if P' is so defined that there exists a property P applicable to a space such that:

(a) P is a homeomorphic property (of a space).

(b) A possesses P' if and only if $\exists$ a subspace (S,ρ') of (S,ρ) such that $S' = A$ and (S',ρ') possesses P.

(Condition (a) ensures that, provided $S' = A$, condition (b) is independent of the choice of subspace (S',ρ').)

For example, it will be recalled that, in Section 2.3, a subset A of a space (S,ρ) is said to be *isolated* if and only if $A \cap A' = \varnothing$; that is, in the notation of Section 2.5, $A'^A = \varnothing$. Clearly then the property P' (applicable to a subset of a space) of being isolated is so defined that a subset A possesses P' if and only if some subspace (A,ρ') of (S,ρ) possesses the property P of being *discrete*. Since P is a homeomorphic property of a space, P' must consequently be a homeomorphic property of a subset. It is clear too that if P is a hereditary homeomorphic property of a space (as is the case above) and if P' is a property of a subset defined in terms of P as in (b), then first, every subset of a space possessing P will possess P', and, secondly, if A is a subset of an arbitrary space such that A possesses P', every non-null subset of A possesses P'.

By contrast, the property (applicable to a subset of a space) of being closed or open is not so defined and indeed is not a homeomorphic property; that is, if, given spaces (S,ρ), (S',ρ'), the subsets A,B of S,S' respectively are (ρ,ρ')-homeomorphic, the statement '$A \in \mathscr{G}_\rho$' (respectively '$A \in \mathscr{F}_\rho$') does *not* imply '$B \in \mathscr{G}_{\rho'}$' (respectively '$B \in \mathscr{F}_{\rho'}$').

Example 2.6.13 $(S,\rho) = (S'\rho') = H^\infty$; $A = S$; B: the set of those elements $\{x_i\}$ of S with $x_1 = 0$. By Example 2.6.11 above, (A,ρ_A) $(=(S,\rho))$ and (B,ρ'_B) are isometric and hence homeomorphic. However, although, trivially, $A \in \mathscr{G}_\rho$, B is nowhere dense in S', so that: ${}^{\rho'}B^\circ \subseteq {}^{\rho'}(\bar{B})^\circ = \varnothing \subset B$; that is, $B\,\omega\,\mathscr{G}_{\rho'}$.

Example 2.6.14 S: set of positive real numbers, S': R, with usual metrics. $A = \bigcup_{n \geq 1} (n^{-1}) \subset S$; $B = \bigcup_{n \geq 1} (-n^{-1}) \subset S'$. Since A has no cluster points (in S), $A \in \mathscr{F}_\rho$ and (A,ρ_A) is discrete. Also, since the only cluster point of B (in S') is 0, $B\, \omega\, \mathscr{F}_{\rho'}$ while (B,ρ'_B) is again discrete. Since the function f from A onto B given by: $f(x) = -x$ for each x in A, is (1,1) it follows (by Example 2.6.8) that f is a (ρ_A,ρ'_B)-homeomorphism; that is, by definition, f is a (ρ,ρ')-homeomorphism from A onto B, although $A \in \mathscr{F}_\rho$ while $B\, \omega\, \mathscr{F}_{\rho'}$.

See also Exercise 8 below and Section 3.3, Exercise 3.

In Part I, it was noted that if f is any function from S into S', with graph T, then the function g from S into $S \times S'$ where $g(x) = \{x,f(x)\}$, for x in S, is a (1,1) function from S onto T.

THEOREM 2.45* If (S'',ρ'') is a product space of the spaces (S,ρ), (S',ρ') and f is a function from S into S', then f is (ρ,ρ')-continuous if and only if g is (ρ,ρ'')-continuous. Then, if T is the graph of f on S, and (T,ρ_1) a subspace of (S'',ρ''), g is a (ρ,ρ_1)-homeomorphism.

PROOF Supposing first that f is (ρ,ρ')-continuous, let G,G' belong to $\mathscr{G}_\rho,\mathscr{G}_{\rho'}$ respectively. Then, if $x \in S$:

$$g(x) \in G \times G' \text{ if and only if } x \in G \text{ and } f(x) \in G';$$

that is, $g^{-1}(G \times G') = G \cap f^{-1}(G')$, a member of $\mathscr{G}_\rho$ (by Theorem (2.36). By Definition 22 and Note 21, g is thus (ρ,ρ'')-continuous. Further, g^{-1} when restricted to T is a single-valued function which coincides with the restriction to T of the projection of $S \times S'$ onto S. By Theorem 2.38, g^{-1} is thus (ρ_1,ρ)-continuous.

Conversely, if g is given to be (ρ,ρ'')-continuous, G' is in $\mathscr{G}_{\rho'}$ and $x \in S$: $f^{-1}(G') = g^{-1}(S \times G')$, where, by definition of product space, $S \times G' \in \mathscr{G}_{\rho''}$. Hence, by Theorem 2.36, the continuity of g implies that of f.

THEOREM 2.46 If (S',ρ') is a product space of (S,ρ), (S,ρ), the diagonal Δ_S belongs to $\mathscr{F}_{\rho'}$.

PROOF If $\{x,y\} \in C_{S'}(\Delta_S)$, $x \neq y$; hence, by Theorem 2.17, Corollary, $\exists$ members G,G' of $\mathscr{G}_\rho$ with x in G, y in G' and $G \cap G'$ null. But the latter is equivalent to: $G \times G' \subseteq C_{S'}(\Delta_S)$; hence, since $G \times G' \in \mathscr{G}_{\rho'}$, $C_{S'}(\Delta_S)$ belongs to $\mathscr{N}_{\rho'}(\{x,y\})$. Thus $C_{S'}(\Delta_S) \in \mathscr{G}_{\rho'}$.

COROLLARY I: Given spaces (S,ρ), (S',ρ') and (ρ,ρ')-continuous functions f,g from S into S', the set of elements x of S where $f(x) = g(x)$, belongs to $\mathscr{F}_\rho$.

To establish this corollary, note that if (S'',ρ'') is a product space of (S',ρ'), (S',ρ'), the function h from S into S'' where $h(x) = \{f(x),g(x)\}$, for x in S, is (ρ,ρ'')-continuous. The second corollary, which provides a generalization of Theorem 2.46, follows from the first:

COROLLARY II: Given spaces (S,ρ), (S',ρ'), let f be a (ρ,ρ')-continuous function from S into S'; if (S'',ρ'') is a product space of (S,ρ), (S',ρ'), the graph of f on S belongs to $\mathscr{F}_{\rho''}$.

In Section 2.1 it was noted that any normed (vector) space $[S,v]$ gives rise to a metric space (S,ρ_v) where $\rho_v(x,y) = v(x - y)$. With this notation:

THEOREM 2.47 Given a normed (vector) space $[S,v]$ and two distinct points x,y of S, let ρ' be the restriction of ρ_v to the segment $S' \equiv \langle x,y \rangle$; if ρ'' is the restriction of ρ_1 to the interval $S'' \equiv [0,1]$ of R, then the spaces (S',ρ'), (S'',ρ'') are homeomorphic.

PROOF Define a function f from S'' into S':
for t in S'', $f(t) = (1 - t)x + ty$. Clearly f is (1,1) onto S', and, for t, u in S'':

$$\rho'(f(t),f(u)) = v(f(t) - f(u)) = |t - u|v(x - y) = v(x - y)\rho''(t,u).$$

Since $v(x - y)$ is non-zero, and independent of t,u in S'', clearly f is a (ρ'',ρ')-homeomorphism.

Worked Exercises

1.* Given a space (S,ρ), let $\{A_i\}$, $i \geqslant 1$, be a covering of S such that $A_i \subseteq A^\circ_{i+1}$ for each $i \geqslant 1$. If (S',ρ') is a second space and f a function from S into S' such that its restriction f_{A_i} is continuous on A_i for each i, show that f is continuous on S.

Solution: Since $\{A^\circ_{i+1}\}$, $i \geqslant 1$, forms a covering of S, it is clear that, for each G' in $\mathscr{G}_{\rho'}$:

$$f^{-1}(G') = \bigcup_{i \geqslant 1} (f^{-1}(G') \cap A^\circ_{i+1}) = \bigcup_{i \geqslant 1} f_i^{-1}(G') \tag{1}$$

where f_i denotes the restriction of f to A°_{i+1}. But since f_i is also the restriction to A°_{i+1} of the function $f_{A_{i+1}}$, it is continuous on A°_{i+1}. Hence, from Theorem 2.36, $f_i^{-1}(G')$ is open relative to A°_{i+1}, and hence, by Theorem 2.27(b), belongs to $\mathscr{G}_\rho$. The required result then follows from (1) and Theorem 2.36.

2. Given spaces (S,ρ), (S',ρ'), and a (ρ,ρ')-continuous (1,1) function f from S onto S', show that f is a (ρ,ρ')-homeomorphism if and only if:

$$\rho'' \leqslant \rho' \text{ for any metric } \rho'' \text{ on } S' \text{ such that } f \text{ is } (\rho,\rho'')\text{-continuous} \quad (2)$$

Solution: By Definition 30, it suffices to show that f is (ρ,ρ')-open if and only if (2) holds. If, first, f is given to be (ρ,ρ')-open, let ρ'' be a metric on S' such that f is (ρ,ρ'')-continuous. Then if $G' \in \mathscr{G}_{\rho''}$, it follows that $f^{-1}(G') \in \mathscr{G}_\rho$, and hence (since f is open) $f\{f^{-1}(G')\} \in \mathscr{G}_{\rho'}$; that is, since f is *onto* S', $G' \in \mathscr{G}_{\rho'}$. Thus $\rho'' \leqslant \rho'$.

Conversely, suppose that (2) holds. If ρ'' is the function from $S' \times S'$ into R obtained by writing for each x',y' in S', $\rho''(x',y') = \rho(x,y)$, where $x = f^{-1}(x')$, $y = f^{-1}(y')$, then ρ'' is clearly a metric on S' such that f is a (ρ,ρ'')-isometry and hence *a fortiori* a (ρ,ρ'')-homeomorphism. That is, first, f is (ρ,ρ'')-continuous, implying by (2) that $\mathscr{G}_{\rho''} \subseteq \mathscr{G}_{\rho'}$ while, secondly, f is (ρ,ρ'')-open. Hence, if $G \in \mathscr{G}_\rho$, then $f(G) \in \mathscr{G}_{\rho''}$, implying: $f(G) \in \mathscr{G}_{\rho'}$; that is f is (ρ,ρ')-open.

Exercises for Solution

1.* Given spaces (S,ρ), (S',ρ') show that a function f from S into S' is continuous if and only if for each $Y \subseteq S'$: $f^{-1}({}^{\rho'}Y^\circ) \subseteq {}^{\rho}(f^{-1}(Y))^\circ$.

2. Given spaces (S,ρ), (S',ρ'), and subsets A_1,A_2 of S such that $A_1 \cap A_2 \neq \varnothing$, let f,g be continuous functions from A_1,A_2 respectively into S' such that $f(x) = g(x)$ on $A_1 \cap A_2$. If a function h be defined from $A_1 \cup A_2$ into S' by writing $h(x) = f(x)$ for $x \in A_1$, and $h(x) = g(x)$ for $x \in A_2$, show that:

(a) h need not be continuous on $A_1 \cup A_2$;

(b)* if each A_i is open relative to $A_1 \cup A_2$, h is continuous.

3. If (S,ρ), (S',ρ') are spaces, $A \subseteq S$, and f a function from S into S', show whether or not the following statements are true:

(a) if f is open (in S), f_A is open in A.

(b) if f is closed (in S), f_A is closed in A.

If not, find* simple conditions which could be imposed on A to ensure their truth.

4.* Given a space (S,ρ), a real-valued function f on S is said to be **(ρ,ρ_1)-upper semi-continuous** if $f^{-1}\{]\leftarrow,a[\} \in \mathscr{G}_\rho$ for each a in R. If $\{f_i\}$, $i \in I$, is a family of upper-semi-continuous functions such that $g(x) \equiv \inf_i f_i(x)$ exists for each x in S, show that g is upper semi-continuous.

5. (a) If f is the function on R such that $f(x) = x$ if x is rational, and $f(x) = 2x$ otherwise, show that a metric ρ can be defined on R such that f becomes a (ρ,ρ_1)-isometry, where ρ_1 is the usual metric on R.

(b) If S' denotes the open interval $]-1,1[$ of R, show that the function given by: $\rho'(x,y) = |x/(1 - |x|) - y/(1 - |y|)|$ is a metric on S' such that (S',ρ') and $(R)_1$ are isometric.

(c) Show that $(R)_1$ and $(R^2)_1$ are *not* isometric.

6. Deduce from Ex. 2 of Section 2.1 that ∃ a metric space containing exactly *four* elements which cannot be isometrically imbedded in H^∞.

7. If, given spaces (S,ρ), (S',ρ') and continuous functions f,g from S into S', there exists a dense subset X of S such that $f(x) = g(x)$ everywhere in X, show that $f = g$.

8. Given spaces (S,ρ), (S',ρ') and an arbitrary non-null subset A of S, show that ∃ a metric ρ'' on $S'' \equiv A \times S'$ such that, to each (ρ,ρ')-continuous function f from A into S', there corresponds a (different) member T of $\mathscr{F}_{\rho''}$ such that A,T are (ρ,ρ'')-homeomorphic (as subsets of S,S'' respectively).

9. If P is an isometric property of a space, show that a given space (S,ρ) is homeomorphic to some space possessing P if and only if ∃ an equivalent metric ρ' on S such that (S,ρ') possesses P.

10.* If (S'',ρ'') is a product space of (S,ρ) and (S',ρ'), and $x_0 \in S$, show that the sets $(x_0) \times S'$ and S' are (ρ'',ρ')-homeomorphic.

CHAPTER 3

Types of Metric Space

3.1 Separable and Completely Separable Spaces

DEFINITION 1* A space (S,ρ) is said to be **separable** if S contains an enumerable dense subset X; that is, $\overline{X} = S$.

More generally, a *subset* A of S is said to be separable (w.r.t.ρ) if some subspace (A,ρ') of (S,ρ) is separable; that is, if A contains an enumerable subset, dense in A. It is clear from Note 25, Chapter 2, that the property of separability is homeomorphic both when applied to a space and to a subset. More generally, indeed, we have:

THEOREM 3.1* Let spaces (S,ρ), (S',ρ') be such that there exists a (ρ,ρ')-continuous function f from S onto S'; then if (S,ρ) is separable, so is (S',ρ').

PROOF Let X be enumerable subset of S with ${}^{\rho}\overline{X} = S$. Then $S' = f(S) = f({}^{\rho}\overline{X}) \subseteq {}^{\rho'}\overline{f(X)}$ by Theorem 2.39. Since $f(X)$ is clearly enumerable, result follows.

COROLLARY If ρ,ρ' are metrics defined on a non-null set S with $\rho' \leqslant \rho$ and if (S,ρ) is separable, so is (S',ρ').

THEOREM 3.2* A product space (S,ρ) of a finite sequence of spaces $\{(S_i,\rho_i)\}$, $1 \leqslant i \leqslant n$, is separable if and only if each space (S_i,ρ_i) is separable.

The proof is left to the reader.

Example 3.1.1 $(R)_1$ is separable, since $Q' = R$. Hence, by Theorem 3.2, (R^n,ρ_i) is separable for $i = 1,2,3$.

Example 3.1.2 $(S,\rho) \equiv H^{\infty}$ is separable. To see this, let X be the subset of S of all elements $x \equiv \{x_i\}$, $i \geqslant 1$, such that: $x_i \in Q$, $i \geqslant 1$, and $\exists\, i'$ (dependent on x) such that $x_i = 0$ for $i > i'$. By Theorem 1.5, X is enumerable. Secondly, $X' = S$. For, given an arbitrary element $y \equiv \{y_i\}$ of S, and $\varepsilon > 0$, $\exists N$ (dependent on y) such that $\sum_{N+1}^{\infty} y_i^2 < \frac{1}{2}\varepsilon$. Choose a member x' of X such that: for $1 \leqslant i \leqslant N$, $y_i < x_i' < y_i + 2\varepsilon/3N$; for $i > N$, $x_i' = 0$. Then $x' \neq y$ and:

$$(\rho(x',y))^2 = \sum_{i=1}^{N} (y_i - x_i')^2 + \sum_{N+1}^{\infty} y_i^2 < \varepsilon^2.$$

Example 3.1.3 If S is the set of continuous functions f from the unit interval into R, and metrics ρ_1,ρ_2 are defined on S as in Example 2.1.3, (S,ρ_i) is separable for $i = 1,2$. Since (by Example 2.4.1) $\rho_2 < \rho_1$, it suffices by Theorem 3.1, Corollary, to show that (S,ρ_1) is separable. Clearly the subset X of S containing all polynomials in x with rational coefficients is enumerable. It remains to show that $\bar{X} = S$. First, by Weierstrass's Approximation Theorem, (e.g., Apostol, Reference [1], p. 481) given f in S, and $\varepsilon > 0$, $\exists$ a polynomial h such that $|f(x) - h(x)| < \varepsilon/2$ for $0 \leqslant x \leqslant 1$. Suppose $h(x) = b_0x^n + b_1x^{n-1} + \ldots + b_n$. For each i, choose a rational a_i such that $|b_i - a_i| < \varepsilon/2(n+1)$, and let g be the member of X such that: $g(x) = a_0x^n + \ldots + a_n$. Then, for $0 \leqslant x \leqslant 1$: $|h(x) - g(x)| \leqslant |b_0 - a_0| + \ldots + |b_n - a_n| < \varepsilon/2$ so that, by the choice of h, it is clear that

$$\rho_1(f,g) = \max_{0 \leqslant x \leqslant 1} |f(x) - g(x)| < \varepsilon.$$

Definition 2* A space (S,ρ) is said to be **completely separable** (or to satisfy the Second Axiom of Countability) if there exists an enumerable base for $\mathscr{G}$.

Just as for separability, this property can be extended to apply to a subset of a space; clearly they are again homeomorphic properties.

Theorem 3.3* The property of complete separability (as applicable to a space) is hereditary.

Proof Let (A,ρ') be an arbitrary subspace of a completely separable space (S,ρ). If $\mathscr{G}' \equiv \{G_i\}$, $i \geqslant 1$, is an (enumerable) base for $\mathscr{G}$, write $G_i' = G_i \cap A$ for $i \geqslant 1$. To show that $\mathscr{G}_A' \equiv \{G_i'\}$, $i \geqslant 1$, forms a base for the set $\mathscr{G}_A$ (of open sets of (A,ρ')), we note first that, clearly, $\mathscr{G}_A' \subseteq \mathscr{G}_A$; secondly, given x in A and X in $\mathscr{N}_A(x)$ (in the notation of Section 2.5) $\exists$ Y in $\mathscr{N}(x)$ such that $X = Y \cap A$; further, since $\mathscr{G}'$ is a base for $\mathscr{G}$, $\exists$ integer i' such that $x \in G_{i'} \subseteq Y$, implying: $x \in G_{i'}' \subseteq X$.

A consequence of Theorem 3.3 is that if (S,ρ) is a completely separable *space*, each *subset* is completely separable; indeed, each *subset* of a completely separable subset of an arbitrary space is completely separable.

DEFINITION 3* Given a space (S,ρ), a covering $\{G_i\}$, $i \in I$, of a subset A of S is said to be a **ρ-open covering** of A (in S) if G_i belongs to $\mathscr{G}_\rho$ for each i in I.

If no ambiguity is possible, $\{G_i\}$ is said simply to be open.

DEFINITION 4* A space (S,ρ) is said to possess the **Lindelöf property** (or be a 'Lindelöf-space') if any open covering of S contains an enumerable sub-covering (of S).

The above notion can as usual be extended to be applicable to any subset of a space and the properties will be homeomorphic; that is, given a space (S,ρ), a subset A of S will be said to possess the Lindelöf property (or be a 'Lindelöf set') if there exists a subspace (A,ρ') of (S,ρ) with this property; in other words, if each ρ'-open covering of A (in A) contains an enumerable sub-covering. However, it will be seen to be often convenient to express the latter property in terms of ρ-open subsets of S, rather than ρ'-open subsets of A; that is, we have:

THEOREM 3.4* Given a space (S,ρ), a subset A is a Lindelöf set if and only if any ρ-open covering of A (in S) contains an enumerable sub-covering of A.

The proof is left to the reader.

THEOREM 3.5 Given a space (S,ρ), and a subset A of S, the following five statements are equivalent:

(a) A is separable.
(b) A is completely separable.
(c) A is a Lindelöf set.
(d) Every non-countable subset of A possesses at least one point of condensation which is a member of A.
(e) Every non-countable subset of A possesses at least one cluster point (a member of A or otherwise).

PROOF First, (a) implies (b). Taking $A = S$ (without loss of generality), let X be an enumerable dense subset of S. Then the set $\mathscr{B}$ of all subsets of S of the form $N_r(x)$, where $x \in X$ and $r \in Q$, is enumerable. It remains to show that $\mathscr{B}$ forms a base for $\mathscr{G}$. Given x in S, and X in $\mathscr{N}(x)$, $\exists$ (real) $\varepsilon > 0$ such that $N_\varepsilon(x) \subseteq X$. Since X is dense, $\exists$ a member x' of X with $\rho(x',x) < \varepsilon/3$; choose a member r' of Q with $\varepsilon/3 < r' < 2\varepsilon/3$, and write $G = N_{r'}(x')$, a member of $\mathscr{B}$. Then, $x \in G$, and if y is any member of G,

$$\rho(x,y) \leqslant \rho(x',x) + \rho(x',y) < \varepsilon/3 + r' < \varepsilon,$$

i.e., $G \subseteq N_\varepsilon(x)$. Thus $x \in G \subseteq X$ and the result follows from Theorem 2.4.

Secondly, ((b) implies (c))*. Taking again $A = S$, let $\mathscr{G}' \equiv \{G'_j\}$, $j \geqslant 1$, be an (enumerable) base for $\mathscr{G}$ and $\{\mathscr{G}_i\}$, $i \in I$, an arbitrary given open covering of S. Corresponding to each x in S, choose a member $i(x)$ of I, (i.e., $i(x)$ is a function of x) such that $x \in G_{i(x)}$. By Theorem 2.4, $\exists$ an integer $j(x)$, (depending on x and $i(x)$ and hence ultimately on x) such that $x \in G'_{j(x)} \subseteq G_{i(x)}$. But, since the set of all (distinct) sets $G'_{j(x)}$, for x in S, is enumerable, $\exists$ a sequence $\{x_n\}$, $n \geqslant 1$, of elements of S such that, for each x in S, $\exists$ an integer n (a function of x) such that $G'_{j(x)} = G'_{j(x_n)}$. Then:

$$S = \bigcup_{x \in S} G'_{j(x)} = \bigcup_{n \geqslant 1} G'_{j(x_n)} \subseteq \bigcup_{n \geqslant 1} G_{i(x_n)},$$

i.e., the sequence $\{G_{i(x_n)}\}$, $n \geqslant 1$, is a covering of S.

Thirdly, ((c) implies (d))*. If (d) does not hold for some subset A of S, $\exists$ a non-enumerable subset X of A such that, to each member x of A, there corresponds a member G_x of $\mathscr{G}_\rho$ containing x with $G_x \cap X$ enumerable. Since the family $\{G_x\}$, $x \in A$, form a ρ-open covering of A (in S), it follows by assumption (c) and Theorem 3.4 that $\exists$ a sequence $\{x_i\}$, $i \geqslant 1$, of members of A such that $\{G_{x_i}\}$, $i \geqslant 1$, is a covering of A. Hence, if $Y = \bigcup_{i \geqslant 1} G_{x_i}$:

$$X = Y \cap X = \bigcup_{i \geqslant 1} (G_{x_i} \cap X). \tag{1}$$

Since the expression on the right-hand side of (1) is an enumerable set, a contradiction is obtained.

Fourthly, it is immediate that: ((d) implies (e))*.

Finally, to prove that (e) implies (a), let A be a subset of S containing at least two members; choose a positive integer n_0 such that $\rho(x,y) \geqslant n_0^{-1}$ for some pair x,y of members of A. For each integer $n \geqslant n_0$, let $\{X_i^{(n)}\}$, $i \in I_n$, denote the family of all distinct subsets of A such that, for each i in I_n, and x,y in $X_i^{(n)}$, $\rho(x,y) \geqslant n^{-1}$. The members of this family, when partially ordered by inclusion, form a poset $E^{(n)}$ which, by 'The Maximal Principle' (Theorem 1.10, Corollary) contains a maximal chain $C^{(n)}$; that is, if $C^{(n)} = \{X_i^{(n)}\}$, for i in $I'_n \subseteq I_n$:

(i) for each i, i' in I'_n, either $X_i^{(n)} \subseteq X_{i'}^{(n)}$ or $X_{i'}^{(n)} \subseteq X_i^{(n)}$;

(ii) if $i' \in I_n - I'_n$, $\exists\, i''$ in I'_n such that neither $X^{(n)}_{i'} \subseteq X^{(n)}_{i''}$ nor $X^{(n)}_{i''} \subseteq X^{(n)}_{i'}$ (otherwise the family: $\{X^{(n)}_i\}$, $i \in I'_n \cup (i')$, is a chain in $E^{(n)}$ properly containing $C^{(n)}$).

Then, if $X^{(n)} = \bigcup_{i \in I'_n} X^{(n)}_i$:

(i′) if x,y are distinct members of $X^{(n)}$, $\rho(x,y) \geqslant n^{-1}$. This is clear since by (i) $\exists$ a member i of I'_n such that x,y are both in $X^{(n)}_i$;

(ii′) if $x \in A$, $\exists\, y$ in $X^{(n)}$ (y depending on the choice of x) with: $\rho(x,y) < n^{-1}$. For, if not, $\rho(x,y) \geqslant n^{-1}$ for every member y of $X^{(n)}$; that is, the set $X' \equiv X^{(n)} \cup (x)$ is a member of the family $\{X^{(n)}_i\}$, $i \in I_n$. If $X' = X^{(n)}_{i_1}$, where $i_1 \in I_n$, then $X^{(n)}_i \subset X^{(n)}_{i_1}$ for every i in I'_n, contradicting (ii).

If then, in turn, $X = \bigcup_{n \geqslant n_0} X^{(n)}$:

(i″) X is dense in A. For if $x \in A$, ε is positive, and $n_1 \geqslant \max(n_0, \varepsilon^{-1})$ then, by (ii′) $\exists$ member y of $X^{(n_1)}$ (and hence of X) with $\rho(x,y) < \varepsilon$. Thus: $A \subseteq \bar{X}$.

(ii″) X is enumerable. For, if not, $\exists\, n_1 \geqslant n_0$ such that $X^{(n_1)}$ is non-enumerable; then by assumption (e) (applied for the first time in the present argument!) $X^{(n_1)}$ possesses a cluster point x_1, somewhere in S. It follows from Theorem 2.5 that $\exists$ two distinct elements x,y in $X^{(n_1)}$ with $\rho(x,x_1)$ and $\rho(y,x_1)$ each less than $1/2n_1$; but this would imply: $\rho(x,y) < 1/n_1$, contradicting (i′).

COROLLARY The property of separability is hereditary.

Example 3.1.4 (R^n,ρ_i), $1 \leqslant i \leqslant 3$, H^∞, and the spaces (S,ρ_i), $i = 1,2$, of Example 3.1.3 are completely separable, and are Lindelöf spaces.

Example 3.1.5 S: set of bounded functions f from $[0,1]$ into R; $\rho_1(f,g) = \sup_{0 \leqslant x \leqslant 1} |f(x) - g(x)|$ for f,g in S. (S,ρ) is *not* separable. For if it were, the family $\{f_t\}$, $0 < t < 1$, where:

$$\text{for } 0 < t < 1: \quad f_t(x) = \begin{cases} 1 & \text{for } x = t \\ 0 & \text{for } 0 \leqslant x < t \text{ or } t < x \leqslant 1 \end{cases}$$

would constitute, by the Corollary above, a separable subset A of S which, by Theorem 3.5, would possess a point of condensation f_{t_0}, say (that is, belonging to A itself). Since, however, $\rho(f_t,f_{t'}) = 1$ for distinct t,t', a contradiction is obtained.

DEFINITION 5 Given a space (S,ρ), a subset A of S is said to be **totally bounded** (w.r.t.ρ) if, to each positive number ε, there corresponds a finite sequence $\{x_i\}$, $1 \leqslant i \leqslant n$, of elements of A such that $\{N_\varepsilon(x_i)\}$, $1 \leqslant i \leqslant n$, forms a covering of A.

Clearly any totally bounded set is bounded. If S itself is totally bounded, the *space* (S,ρ) is said to be totally bounded.

THEOREM 3.6 Given a space (S,ρ), any totally bounded subset A of S is separable.

PROOF Corresponding to each positive integer n, $\exists$ a finite sequence $\{x_{n,i}\}$, $1 \leqslant i \leqslant m_n$ (where m_n depends on n) of members of A such that

$$A \subseteq \bigcup_{1 \leqslant i \leqslant m_n} N_{1/n}(x_{n,i}) \tag{1}$$

If $X = \bigcup_{n \geqslant 1} \left(\bigcup_{1 \leqslant i \leqslant m_n} (x_{n,i}) \right)$, X is clearly enumerable.

Further, X is dense in A, for, given $x \in A$, and $\varepsilon > 0$, let n_1 be an integer $\geqslant \varepsilon^{-1}$; then, by (1), $\exists$ integer i' with $1 \leqslant i' \leqslant m_{n_1}$ such that $x \in N_{1/n_1}(x_{n_1,i'})$; that is: $x_{n_1,i'} \in N_{1/n_1}(x) \subseteq N_\varepsilon(x)$ and so $N_\varepsilon(x) \cap X \neq \varnothing$. Thus $x \in \bar{X}$.

Example 3.1.6 S: arbitrary infinitely enumerable set. If ρ_0 is a metric defined on S as in Note 1 of Chapter 2, (S,ρ_0) is a bounded, separable space which, however, is *not* totally bounded, since, for any finite sequence $\{x_i\}$, $1 \leqslant i \leqslant n$,

$$\bigcup_{1 \leqslant i \leqslant n} N_k(x_i) = \bigcup_{1 \leqslant i \leqslant n} (x_i) \subset S.$$

There is a further instance of this in Example 3.3.4.

Worked Exercises

1. If, given a space (S,ρ), A is a separable subset of S, X is a non-enumerable subset of A, and T denotes the set of points of condensation of X, show that $X - T$ is enumerable. Hence show that T is dense-in-itself.

Solution: If, first, $X - T$ were non-enumerable, then, since $X - T \subseteq A$, it would follow from Theorem 3.5, Corollary, that $X - T$ would be separable and hence (by Theorem 3.5) possess a point of condensation x' which is a member of $X - T$ itself. But x' must *a fortiori* be a point of condensation of X; that is, $x' \in T$, giving a contradiction. If, secondly, T were *not* dense-in-itself, $\exists\, x''$ in T such that $Y \cap T = (x'')$ for some member Y of $\mathcal{N}(x'')$. Then: $Y \cap X = (Y \cap (X \cap T)) \cup (Y \cap (X - T)) \subseteq (Y \cap T) \cup (X - T) = (x'') \cup (X - T)$, which is enumerable, by the first part. But this contradicts the definition of T.

2. If (S,ρ) is a space where any collection of mutually disjoint open sets is enumerable, show that it must be separable.

Solution: It is clear from the last part of the proof of Theorem 3.5 that, for an *arbitrary* space (S,ρ), $\exists$ a positive integer n_0 and a sequence $\{X^{(n)}\}$, $n \geqslant n_0$, of subsets of S such that:

(i′) $\rho(x,y) \geqslant n^{-1}$ for any distinct members x,y of $X^{(n)}$

(i″) $X \equiv \bigcup_{n \geqslant n_0} X^{(n)}$ is dense (in S).

Suppose now that (S,ρ) is *not* separable; it follows from (i″) that $\exists\, n_1 \geqslant n_0$ such that $X^{(n_1)}$ is *not* enumerable. Write $r = n_1^{-1}$ and, for each x in $X^{(n_1)}$, write $G_x = N_{r/2}(x)$. It is easily seen from (i′) that $\{G_x\}$ is a family of mutually disjoint sets, giving a contradiction with hypothesis.

Exercises for Solution

1. Prove the *converse* of Worked Ex. 2.

2. If S denotes the set of complex numbers z, show that the function given by:

$$\rho(z,z') = \begin{cases} |z - z'| \text{ if } z,z' \text{ are collinear with origin } 0 \\ |z| + |z'| \text{ otherwise} \end{cases}$$

is a metric on S such that (S,ρ) is *not* separable.

3. (S,ρ) is a space such that, corresponding to each x in S, $\exists\, r_x > 0$ such that $N_{r_x}(x)$ is separable. Show (cf. Worked Ex. of Section 2.5) that $\exists$ a family $\{X_i\}$, $i \in I$, of subsets of S such that:

(a) for each i in I, $X_i = N_{\varepsilon_i}(x_i)$ where $x_i \in S$, $0 < \varepsilon_i < r_{x_i}$;

(b) $X_i \cap X_j = \varnothing$ for distinct i,j in I;

(c) $X \equiv \bigcup_{i \in I} X_i$ is dense (in S);

(d) for each i in I, $\exists$ an enumerable subset Y_i of X_i such that $Y \equiv \bigcup_i Y_i$ is dense (in S);

(e) for each x in S and $0 < \varepsilon < r_x$, $N_\varepsilon(x) \cap X_i$ is non-null only for an enumerable set of indices i;

(f) Y possesses *no* points of condensation.

4. If (S',ρ') is the space of Ex. 6 in Section 2.1, (S,ρ) is an arbitrary separable space, and $\{a_i\}$, $i \geqslant 1$, a sequence of elements of S such that $X \equiv \bigcup_{i \geqslant 1} (a_i)$ is dense in S, let f be the function from S into S' such that, for each x in S and $i = 1,2,\ldots$: $(f(x))_i = \rho(a_{i+1},x) - \rho(a_{i+1},a_1)$. With the help of Ex. 9 of Section 2.3, show that f is a homeomorphism of (S,ρ) onto a subspace of (S',ρ'). Hence show that a given space (S,ρ) can be homeomorphically imbedded in (S',ρ') if and only if (S,ρ) is separable.

3.2 Compact and Countably Compact Spaces

A strengthening of the Lindelöf Property of Definition 4 appears in:

DEFINITION 6* A space (S,ρ) is said to be **compact** if any open covering of S contains a finite sub-covering (of S).

As for the Lindelöf Property in Section 3.1, compactness is extended to apply to a subset of a space, and in either sense of the term it is a homeomorphic property. An analogue of Theorem 3.4 reads:

THEOREM 3.7* Given a space (S,ρ), a subset A is compact if and only if any ρ-open covering of A (in S) contains a finite sub-covering of A.

THEOREM 3.8* A space (S,ρ) is compact if and only if: for any family $\{F_i\}$, $i \in I$, of non-null closed sets having the finite intersection property,

$$\bigcap_i F_i \text{ is non-null.} \qquad (1)$$

PROOF It is equivalent to show that (S,ρ) is compact if and only if any family $\{F_i\}$, $i \in I$, of non-null closed sets with $\bigcap_i F_i = \varnothing$ **contains** a finite sequence $\{F_{i_r}\}$, $1 \leqslant r \leqslant n$, such that $\bigcap_{1 \leqslant r \leqslant n} F_{i_r} = \varnothing$.

But, if $G_i = C(F_i)$, for i in I, the statements '$\bigcap_i F_i = \varnothing$' and '$\bigcap_{1 \leqslant r \leqslant n} F_{i_r} = \varnothing$' are respectively equivalent to '$\bigcup_i G_i = S$' and '$\bigcup_{1 \leqslant r \leqslant n} G_{i_r} = S$'; so the result follows from Theorem 2.12.

COROLLARY* If (S,ρ) is compact, I is a totally ordered set, and $\{F_i\}$, $i \in I$, a corresponding family of non-null closed sets such that $F_j \subseteq F_i$ for $i < j$ in I, then $\bigcap_i F_i$ is non-null.

It is shown later (Theorem 4.23) that the condition (1) in Theorem 3.8 can be replaced by a weaker form.

DEFINITION 7* A space (S,ρ) is said to be **countably compact** if every infinite subset X of S possesses at least one cluster point.

When the above property is extended in the usual way to apply to a subset of a space, it is clear that a subset A will be countably compact if and only if every infinite subset of A possesses a cluster point *belonging to* A. The properties are again homeomorphic.

The suitability of the term 'countably compact' is seen from:

THEOREM 3.9. A space (S,ρ) is countably compact if* and only if any *enumerable* open covering of S contains a finite sub-covering.

PROOF (a) Given that (S,ρ) is countably compact, suppose that $\exists$ an enumerable open covering $\{G_i\}$, $i \geqslant 1$, of S containing *no* finite sub-covering; then, for each positive integer n,

$$K_n \equiv C(\bigcup_{1\leqslant i\leqslant n} G_i) \in \mathscr{F} \text{ and is non-null.}$$

If $\{x_n\}$, $n \geqslant 1$, is a given sequence of elements of S such that $x_n \in K_n$ for $n \geqslant 1$, then $H \equiv \bigcup_{n\geqslant 1} (x_n)$ contains only a finite number of (distinct) members. For if not, H possesses a cluster point x, somewhere in S. By Theorem 2.5, it then is clear that, for *each* positive integer m, each member Y of $\mathscr{N}(x)$ contains an infinity of terms of $\{x_n\}$ with $n \geqslant m$; that is, x is a cluster point of $H_m \equiv \bigcup_{n\geqslant m} (x_n) \subseteq K_m$. That is, since $K_m \in \mathscr{F}$, $x \in K_m$, clearly contradicting the assumption that $\{G_i\}$ is a covering of S. Hence, (since H has been seen to contain only a finite number of elements) $\exists$ an element y in H such that for any integer m, $x_n = y$ for some $n > m$, implying that $y \in K_m$, all m. But this yields a contradiction just as before.

(b)* Given that each enumerable open covering of S contains a finite sub-covering, suppose that $\exists$ an infinite subset X of S possessing no cluster points. By Theorem 1.5, X contains an infinitely enumerable set H; let its members be enumerated as: $\{x_n\}$, $n \geqslant 1$. Then, for each n, x_n is not a cluster point of H; that is, there corresponds a member $G^{(n)}$ of $\mathscr{G}$ containing x_n such that $G^{(n)} \cap H = (x_n)$. Again, each x in $C(H)$ is not a cluster point of H, so that there corresponds a member G_x of $\mathscr{G}$ containing x such that $G_x \cap H$ is null. If $G = \bigcup_{C(H)} G_x$, clearly G and the sets $G^{(n)}$, $n \geqslant 1$, together form an enumerable open covering of S. But, since for each m, $x_{m+1}\,\omega\,(\bigcup_{1\leqslant n\leqslant m} G^{(n)}) \cup G$, this enumerable covering of S contains *no* finite sub-covering, contradicting assumption.

COROLLARY I* A compact space is countably compact.

COROLLARY II A countably compact space possessing the Lindelöf property is compact.

THEOREM 3.10 A countably compact space (S,ρ) is totally bounded.

PROOF If not, $\exists$ positive ε such that $S \supset \bigcup_{1 \leqslant i \leqslant n} N_\varepsilon(x_i)$ for any finite sequence $x_1, \ldots, x_n$ of elements of S. Choose y_1 in S; by assumption, $\exists$ an element y_2 in $C(N_\varepsilon(y_1))$; that is, $\rho(y_1,y_2) \geqslant \varepsilon$. We go on to construct a sequence $\{y_i\}$, $i \geqslant 1$, such that $\rho(y_i,y_j) \geqslant \varepsilon$ for distinct integers i,j. This is done recursively as follows: if, given $i > 2$, the elements $y_1, \ldots, y_{i-1}$ have been chosen so that $\rho(y_j,y_k) \geqslant \varepsilon$ for $1 \leqslant j < k \leqslant i-1$, there exists, by assumption, an element y_i in

$$C\Big(\bigcup_{1 \leqslant k \leqslant i-1} N_\varepsilon(y_k)\Big);$$

then $\rho(y_j,y_k) \geqslant \varepsilon$ for $1 \leqslant j < k \leqslant i$.

Since (S,ρ) is countably compact, the sequence $\{y_i\}$ has a cluster point x somewhere in S; hence, by Theorem 2.5, $\exists$ distinct i,j such that y_i,y_j both belong to $N_{\varepsilon/2}(x)$. But this implies: $\rho(y_i,y_j) < \varepsilon$.

COROLLARY A space (S,ρ) is compact if it is countably compact.

To establish the corollary, note that, by Theorem 3.10, (S,ρ) is totally bounded, and consequently it is separable, by Theorem 3.6; hence, by Theorem 3.5, it has the Lindelöf property, and so is compact by Corollary II to Theorem 3.9.

DEFINITION 8* A space (S,ρ) is said to be **sequentially compact** if every sequence of elements of S contains a convergent subsequence.

THEOREM 3.11 A space is countably compact if* and only if it is sequentially compact.

The proof is almost immediate from Theorem 2.21.

A consequence of Theorem 3.9, Corollary I, Theorem 3.10, Corollary, and Theorem 3.11 is that the terms 'compact', 'countably compact' and 'sequentially compact' are all equivalent for any space (S,ρ).

THEOREM 3.12* If (S,ρ) is compact, any closed non-null subset F of S is compact.

PROOF If $\{G_i\}$, $i \in I$, is an arbitrary ρ-open covering of F (in S), then the members of this family form, together with $C(F)$, a ρ-open covering of S itself. Hence, by assumption, $\exists$ a finite sequence $\{G_{i_r}\}$, $1 \leqslant r \leqslant n$, of members of this family such that: $S = \bigcup_{1 \leqslant r \leqslant n} G_{i_r} \cup C(F)$. Then:

$$F = S \cap F = ((\bigcup_{1 \leqslant r \leqslant n} G_{i_r}) \cap F) \cup (C(F) \cap F) = (\bigcup_{1 \leqslant r \leqslant n} G_{i_r}) \cap F$$

i.e., $\{G_{i_r}\}$, $1 \leqslant r \leqslant n$, is a covering of F.

So, by Theorem 3.7, F is compact.

The following result can be compared with Theorem 2.17:

THEOREM 3.13 Given a space (S,ρ), X a compact proper subset of S, and x in $C(X)$, there exist open sets G_i, $i = 1,2$, such that $G_1 \cap G_2 = \emptyset$, $X \subseteq G_1$ and $x \in G_2$.

PROOF Corresponding to each y in X, by Theorem 2.17, Corollary, $\exists$ disjoint members G_y, H_y of $\mathscr{G}_\rho$ such that $x \in G_y$, $y \in H_y$. Since $\{H_y\}$, $y \in X$, constitutes a ρ-open covering of X (in S), by Theorem 3.7 $\exists$ a finite sequence $\{y_1, \ldots, y_n\}$ of members of X such that $X \subseteq G_1 \equiv \bigcup_{1 \leqslant i \leqslant n} H_{y_i}$. Then $G_1 \in \mathscr{G}$, and if $G_2 = \bigcap_{1 \leqslant i \leqslant n} G_{y_i}$, G_1 and G_2 have the desired properties.

COROLLARY If X is a compact subset of S then X is closed and (totally) bounded.

PROOF If $X \subset S$, the above Theorem shows that, to each member x of $C(X)$, there corresponds a member G_x of $\mathscr{G}$ such that $x \in G_x \subseteq C(X)$. Then $C(X) = \bigcup_{C(X)} G_x$ and so $X \in \mathscr{F}$.

The rest of the proof follows immediately from Theorem 3.9, Corollary I and Theorem 3.10.

THEOREM 3.14* Given spaces (S,ρ), (S',ρ'), and a compact subset A of S, let f be a (ρ,ρ')-continuous function from A into S'; then $f(A)$ is compact.

PROOF There is no loss of generality in taking $A = S$. If $\{H_i\}$, $i \in I$, is an arbitrary ρ'-open covering of $f(S)$ (in S'), $S = f^{-1}(\bigcup_i H_i) = \bigcup_i f^{-1}(H_i)$, where $f^{-1}(H_i) \in \mathscr{G}_\rho$ for each i. Hence, by assumption, $\exists$ a finite sequence $\{i_1, \ldots, i_n\}$ of members of I such that: $\{f^{-1}(H_{i_r})\}$, $1 \leqslant r \leqslant n$, is a covering of S, so that:

$$f(S) = \bigcup_{1 \leqslant r \leqslant n} f(f^{-1}(H_{i_r})) \subseteq \bigcup_{1 \leqslant r \leqslant n} H_{i_r}.$$

That is, (by Theorem 3.7) $f(S)$ is compact.

The next theorem, on a product of compact spaces, can be

proved by more elementary methods (e.g., HALL and SPENCER, Reference [2] pp. 84–5); that is, it can be quite readily proved for the case $n = 2$ (applying Ex. 10, Section 2.6) and extended by induction. The argument given here is perhaps, however, of more value from at least two points of view: first, it can be extended, with scarcely any modification, to apply to an arbitrary family of compact spaces (see Note 3 of Chapter 4), and, secondly, it makes use of an important technique based on Tukey's Lemma (of Theorem 1.10). A stimulating discussion of some of the points involved appears in HOCKING and YOUNG, Reference [4] pp. 25–28; although appeal is made there rather to the Maximal Principle (a Corollary to Tukey's Lemma), the approach is essentially the same.

THEOREM 3.15* A product space (S,ρ) of a finite sequence of spaces $\{(S_i,\rho_i)\}$, $1 \leqslant i \leqslant n$, is compact if and only if each space (S_i,ρ_i) is compact.

PROOF If (S,ρ) is compact, the (ρ,ρ_i)-continuity of the projection π_i of S onto S_i implies, by Theorem 3.14, the compactness of each space (S_i,ρ_i). Given, conversely, that each space (S_i,ρ_i) is compact, it will suffice (by Theorem 3.8) for the proof of the compactness of (S,ρ) to show that if $\mathscr{X}_0 \equiv \{X_j\}$, $j \in I$, is a given family of subsets of S (not necessarily in $\mathscr{F}_\rho$) having the finite intersection property, then $\bigcap_j {}^\rho\overline{X}_j$ is non-null. If $\mathscr{S}$ is the subset of $P(P(S))$ of all families $\mathscr{X}$ of members of $P(S)$ which possess the finite intersection property, $\mathscr{S}$ is seen to be of *finite character* as a subset of $P(P(S))$. If, then, the members of $\mathscr{S}$ are partially ordered by inclusion (that is, given $\mathscr{X} \equiv \{X_k\}$, $k \in K$, and $\mathscr{Y} \equiv \{Y_l\}$ $l \in L$, in $\mathscr{S}$, by writing $\mathscr{X} \leqslant \mathscr{Y}$ if and only if for each k in K, $\exists$ l in L such that $K_k = Y_l$) it follows immediately from Tukey's Lemma (Theorem 1.10) that $\mathscr{S}$ has a maximal member $\mathscr{X}_1$ such that $\mathscr{X}_0 \leqslant \mathscr{X}_1$. If $\mathscr{X}_1 = \{Y_m\}$, $m \in M$, then its maximality in $\mathscr{S}$ implies:

(a) if X is a subset of S such that $Y_m \subseteq X$ for some m in M, then $X \in \mathscr{X}_1$;

(b) if $\{m_1,\ldots,m_r\}$ is a finite sequence of members of M, then $\bigcap_{1\leqslant t\leqslant r} Y_{m_t} \in \mathscr{X}_1$;

(c) if X is a subset of S such that $X \cap Y_m \neq \varnothing$ for all m in M, then $X \in \mathscr{X}_1$.

Now, for each i, the family $\{\overline{{}^{\rho_i}\pi_i(Y_m)}\}$, $m \in M$, of members of $\mathscr{F}_{\rho_i}$ has the finite intersection property, for if $\{m_1,\ldots,m_r\}$ is a finite sequence of members of M, $\exists$ (since $\mathscr{X}_1 \in \mathscr{S}$) an element $x \equiv \{x_1, \ldots, x_n\}$ of S with $x \in \bigcap_{1 \leqslant t \leqslant r} Y_{m_t}$; then:

$$\pi_i(x) \in \pi_i(Y_{m_t}) \subseteq {}^{\rho_i}\overline{\pi_i(Y_{m_t})} \text{ for } 1 \leqslant t \leqslant r.$$

Hence, since (S_i, ρ_i) is compact, it follows that $\exists$ an element y_i of S_i such that

$$y_i \in \bigcap_{m \in M} {}^{\rho_i}\overline{\pi_i(Y_m)} \tag{1}$$

If, then, $y \equiv \{y_1, \ldots, y_n\}$ in S, we show that:

$$y \in \bigcap_{m \in M} {}^{\rho}\overline{Y}_m \tag{2}$$

Given an arbitrary member G of $\mathscr{G}_\rho$ containing y, $\exists$ (by the definition of product space) for each i, a member G_i of $\mathscr{G}_{\rho_i}$ containing y_i such that $\prod_{1 \leqslant i \leqslant n} G_i \subseteq G$; then, by (1), $G_i \cap \pi_i(Y_m) \neq \varnothing$, and, hence, $\pi_i^{-1}(G_i) \cap Y_m \neq \varnothing$ for each m in M. Hence, by (c) above,

$$\pi_i^{-1}(G_i) \in \mathscr{X}_1 \qquad \text{for } 1 \leqslant i \leqslant n,$$

and so, in turn by (b): $\prod_{1 \leqslant i \leqslant n} G_i = \bigcap_{1 \leqslant i \leqslant n} \pi_i^{-1}(G_i) \in \mathscr{X}_1$ and so, by (a), $G \in \mathscr{X}_1$, implying (since $\mathscr{X}_1 \in \mathscr{S}$) that $G \cap Y_m \neq \varnothing$, for all m in M, i.e., $y \in {}^{\rho}\overline{Y}_m$, all $m \in M$, yielding (2). Since $\mathscr{X}_0 \leqslant \mathscr{X}_1$, it follows finally that $y \in \bigcap_j {}^{\rho}\overline{X}_j$, completing the proof.

For the space $(R^n)_1$, a converse of Theorem 3.13, Corollary can be proved:

THEOREM 3.16 Any closed, bounded, subset of $(R^n)_1$ is compact.

PROOF *Case 1:* $n = 1$; $X =$ closed interval $[a,b]$. The remarks after Theorem 3.11 show that it will suffice here to sketch the proof of Weierstrass's result that X is sequentially compact. Given a sequence $\{x_i\}$, $i \geqslant 1$, of members of X and using the fact that if an interval A contains a sequence of members of X, one at least of the half-intervals composing A contains a subsequence, we construct a subsequence $\{x_{i_r}\}$, $r \geqslant 1$, of $\{x_i\}$ and sequences $\{a_r\}$, $\{b_r\}$, $r \geqslant 1$, also of members of X, such that, for $r \geqslant 1$:

$$a_r \leqslant x_{i_r} \leqslant b_r; \qquad a_r \leqslant a_{r+1}; \qquad b_{r+1} \leqslant b_r;$$

$$b_r - a_r = 2^{1-r}(b - a) \tag{1}$$

If λ, μ are respectively the limits of the bounded monotonic sequences $\{a_r\}$, $\{b_r\}$, it is clear from (1) that $\lambda = \mu$, and so that $\lim_r x_{i_r} = \lambda$, where $\lambda \in X$.

Case 2: $n > 1$; $X = \prod_{1 \leqslant i \leqslant n} X_i$, where X_i is a closed interval of R. Immediately from Case 1, and Theorem 3.15, X is compact.

Case 3: $n \geqslant 1$: X arbitrary (closed, bounded). If $D(X) = k$, clearly X can be wholly contained in a 'generalized cube' Y in R^n (of side k); that is, for each i, $\exists$ closed interval Y_i in R such that $X \subseteq \prod_{1 \leqslant i \leqslant n} Y_i$. But, by Case 2, Y is compact; since X is closed relative to Y, it follows by Theorem 3.12 that X is compact.

Note 1 The result of Theorem 3.16 does not hold for an arbitrary space (S,ρ).

Example 3.2.1 $S = R$, $\rho(x,y) = |x - y|/(1 + |x - y|)$ for x,y in R. If $X = S$, X is closed and bounded. However (S,ρ_1) is not compact (since J is a discrete subset of S (w.r.t.ρ_1), (S,ρ_1) is not sequentially compact) and $\rho_1 \equiv \rho$ (see Theorem 2.23, Corollary II). Hence, since compactness is a homeomorphic property of a space, (S,ρ) is not compact; that is X is not compact.

Example 3.2.2 $(S,\rho) = H^\infty$; for each $x \equiv \{x_i\}$ in S, and $\varepsilon > 0$, $X \equiv \overline{N_\varepsilon(x)}$ is closed, bounded, but is not compact; that is, X is not sequentially compact. For, corresponding to each $n \geqslant 1$, let $y^{(n)} = \{y_i^{(n)}\}$, $i \geqslant 1$, in S, where: $y_i^{(n)} = x_i$ if $i \neq n$ and $y_i^{(n)} = x_i + \varepsilon/2$ if $i = n$. Then each $y^{(n)} \in X$, but $\rho(y^{(n)},y^{(m)}) = \varepsilon/2^{\frac{1}{2}}$ for $m \neq n$. Hence (as in the argument ending the proof of Theorem 3.10) $\{y^{(n)}\}$, $n \geqslant 1$, has no cluster point.

°An easy deduction from Example 3.2.2 is that any compact subset of H^∞ must necessarily be nowhere dense. An example of such a subset is the so-called 'Hilbert cube'; that is, the subset A of all elements $x \equiv \{x_i\}$ with $|x_i| \leqslant i^{-1}$ for $i \geqslant 1$. To see this, note first that if $\{y^{(n)}\}$, $n \geqslant 1$, is a sequence of points of A and if $y \equiv \{y_i\} \in A$, then $y^{(n)} \underset{\rho}{\rightarrow} y$ if (and only if) $y_i^{(n)} \underset{\rho_1}{\rightarrow} y_i$ for each i. (1)

For, given $\varepsilon > 0$, choose a positive integer K such that $\sum_{K+1}^{\infty} i^{-2} < \varepsilon^2/8$; if n_0 is a positive integer such that for $1 \leqslant i \leqslant K$, $|y_i^{(n)} - y_i| < \varepsilon/(2K)^{\frac{1}{2}}$ for any $n \geqslant n_0$, then clearly $\rho(y^{(n)},y) < \varepsilon$ for any $n \geqslant n_0$. (Cf. Ex. 9, Section 2.3.)

If, now, $\{x^{(n)}\}$, $n \geqslant 1$, is an arbitrary sequence of points of A, then $\{x_1^{(n)}\}$, $n \geqslant 1$, is a sequence of points of the interval $[-1,1]$

of R; hence by Theorem 3.16 $\exists$ a subsequence $\{x^{(m,1)}\}$, $m \geqslant 1$, of $\{x^{(n)}\}$ and a point y_1 in $[-1,1]$ such that $x_1^{(m,1)} \underset{\rho_1}{\rightarrow} y_1$. Again $\{x_2^{(m,1)}\}$, $m \geqslant 1$, is a sequence of points in the interval $[-\frac{1}{2},\frac{1}{2}]$ and so $\exists$ a subsequence $\{x^{(m,2)}\}$, $m \geqslant 1$, of $\{x^{(m,1)}\}$ and a point y_2 in $[-\frac{1}{2},\frac{1}{2}]$ such that $x_2^{(m,2)} \underset{\rho_1}{\rightarrow} y_2$, and so on. That is, a succession $\{x^{(m,p)}\}$ of subsequences of $\{x^{(n)}\}$ and a sequence $\{y_p\}$, $p \geqslant 1$, of real numbers are recursively obtained such that: (a) for each $p > 1$, $\{x^{(m,p)}\}$ is a subsequence of $\{x^{(m,p-1)}\}$ and, for each $p > 1$: (b) $|y_p| \leqslant p^{-1}$ and (c) $x_p^{(m,p)} \underset{\rho_1}{\rightarrow} y_p$.

Then the points $y^{(p)} \equiv x^{(p,p)}$, $p \geqslant 1$, form a subsequence of $\{x^{(n)}\}$ such that for each $i \geqslant 1$ the numbers $\{y_i^{(p)}\}$, $p \geqslant i$, form a subsequence of $\{x_i^{(m,i)}\}$, $m \geqslant 1$. Hence, by (c) and (1) above, A is (sequentially) compact.

THEOREM 3.17 Given a space (S,ρ), a subset A of S is compact (a) if and (b)* only if each (ρ,ρ_1)-continuous function f from A into R is bounded on A (where ρ_1 is the usual metric on R). Then f attains in A its supremum and infimum.

PROOF (Taking $A = S$) suppose first that S is compact. Then $f(S)$ is compact and so is a bounded and closed subset of R (by Theorem 3.14 and Theorem 3.13, Corollary). It follows from Example 2.3.10, that $f(S)$ contains its supremum and infimum.

Conversely, if S is *not* compact, $\exists$ a sequence $\{x_i\}$, $i \geqslant 1$, of (distinct) elements of S such that $X \equiv \bigcup_{i \geqslant 1} (x_i)$ is discrete; in particular, then, for each $i \geqslant 1$, $\exists$ number $\varepsilon_i > 0$ such that $X \cap N_{\varepsilon_i}(x_i) = (x_i)$. If $\delta_i = \min(\varepsilon_i, i^{-1})$, define a function f_i from S into R:

$$\text{for } x \text{ in } S,\ f_i(x) = \begin{cases} i(1 - 2\rho(x,x_i)\delta_i^{-1}) & \text{if } \rho(x,x_i) \leqslant \frac{1}{2}\delta_i \\ 0 & \text{if } \rho(x,x_i) > \frac{1}{2}\delta_i \end{cases}$$

For each x in S, x is not a cluster point of X; hence $\exists\, i_0$ (depending on choice of x) such that $x_i \omega N_{\delta_i}(x)$ for $i > i_0$; that is, $f_i(x) = 0$ for i sufficiently large, and so a function f from S into R can be defined by writing: $f(x) = \sum_1^{\infty} f_i(x)$ for each x in S. Then f is (ρ,ρ_1)-continuous. For, given x in S, $\exists$ a number $k > 0$ and positive integer i_1 (where k,i_1 depend on choice of x) such that $\rho(x,x_i) > 2k$

for all $i \geqslant i_1$; hence, for y in $N_k(x)$, clearly $\rho(y,x_i) > k$ for $i \geqslant i_1$. If, further, an integer i_2 is chosen so that $\delta_i < 2k$ for all $i \geqslant i_2$ and if $i_3 = \max(i_1,i_2)$, it is clear that $\rho(y,x_i) > \frac{1}{2}\delta_i$, that is, $f_i(x) = f_i(y)$ $(= 0)$ for $i \geqslant i_3$ so that

$$|f(x) - f(y)| \leqslant \sum_{i=1}^{i_3} |f_i(x) - f_i(y)| \quad \text{for } y \text{ in } N_k(x). \tag{1}$$

But it is easily verified that $|f_i(x) - f_i(y)| \leqslant 2i\delta_i^{-1}\rho(x,y)$; hence if $\eta = \min\{k,\frac{1}{2}i^{-1}\delta_i i_3^{-1}\varepsilon\}$, $1 \leqslant i \leqslant i_3$, η depends ultimately on x, ε and for y in $N_\eta(x)$, it follows from (1) that: $|f(x) - f(y)| < \varepsilon$. However $f(S)$ is not bounded, for: $f(x_i) \geqslant f_i(x_i) \geqslant i$ for each $i \geqslant 1$.

THEOREM 3.18 Given spaces (S,ρ), (S',ρ') with (S,ρ) compact, any (ρ,ρ')-continuous function f from S into S' is (ρ,ρ')-closed.

PROOF If $F \in \mathscr{F}_\rho$, F is compact, hence $f(F)$ is compact, and hence $f(F) \in \mathscr{F}_{\rho'}$ (applying in turn Theorems 3.12, 3.14, 3.13 Corollary).

COROLLARY If (S,ρ), (S',ρ'), f are as above, and, in addition, f is (1,1) onto S', then f is a (ρ,ρ')-homeomorphism.

Example 2.6.7 shows that the compactness of (S,ρ) is an essential condition in Theorem 3.18 and its corollary.

If (S',ρ') is compact, there is the following converse of Corollary II to Theorem 2.46.

THEOREM 3.19* If (S'',ρ'') is a product space of (S,ρ) and (S',ρ'), where the latter is compact, and f is a function from S into S' such that its graph T on S belongs to $\mathscr{F}_{\rho''}$, then f is (ρ,ρ')-continuous.

PROOF Given F' in $\mathscr{F}_{\rho'}$, let x be any member of

$$\overline{{}^{\rho}f^{-1}(F')}. \tag{1}$$

If the members of $\mathscr{N}_\rho(x)$ are indexed as $\{X_i\}$, $i \in I$, let $\{i_i, \ldots, i_r\}$ be any finite sequence in I; then (by Theorem 2.3) $X \equiv \bigcap_{1 \leqslant s \leqslant r} X_{i_s} \in \mathscr{N}_\rho(x)$ and so, by (1): $X \cap f^{-1}(F') \neq \varnothing$. Hence clearly the family $\{\overline{{}^{\rho'}f(f^{-1}(F') \cap X_i)}\}$, $i \in I$, of members of $\mathscr{F}_{\rho'}$ possesses the finite intersection property; so, by Theorem 3.8, $\exists\, z$ in

$$\bigcap_{i \in I} \overline{{}^{\rho'}f(f^{-1}(F') \cap X_i)}$$

Now if G'' is an arbitrary member of $\mathscr{G}_{\rho''}$ containing $\{x,z\}$, there exist, by definition of product space, members G,G' of $\mathscr{G}_\rho$, $\mathscr{G}_{\rho'}$ respectively containing x,z such that $G \times G' \subseteq G''$; but $z \in \overline{{}^{\rho'}f(f^{-1}(F') \cap G)}$, since $G \in \mathscr{N}_\rho(x)$; hence:

$$\varnothing \neq G' \cap f(f^{-1}(F') \cap G) \subseteq G' \cap f(G)$$

that is

$$\varnothing \subset (G \times G') \cap T \subseteq G'' \cap T.$$

So $\{x,z\} \in {}^{\rho''}\overline{T} = T$ (by assumption); that is,

$$f(x) = z \in {}^{\rho'}\overline{f(f^{-1}(F'))} \subseteq {}^{\rho'}\overline{F}' = F';$$

that is $x \in f^{-1}(F')$. Hence, by (1), $f^{-1}(F') \in \mathscr{F}_\rho$, and so f is (ρ,ρ')-continuous.

Note 2 The compactness of (S',ρ') is an essential condition in Theorem 3.19.

Example 3.2.3 Let (S,ρ) be an arbitrary non-discrete space, and ρ' a discrete metric on $S' = S$. If f is the identity function on S, the graph T of f on S coincides with the diagonal Δ_S. Since $\mathscr{G}_\rho \subset \mathscr{G}_{\rho'}$, it follows immediately from the proof of Theorem 2.45 that $\Delta_S \in \mathscr{F}_{\rho''}$; at the same time, however, '$\mathscr{G}_\rho \not\supseteq \mathscr{G}_{\rho'}$' implies that f is *not* (ρ,ρ')-continuous. (Cf. Worked Exercise 1, Chapter 5.)

The well-known concept in real variable theory of uniform continuity of a function can be extended as follows:

DEFINITION 9 Given spaces (S,ρ), (S',ρ'), $A \subseteq S$, a function f from A into S' is said to be **uniformly (ρ,ρ')-continuous** on A if, for each positive ε, there exists positive δ (dependent on the choice of ε) such that $\rho'(f(x),f(y)) < \varepsilon$ for any pair x,y of elements of S with $\rho(x,y) < \delta$.

THEOREM 3.20 Given spaces (S,ρ), (S',ρ'), and a compact subset A of S, any function f from A into S' which is (ρ,ρ')-continuous on A is *uniformly* (ρ,ρ')-continuous on A.

PROOF There is no loss of generality in taking $A = S$. We show, as a preliminary result, that if $\mathscr{H} \equiv \{G_i\}$, $1 \leqslant i \leqslant n$, is a (finite) ρ-open covering of S, $\exists$ a corresponding positive number† $d(\mathscr{H})$ such that, for each subset X of S with $D(X) < d$, $X \subseteq G_i$ for some i (depending on the choice of X). (1)
If not, $\exists$ a ρ-open covering $\mathscr{H}$ of S such that, to each positive integer m, there corresponds a subset X_m of S with $D(X_m) < m^{-1}$ and such that $X_m \not\subseteq G_i$ for $1 \leqslant i \leqslant n$. For each $m \geqslant 1$, choose x_m in X_m; since S is compact, it is sequentially compact, so that $\exists$ a subsequence $\{x_{m_r}\}$, $r \geqslant 1$, of $\{x_m\}$ and an element x of S such that:

† $d(\mathscr{H})$ is often called the *Lebesgue Number* of $\mathscr{H}$.

$x_{m_r} \underset{\rho}{\rightarrow} x$. Since $\mathscr{H}$ covers S, $x\,\omega\, C(G_{i'}) = {}^{\rho}\overline{C(G_{i'})}$ for some i' (with $1 \leqslant i' \leqslant n$); since clearly $C(G_{i'}) \neq \varnothing$, it follows by Theorem 2.6, that $d \equiv \rho(x, C(G_{i'})) > 0$. Since $\lim \rho(x_{m_r}, x) = 0$, $\exists$ integer r_0 with $m_{r_0} > 2d^{-1}$, and such that $\rho(x_{m_{r_0}}, x) < d/2$. Then, for any element y in $X_{m_{r_0}}$:

$$\rho(x,y) < d/2 + m_{r_0}^{-1} < d, \text{ since } D(X_{m_{r_0}}) < m_{r_0}^{-1}.$$

Consequently, by choice of d, $y\,\omega\, C(G_{i'})$; hence $X_{m_{r_0}} \subseteq G_{i'}$, a contradiction; thus (1) is established.

To prove the theorem, choose an arbitrary $\varepsilon > 0$; then since the family $\{N^{\rho'}_{\varepsilon/2}(y)\}$, $y \in S'$, is a ρ'-open covering of S', it follows from the (ρ,ρ')-continuity of f that the family $\{f^{-1}(N^{\rho'}_{\varepsilon/2}(y))\}$, $y \in S'$, is a ρ-open covering of S; hence $\exists$ a finite sequence $\{y_1, \ldots, y_n\}$ of members of S' such that $\mathscr{H}_\varepsilon \equiv \{f^{-1}(N^{\rho'}_{\varepsilon/2}(y_i))\}$, $1 \leqslant i \leqslant n$, covers S. If $\delta = d(\mathscr{H}_\varepsilon)$ (of (1) above), then δ depends ultimately on ε; if x,y are any elements of S such that $\rho(x,y) < \delta$, $X \equiv (x,y)$ has its diameter less than δ; hence $\exists i$ such that $x,y \in f^{-1}(N^{\rho'}_{\varepsilon/2}(y_i))$. Clearly: $\rho'(f(x), f(y)) < \varepsilon$.

Note 3 The compactness of A is an essential condition in Theorem 3.20.

Example 3.2.4 $(S,\rho) = (S',\rho') = (R)_1$; $A = N_1(0) - (0)$. For $x \in A$, $f(x) = |x|^{-1}$. f is clearly continuous on A, but not uniformly.

THEOREM 3.21 Given space (S,ρ), let X,Y be non-null subsets of S such that X is compact, and Y is closed. Then:

(a) if $X \cap Y = \varnothing$, $\rho(X,Y) > 0$;

(b) if Y is, in addition, compact, there exist members x_0, y_0 of X,Y respectively such that: $\rho(x_0,y_0) = \rho(X,Y)$.

PROOF By definition of $\rho(X,Y)$, $\exists$ sequences $\{x_i\}$, $i \geqslant 1$, and $\{y_i\}$, $i \geqslant 1$, of elements of X and Y respectively such that

$$\rho(X,Y) = \lim_i \rho(x_i, y_i) \tag{1}$$

Since X is compact, $\exists$ a subsequence $\{x_{i_r}\}$, $r \geqslant 1$, of $\{x_i\}$ and an element x_0 of X such that

$$x_{i_r} \underset{\rho}{\rightarrow} x_0 \tag{2}$$

Now, suppose (i) that $X \cap Y = \varnothing$; then, by (1):

$$\rho(X,Y) = \lim_r \rho(x_{i_r}, y_{i_r}) = \lim_r \rho(x_0, y_{i_r}) \qquad \text{by (2)}$$

$$\geqslant \rho(x_0, Y) > 0, \quad \text{since } x_0 \omega Y = \overline{Y}.$$

Secondly, suppose (ii) that Y also is compact. Then $\{y_{i_r}\}$ will contain a subsequence $\{y_{i_{r_s}}\}$, $s \geqslant 1$, such that $y_{i_{r_s}} \underset{\rho}{\rightarrow} y_0$, where $y_0 \in Y$.

Then, from (1), and (2):

$$\rho(X,Y) = \lim \rho(x_{i_{r_s}}, y_{i_{r_s}}) = \rho(x_0, y_0).$$

DEFINITION 10* A space (S,ρ) is said to be **locally compact** if, for each x in S, there exists a member G of $\mathscr{G}$ containing x such that $\bar{G}$ is compact.

By the usual means, the property of local compactness is extended to apply to a subset of a space, and they are homeomorphic properties. Any compact space is clearly locally compact.

THEOREM 3.22 A space (S,ρ) is locally compact if and only if one of the following three (equivalent) conditions is satisfied:

(a) for each x in S, (at least) one of the members of $\mathscr{N}(x)$ is compact.

(b) for each x in S, there exists positive ε such that $\overline{N_\varepsilon(x)}$ is compact.

(c)* the subset $\mathscr{G}'$ of $\mathscr{G}$ containing those members G such that $\bar{G}$ is compact forms a base for $\mathscr{G}$.

The proof of the equivalence of local compactness and property (a) depends on the Corollary to Theorem 3.13 and on Theorem 3.12. Property (c) should be compared with the definition of local compactness as it appears in HALL and SPENCER, Reference [2] p. 218 (using Theorem 2.4).

Example 3.2.5 By Theorem 3.16, $(R^n)_1$ is locally compact (though not compact).

Example 3.2.6 By Example 3.2.2, H^∞ is not locally compact.

Example 3.2.7 Clearly any discrete space (S,ρ) is locally compact (though not compact if S is infinite).

An analogue of Theorem 3.12:

THEOREM 3.23* If (S,ρ) is locally compact, any closed subset F of S is locally compact.

PROOF That is, if $x \in F$, it must be shown that $\exists$ a member G' of $\mathscr{G}_F$ such that $x \in G'$ and $\bar{G}'^F$ is compact. But if G is a subset of S such that $x \in G \in \mathscr{G}$ and $\bar{G}$ is compact, $G' \equiv G \cap F$ satisfies these requirements, for, first, $\bar{G}'$ is, *a fortiori*, closed relative to the compact set $\bar{G}$ and so is itself compact (by Theorem 3.12), and, secondly, $\bar{G}'$ coincides with its closure $\bar{G}'^F$ relative to F (since $F \in \mathscr{F}$).

Note 4 The condition in Theorem 3.23 that F be closed is essential.

Example 3.2.8 $(S,\rho) = (R)_1$; $A = Q$. Then, although $(R)_1$ has been seen to be locally compact, (A,ρ_A) is not locally compact; that is, for any $\varepsilon > 0$, $\bar{N}^A_\varepsilon$ is not compact, where $N_\varepsilon =]-\varepsilon,\varepsilon[\cap A$, the ε-neighbourhood of 0 in A. For, if $z \in]-\varepsilon,\varepsilon[\cap C(A)$, $z \in A'$; hence (by Theorem 2.21) $\exists$ a sequence $\{x_i\}$, $i \geqslant 1$, of members of N_ε such that:

$$x_i \underset{\rho}{\to} z. \tag{1}$$

Now if $\{x_i\}$ contained a subsequence $\{x_{i_r}\}$ such that $x_{i_r} \underset{\rho A}{\to} x$, where $x \in A$, then also: $x_{i_r} \underset{\rho}{\to} x$; however, since $x \neq z$, this would contradict (1).

A partial analogue of Theorem 3.14:

THEOREM 3.24 Given spaces (S,ρ), (S',ρ') and a locally compact subset A of S, let f be a (ρ,ρ')-continuous and (ρ,ρ')-open function from A into S; then $f(A)$ is locally compact.

PROOF There is, as usual, no less of generality in taking $A = S$, or taking f *onto* S'. Given $y = f(x)$ in S', $\exists$ a member G of $\mathscr{G}_\rho$ containing x such that ${}^\rho\bar{G}$ is compact. Then since f is open, $f(G) \in \mathscr{G}_{\rho'}$ and, since f is continuous, $f({}^\rho\bar{G})$ is compact (by Theorem 3.14); that is, $f({}^\rho\bar{G})$ is a compact member of $\mathscr{N}_{\rho'}(y)$; hence, by Theorem 3.22, S' is locally compact.

Note 5 The condition in Theorem 3.24 that f be open is essential.

Example 3.2.9 $(S',\rho') = H^\infty$; $S = S' = A$; ρ a discrete metric on S; f the identity function on S. By Example 3.2.7, (S,ρ) is locally compact, and f is clearly (ρ,ρ')-continuous; however, as noted in Example 3.2.6, (S',ρ') is not locally compact.

An analogue of Theorem 3.15:

THEOREM 3.25* A product space (S,ρ) of a finite sequence of spaces $\{(S_i,\rho_i)\}$, $1 \leqslant i \leqslant n$, is locally compact if and only if each space (S_i,ρ_i) is locally compact.

The proof is left to the reader.

Worked Exercises

1. Given a space (S,ρ), a non-null subset A of S is said to be **relatively compact** if $\exists$ a compact subset X of S such that $A \subseteq X$. Show that A is relatively compact if and only if one of the following (equivalent) conditions is satisfied:

(a) $\bar{A}$ is compact;

(b) every infinite subset of A possesses at least one cluster point.

Solution: Given *first* that A is relatively compact, let X be a compact subset of S containing A. Then: $\bar{A} \subseteq \bar{X} = X$ (by Theorem 3.13, Corollary). Since $\bar{A}$ is *a fortiori* closed relative to X, (a) follows from Theorem 3.12. Given *secondly* that (a) holds, it is immediate (since $\bar{A}$ is countably compact) that (b) holds. Suppose *finally* that (b) holds. Then, first, A' is countably compact. For, given an infinite subset X of A' (if none exists the result is immediate) $\exists$ an infinite sequence $\{x_i\}$, $i \geqslant 1$, of distinct members of X. Construct an infinite sequence $\{y_i\}$, $i \geqslant 1$, of distinct members of A as follows:

Choose y_1 in $N_1(x_1) \cap A$; if, given $i > 1$, $y_1, \ldots, y_{i-1}$ have been chosen, then it will follow from Theorem 2.5 that $\exists\, y_i$ in $N_{i^{-1}}(x_i) \cap A$ such that $y_i \neq y_j$ for $1 \leqslant j \leqslant i-1$. Now by assumption (b), $Y \equiv \bigcup_{i \geqslant 1} (y_i)$ possesses a cluster point y *in* A'. Choose $\varepsilon > 0$; then, since all the terms of $\{x_i\}$ are distinct, $\exists\, i_0$ such that $\rho(x_i,y) > 0$ for $i \geqslant i_0$. If then i' is chosen so that *both* $i' \geqslant \max(2\varepsilon^{-1},i_0)$ and $y_{i'} \in N_{\varepsilon/2}(y)$ (possible again from Theorem 2.5):

$$0 < \rho(x_{i'},y) \leqslant \rho(x_{i'},y_{i'}) + \rho(y_{i'},y) < 1/i' + \varepsilon/2 \leqslant \varepsilon.$$

Thus y is also a cluster point of X. It follows that $\bar{A}$ is countably compact (and hence compact). For if Z is any infinite subset of $\bar{A}$, write $Z_1 = Z \cap A$, $Z_2 = Z \cap A'$. Then either Z_1 or Z_2 is infinite. In the former case, it follows from (b) that Z_1 possesses a cluster point, in A'; in the latter case, the same holds for Z_2, since A' has been shown to be countably compact. Thus, in either case, Z possesses a cluster point, in $A' \subseteq \bar{A}$. It is thus immediate that A is relatively compact.

2. If (S,ρ) is locally compact, and F a subset of S such that, for every compact subset K of S, $F \cap K$ is null or compact, show that $F \in \mathscr{F}$.

Solution: Given x in $\bar{F}$, let G be a member of $\mathscr{G}$ such that $x \in G$ and $\bar{G}$ is compact. Then, from Worked Ex. (a), Section 2.3

$$x \in \bar{F} \cap G \subseteq \overline{F \cap G} \subseteq \overline{F \cap \bar{G}}. \tag{1}$$

But, since $F \cap \bar{G}$ is compact, it follows from Theorem 3.13, Corollary that $\overline{F \cap \bar{G}} = F \cap \bar{G} \subseteq F$. Hence it follows from (1) that $x \in F$.

Exercises for Solution

1. If (S,ρ), (S',ρ') are spaces, and f a (ρ,ρ')-continuous function from

S into S', let $\{A_i\}$, $i \geqslant 1$, be a sequence of non-null subsets of S such that: (a): $A_{i+1} \subseteq A_i$ for $i \geqslant 1$, (b): $A_i \in \mathscr{F}_\rho$, $i \geqslant 2$, (c): A_1 is compact. Show that: $\varnothing \subset \bigcap_i f(A_i) = f(\bigcap_i A_i)$.

2. Given a space (S,ρ), $X \subseteq S$, and $r > 0$, let $N_r(X)$ denote the set of those elements x of S such that $\rho(x,y) < r$ for some y in X (dependent on x). Show that:

(a) $N_r(X) \in \mathscr{G}$

(b) if K_1, K_2 are subsets of S such that K_1 is compact, $K_2 \in \mathscr{F}$ and $K_1 \cap K_2 = \varnothing$, show that $\exists\, r > 0$ such that: $N_r(K_1) \cap N_r(K_2) = \varnothing$.

3.* If in the Worked Ex. of Section 2.4, (S',ρ') is given to be compact, show that if $A((x)) \neq \varnothing$ and G' is a member of $\mathscr{G}_{\rho'}$ such that $A((x)) \subseteq G'$, then $\exists$ a member i of I such that $A(X_i) \subseteq G'$.

4. Given spaces (S,ρ), (S',ρ'), let f be an isometry of (S,ρ) onto a subspace of (S',ρ'), and g an isometry of (S',ρ') onto a subspace of (S,ρ). If (S,ρ) is compact, show that f is actually an isometry of (S,ρ) onto (S',ρ') itself. [*Hint:* if $h = f \circ g$, $x \in C_S(h(S))$, and $\{x_i\}$, $i \geqslant 0$, is the sequence of elements of S such that $x_0 = x$ and $x_{i+1} = h(x_i)$ for $i \geqslant 0$, show that $\exists\, d > 0$ such that $\rho(x_i,x_j) \geqslant d$ for $i \neq j$.]

5. Given a space (S,ρ), let A be a locally compact subset of S; show that:

(a) A is open relative to $\bar{A}$

(b) A is locally closed (see Ex. 2, Section 2.5).

Show, by means of an example, that A is not necessarily closed (in S) or bounded.

6. Given spaces (S,ρ), (S',ρ'), and a (ρ,ρ')-continuous function f from S into S', let A' be a locally compact subset of S'. If (S,ρ) is compact, show that $f^{-1}(A')$ is locally compact. If, however, (S,ρ) is *not* compact, show by means of an example that $f^{-1}(A')$ need not be locally compact.

3.3 Complete Spaces

DEFINITION 11 A space (S,ρ) is said to be **complete** if every fundamental sequence $\{x_i\}$, $i \geqslant 1$, of members of S converges.

A subset A of S is said to be complete when the restricted subspace (A,ρ_A) is complete.

Example 3.3.1 $(R^n)_1$ is complete. For, since every fundamental sequence is bounded, it is, by Theorem 3.16, contained in a compact (and hence, sequentially compact) subset of R^n. By Theorem 2.20, the sequence converges.

Example 3.3.2 H^∞ is complete. Let $\{x^{(n)}\}$, $n \geqslant 1$, be any fundamental sequence in H^∞; then if, for each n, $x^{(n)} = \{x_i^{(n)}\}$, $i \geqslant 1$, clearly $\{x_i^{(n)}\}$, $n \geqslant 1$, is a fundamental sequence of elements of R for each $i \geqslant 1$. Hence, by the previous example, $\exists$ a member x_i

of R s.t.: $x_i^{(n)} \underset{\rho_1}{\to} x_i$ for each $i \geqslant 1$. It remains to show that Σx_i^2 is convergent, and that

$$x^{(n)} \underset{\rho}{\to} x \equiv \{x_i\}. \tag{1}$$

Given $\varepsilon > 0$, $\exists\, n_0$ (dependent on ε) such that $\rho(x^{(n)},x^{(m)}) < \varepsilon$ for $m > n \geqslant n_0$. Then, for an arbitrarily given positive integer K; and $m,n \geqslant n_0$:

$$\sum_{i=1}^{K} (x_i^{(n)} - x_i^{(m)})^2 \leqslant \sum_{i=1}^{\infty} (x_i^{(n)} - x_i^{(m)})^2 < \varepsilon^2.$$

Hence

$$\overline{\lim_m} \left\{ \sum_{i=1}^{K} (x_i^{(n)} - x_i^{(m)})^2 \right\} \leqslant \varepsilon^2$$

that is,

$$\sum_{i=1}^{K} (x_i^{(n)} - x_i)^2 \leqslant \varepsilon^2 \quad \text{for } n \geqslant n_0 \tag{2}$$

and so

$$\sum_{i=1}^{\infty} (x_i^{(n)} - x_i)^2 \leqslant \varepsilon^2 \quad \text{for } n \geqslant n_0. \tag{3}$$

But, for any such K:

$$\sum_{i=1}^{K} x_i^2 \leqslant 2 \sum_{i=1}^{K} (x_i^{(n_0)} - x_i)^2 + 2 \sum_{i=1}^{K} (x_i^{(n_0)})^2$$

$$\leqslant 2\varepsilon^2 + 2 \sum_{i=1}^{\infty} (x_i^{(n_0)})^2 \quad \text{by (2).}$$

Thus, Σx_i^2 is convergent, and (1) follows from (3).

Thus a complete space need not be (locally) compact.

The relation between the properties of completeness and compactness appears in:

THEOREM 3.26 A space (S,ρ) is compact if and only if it is both complete and totally bounded.

PROOF If (S,ρ) is compact, it is countably compact, so that its total boundedness is a consequence of Theorem 3.10; since, further, (S,ρ) is sequentially compact, an arbitrary fundamental sequence $\{x_i\}$, $i \geqslant 1$, of elements of S contains a convergent subsequence, and so (by Theorem 2.20) is itself convergent.

Conversely, if (S,ρ) is given to be complete and totally bounded, it will be shown that it is (sequentially) compact. Let $\{x_i\}$, $i \geqslant 1$, be an arbitrary sequence of elements of S. Since (S,ρ) is totally bounded, $\exists$ a finite sequence $\{y_{1,1},\ldots,y_{1,n_1}\}$ of elements of S such that $S = \bigcup_{1\leqslant m\leqslant n_1} N_1(y_{1,m})$. If the enumeration of these elements is so conducted that $N_1(y_{1,1})$ contains a subsequence of $\{x_i\}$, let i_1 be the least value of i such that $x_i \in N_1(y_{1,1})$. Again, $\exists$ a finite sequence $\{y_{2,1},\ldots,y_{2,n_2}\}$ of elements of S such that $S = \bigcup_{1\leqslant m\leqslant n_2} N_{\frac{1}{2}}(y_{2,m})$ and $N_1(y_{1,1}) \cap N_{\frac{1}{2}}(y_{2,1})$ contains a subsequence of $\{x_i\}$; let i_2 be the least value of $i > i_1$ such that $x_i \in N_1(y_{1,1}) \cap N_{\frac{1}{2}}(y_{2,1})$, and so on. That is, a subsequence $\{x_{i_r}\}$, $r \geqslant 1$, of $\{x_i\}$ and a sequence $\{y_{r,1}\}$, $r \geqslant 1$, of elements of S are constructed recursively as follows:

given $r > 2$, let elements $y_{1,1},\ldots,y_{r-1,1}$ of S have been determined so that $\bigcap_{1\leqslant s\leqslant r-1} N_{1/s}(y_{s,1})$ contains a subsequence of $\{x_i\}$ and let $i_1 < i_2 < \ldots i_{r-1}$ have been determined so that: $x_{i_t} \in \bigcap_{1\leqslant s\leqslant t} N_{1/s}(y_{s,1})$ for $1 \leqslant t \leqslant r-1$. Then $\exists$ a finite sequence $\{y_{r,1},\ldots,y_{r,n_r}\}$ of elements of S such that $S = \bigcup_{1\leqslant m\leqslant n_r} N_{1/r}(y_{r,m})$ and $\bigcap_{1\leqslant s\leqslant r} N_{1/s}(y_{s,1})$ contains a subsequence of $\{x_i\}$; i_r is chosen as the least integer i greater than i_{r-1} such that $x_i \in \bigcap_{1\leqslant s\leqslant r} N_{1/s}(y_{s,1})$.

Given now $\varepsilon > 0$, let q be the least integer greater than $2\varepsilon^{-1}$; then for $r' > r \geqslant q$, clearly $x_{i_r}, x_{i_{r'}}$ are both members of $N_{1/q}(y_{q,1})$, so that $\rho(x_{i_r},x_{i_{r'}}) < 2q^{-1} < \varepsilon$; that is, the subsequence $\{x_{i_r}\}$, $r \geqslant 1$, of $\{x_i\}$ is a fundamental sequence which, by the completeness of (S,ρ), must converge.

Example 3.3.3 Since $(R^n)_1$ is complete, but not compact, it is not totally bounded.

Example 3.3.4 On R^n, the function ρ such that $\rho(x,y) = \min(1,\rho_1(x,y))$ can be shown to be a bounded metric, equivalent to ρ_1; hence (since separability is a homeomorphic property) (R^n,ρ) is bounded, separable. However (R^n,ρ) is not totally bounded; for, if it were, then, for any ε with $0 < \varepsilon < 1$, $\exists$ a finite sequence $\{x_1,\ldots,x_m\}$ in R^n such that, for each x in R^n, there corresponds i (dependent on the choice of x) such that $\rho(x,x_i) < \varepsilon$; that is, (since $\varepsilon < 1$) $\rho_1(x,x_i) < \varepsilon$, and the previous example would be contradicted.

Example 3.3.5 Completeness, though clearly isometric, is neither a homeomorphic nor a hereditary property of a space. For, if $(S,\rho) = (R)_1$, and $(S',\rho') = (A,\rho_A)$, where $A =]0,1[$, then it was seen in Chapter 2 (Example 2.6.11) that (S,ρ), (S',ρ') are homeomorphic. Since the sequence: $x_i = i^{-1}$, $i \geqslant 2$, is a non-converging ρ'-fundamental sequence of elements of S', the latter space is not, however, complete. (See also Ex. 5 on p. 103).

THEOREM 3.27 If (S,ρ) is complete, any non-null closed subset F of S is complete.

PROOF If $\{x_i\}$, $i \geqslant 1$, is an arbitrary ρ_F-fundamental sequence of elements of F, then (since ρ and ρ_F coincide on F) it is a ρ-fundamental sequence (in S); hence $\exists\, x$ in S such that $x_i \underset{\rho}{\to} x$. But (by Theorem 2.21, Corollary) $x \in {}^{\rho}\overline{F} = F$; that is, $x_i \underset{\rho_F}{\to} x$.

THEOREM 3.28 Given spaces (S_i,ρ_i), $1 \leqslant i \leqslant n$, let ρ be a metric on $S \equiv \prod_{1 \leqslant i \leqslant n} S_i$ such that, for $1 \leqslant i \leqslant n$ and $x \equiv \{x_j\}$, $y \equiv \{y_j\}$ in S:

(a) $\rho_i(x_i,y_i) \leqslant \rho(x,y)$
(b) if $x_j = y_j$ for $j \neq i$, $\rho(x,y) = \rho_i(x_i,y_i)$.

The (S,ρ) is complete if and only if each (S_i,ρ_i) is complete. (1)

The proof is left to the reader.

COROLLARY I If ρ is one of the metrics given in Note 4, Chapter 2, conclusion (1) of Theorem 3.28 holds.

COROLLARY II If (S,ρ) is any product space of complete spaces (S_i,ρ_i), then (S,ρ) is homeomorphic to a complete space.

†THEOREM 3.29 Given an arbitrary space (S,ρ), there exists a complete space (T,ρ') in which (S,ρ) can be isometrically imbedded in such a way that S is dense in T.

PROOF That is, a complete space (T,ρ') is constructed such that, for some dense subset S' of T, the restricted subspace $(S',(\rho')_{S'})$ is isometric to the given space (S,ρ).

On the set E of all ρ-fundamental sequences $\{x_i\}$ of elements of S, an equivalence relation $\mathscr{R}$ is clearly defined by writing $\{x_i\}\ \mathscr{R}\ \{y_i\}$ (for given members $\{x_i\}$, $\{y_i\}$ of E) if and only if $\lim \rho(x_i,y_i) = 0$. If the set of corresponding $\mathscr{R}$-classes is denoted by T, a real-valued function ρ' on $T \times T$ is defined by writing, for each x',y' in T, (see Ex. 7, Section 2.3) $\rho'(x',y') = \lim \rho(x_i,y_i)$, where $\{x_i\} \in x'$, and $\{y_i\} \in y'$. Then, first, $\rho'(x',y')$ is independent

† This Theorem generalizes the well-known method of construction of the real number system for 'Cauchy sequences' of rationals.

of the choice of $\{x_i\}$, $\{y_i\}$ in x',y' respectively, for if $\{x_i\}\ \mathscr{R}\ \{\bar{x}_i\}$ and $\{y_i\}\ \mathscr{R}\ \{\bar{y}_i\}$, and $i \geqslant 1$:

$$\rho(x_i,y_i) \leqslant \rho(x_i,\bar{x}_i) + \rho(\bar{x}_i,\bar{y}_i) + \rho(\bar{y}_i,y_i)$$

so that $\lim \rho(x_i,y_i) \leqslant \lim \rho(\bar{x}_i,\bar{y}_i)$; secondly, it is easily seen that ρ' is a metric on T.

Given now an arbitrarily chosen element x of S, let $f(x)$ denote that element of T which contains the (clearly ρ-fundamental) sequence $\{x_i\}$ with $x_i = x$, for all i. If $x,\bar{x}$ are any two elements of S, clearly $\rho'(f(x), f(\bar{x})) = \rho(x,\bar{x})$; that is, if $S' = f(S)$, f is a $(\rho,\rho'_{S'})$-isometry of S onto S'.

It remains to show that:

(i) S is dense (in T); (ii) (T,ρ') is complete.

Given x' in T, and $\{x_i\}$ in x', $f(x_i)$ is a member of S'; hence (by Theorem 2.21, Corollary) it will suffice for the proof of (i) to show that: $f(x_i) \underset{\rho'}{\rightarrow} x'$ (as elements of T). Now, by the construction of the function f, it is clear that: for each $j \geqslant 1$:

$$\rho'(f(x_j),x') = \lim_i \rho(x_j,x_i). \tag{1}$$

But, since $\{x_i\} \in E$, there exists, for given $\varepsilon > 0$, a corresponding i_0 such that $\rho(x_j,x_i) < \varepsilon/2$ for $i > j \geqslant i_0$; hence, for each $j \geqslant i_0$, $\lim_i \rho(x_j,x_i) \leqslant \varepsilon/2 < \varepsilon$; that is, from (1), $\rho'(f(x_j),x') < \varepsilon$ for $j \geqslant i_0$.

Secondly, to prove (ii), let $\{x'_n\}$, $n \geqslant 1$, be an arbitrary ρ'-fundamental sequence of elements of T; by (i), $x'_n \in {}^{\rho'}\bar{S}'$; hence $\exists\ x_n$ in S such that:

$$\rho'(x'_n, f(x_n)) < n^{-1}. \tag{2}$$

Given $\varepsilon > 0$, $\exists$ an integer $n_0 \geqslant 4\varepsilon^{-1}$ such that $\rho'(x'_m,x'_n) < \varepsilon/2$ for $m > n \geqslant n_0$. Then; for $m > n \geqslant n_0$:

$$\begin{aligned}\rho(x_m,x_n) = \rho'(f(x_m), f(x_n)) &\leqslant \rho'(f(x_m),x'_m) + \rho'(x'_m,x'_n) + \rho'(f(x_n),x'_n)\\ &< m^{-1} + \varepsilon/2 + n^{-1} < \varepsilon \text{ by (2).}\end{aligned}$$

Thus $\{x_n\}$, $n \geqslant 1$, is a member of E; it remains to show that if x' is the member of T containing it, then $x'_n \underset{\rho'}{\rightarrow} x'$. To see this, it is only necessary to note that, of the two terms on the right-hand side of the inequality:

$$\rho'(x'_n,x') \leqslant \rho'(x'_n,f(x_n)) + \rho'(f(x_n),x'),$$

the first tends to 0 by (2), and the second behaves similarly (as seen in the proof of (i)).

Any space which fulfils the requirements of Theorem 3.29 will be called a **completion** of the given space (S,ρ).

Note 6 (In the proof of Theorem 3.29) $f(x)$ contains exactly those members $\{x_i\}$ of E such that $x_i \underset{\rho}{\rightarrow} x$; for $\{x_i\} \in f(x)$ if and only if $\lim \rho(x,x_i) = 0$. Thus $S' = T$, that is, the spaces (S,ρ), (T,ρ') coincide in the above identification, if and only if (S,ρ) is complete.

°DEFINITION 12 A space (S,ρ) is said to be **absolutely closed** if whenever it is isometrically imbedded in a space (T,ρ'), then S is closed (in T) w.r.t.ρ'.

°THEOREM 3.30 A space (S,ρ) is absolutely closed if and only if it is complete.

PROOF If (S,ρ) is absolutely closed, and (T,ρ') is a completion of (S,ρ), then $T = {}^{\rho'}\bar{S} = S$; hence (S,ρ) is itself complete. Conversely, given a complete space (S,ρ), let (T,ρ') be an arbitrary space in which (S,ρ) can be isometrically imbedded. If $x \in {}^{\rho'}\bar{S}$, $\exists$ a sequence $\{x_i\}$, $i \geqslant 1$, of elements of S such that $x_i \underset{\rho'}{\rightarrow} x$; hence $\{x_i\}$ is a ρ'-fundamental sequence (of elements of T). But, since ρ and ρ' coincide on S, $\{x_i\}$ is also a ρ-fundamental sequence (of elements of S); so, by completeness assumption on (S,ρ), $\exists$ an element y in S such that $x_i \underset{\rho}{\rightarrow} y$ (as elements of S); hence, again, $x_i \underset{\rho'}{\rightarrow} y$ (as elements of T). Thus $x = y$; that is, $x \in S$, and so $S \in \mathscr{F}_{\rho'}$.

°COROLLARY The property (applicable to a space) of being absolutely closed is neither homeomorphic nor hereditary.

By Theorem 2.16, the inequality '$\mathscr{F}_\rho \subseteq (\mathscr{G}_\rho)_\delta$' holds for any space (S,ρ); hence the concept now introduced is a generalization of that appearing in Definition 12.

°DEFINITION 13 A space (S,ρ) is said to be an **absolute G_δ-space** if whenever it is isometrically imbedded in a space (T,ρ'), then S is a G_δ-subset of T, w.r.t.ρ'.

Then, analogously to Theorem 3.30:

°THEOREM 3.31 A space (S,ρ) is an absolute G_δ-space if and only if there exists a *complete* space (T,ρ') in which (S,ρ) can be isometrically imbedded in such a way that S is a G_δ-subset of T, w.r.t.ρ'.

PROOF The necessity of the condition is immediate from Theorem 3.29. Conversely, suppose that $\exists$ a complete space

(T,ρ') satisfying the condition; if (T_1,ρ_1) is an *arbitrary* space in which (S,ρ) can be isometrically imbedded, it will be shown that

$$S \in (\mathscr{G}_{\rho_1})_\delta. \tag{1}$$

Since it easily follows from Note 6 that any completion of (S,ρ) can be isometrically imbedded in (T,ρ') and since, secondly, S is clearly a G_δ-subset of any subspace of (T,ρ') containing it, there is no loss of generality in assuming here that (T,ρ') is itself a completion of (S,ρ). Then, since $S \in (\mathscr{G}_{\rho'})_\delta$, $\exists$ a sequence $\{G_n\}$, $n \geqslant 1$, of members of $\mathscr{G}_{\rho'}$ such that:

$$S = \bigcap_{n \geqslant 1} G_n \tag{2}$$

Now let (T_2,ρ_2) be a completion of (T_1,ρ_1). Since (T_2,ρ_2) is a complete space in which (S,ρ) can be isometrically imbedded, (T,ρ') can, as above, be isometrically imbedded in (T_2,ρ_2) and, by Theorem 3.30, $T \in \mathscr{F}_{\rho_2}$ (as a subset of T_2). From (2), $\exists$ a sequence $\{G'_n\}$, $n \geqslant 1$, of members of $\mathscr{G}_{\rho_2}$ such that:

$$S = \bigcap_{n \geqslant 1} (T \cap G'_n) = T \cap (\bigcap_{n \geqslant 1} G'_n) \tag{3}$$

Since $\mathscr{F}_{\rho_2} \subseteq (\mathscr{G}_{\rho_2})_\delta$, it follows from (3) that $S \in (\mathscr{G}_{\rho_2})_\delta$; since (T_1,ρ_1) is a subspace of (T_2,ρ_2), (1) follows.

DEFINITION 14*. A space (S,ρ) is said to be of the **First Category** (of Baire) if there exists a sequence $\{X_i\}$, $i \geqslant 1$, of nowhere-dense subsets of S such that $S = \bigcup_{i \geqslant 1} X_i$.

If (S,ρ) does *not* satisfy the above conditions it is said to be of the **Second Category.** These properties are extended in the usual way to apply to a subset of a space, and they are homeomorphic. By Theorem 2.35, it is clear that the sequence in Definition 14 must necessarily contain an infinity of distinct terms.

Before these notions can be related to the property of completeness, we require a result comparable with Theorem 3.8:

THEOREM 3.32 A space (S,ρ) is complete if and only if for any sequence $\{K_n\}$, $n \geqslant 1$, of bounded closed subsets of S such that:

(a) $\lim D(K_n) = 0$;

(b) $K_{n+1} \subseteq K_n$ for $n \geqslant 1$;

then $\bigcap_{n \geqslant 1} K_n$ is non-null.

PROOF Given that (S,ρ) is complete, let $\{K_n\}$, $n \geqslant 1$, be any sequence of bounded closed subsets of S satisfying conditions (a), (b); for each n, choose x_n in K_n. Since, for $m > n$, $x_m \in K_n$, by (b), it clearly follows from (a) that $\{x_n\}$ is a fundamental sequence, and so $\exists$ x in S such that $x_n \underset{\rho}{\rightarrow} x$; then, since each $K_n \in \mathscr{F}$ and contains all but a finite number of the terms of $\{x_n\}$, it follows that $x \in K_n$.

Conversely, if $\{x_i\}$, $i \geqslant 1$, is an arbitrary fundamental sequence in S, there will correspond, to each positive integer n a (least) integer i_n such that:

$$\rho(x_{i_n},x_i) < 1/2^n \quad \text{for } i \geqslant i_n. \tag{1}$$

If $S_{1/2^{n-1}}(x_{i_n})$, for $n \geqslant 1$, is denoted by K_n, then $\{K_n\}$ is a sequence of bounded closed subsets of S satisfying conditions (a) and (b) above; to see that the latter is satisfied we need only to note that for any element x in K_{n+1}:

$$\rho(x,x_{i_n}) < \rho(x_{i_{n+1}},x_{i_n}) + 1/2^n < 1/2^{n-1}, \quad \text{by (1).}$$

Hence $\exists$ an element y in S such that $\rho(y,x_{i_n}) < 1/2^{n-1}$ for each $n \geqslant 1$; that is, $\{x_i\}$ contains a convergent subsequence, and so is itself convergent.

THEOREM 3.33 If (S,ρ) is a complete space, it is of the Second Category.

PROOF If (S,ρ) were of the First Category, $\exists$ sequence $\{X_i\}$, $i \geqslant 1$, of nowhere dense subsets such that $S = \bigcup_{i \geqslant 1} X_i$. Since X_1 is nowhere dense (in S), $\exists$ (by Theorem 2.34) an element x_1 of S and positive ε_1 such that $N_{\varepsilon_1}(x_1) \cap X_1 = \varnothing$; if $r_1 = \frac{1}{2}\min(1,\varepsilon_1)$, and K_1 denotes $\overline{N_{r_1}(x_1)}$, $K_1 \in \mathscr{F}$ and $K_1 \cap X_1 = \varnothing$; again, $\exists$ x_2 in S and $\varepsilon_2 > 0$ such that $N_{\varepsilon_2}(x_2) \subseteq N_{r_1}(x_1)$ and $N_{\varepsilon_2}(x_2) \cap X_2 = \varnothing$, so that if $r_2 = \frac{1}{2}\min(\frac{1}{2},\varepsilon_2)$, and K_2 denotes $\overline{N_{r_2}(x_2)}$, $K_2 \in \mathscr{F}$, $K_2 \subseteq K_1$, and $K_2 \cap X_2 = \varnothing$, and so on. That is, we construct recursively a sequence $\{K_i\}$, $i \geqslant 1$, of bounded closed subsets of S as follows: given $i > 2$, suppose that $K_1, \ldots, K_{i-1}$ have been constructed so that:

$$K_{i-1} = \overline{N_{r_{i-1}}(x_{i-1})} \subseteq K_{i-2} \ldots \subseteq K_1 \tag{1}$$

(where $0 < r_{i-1} \in R$ and $x_{i-1} \in S$) and:

$$D(K_j) < 2/j,\ K_j \cap X_j = \varnothing \quad \text{for} \quad 1 \leqslant j \leqslant i-1. \tag{2}$$

Then, as before by Theorem 2.34, $\exists$ x_i in S and $\varepsilon_i > 0$ such that $N_{\varepsilon_i}(x_i) \subseteq N_{r_{i-1}}(x_{i-1})$ and $N_{\varepsilon_i}(x_i) \cap X_i = \varnothing$; if $r_i = \frac{1}{2}\min(i^{-1},\varepsilon_i)$, and K_i denotes $\overline{N_{r_i}(x_i)}$, then $K_1, \ldots, K_i$ satisfy (1), (2) with $i - 1$ replaced by i. By Theorem 3.32, $\exists$ an element x in $\bigcap_{i \geqslant 1} K_i$; hence, by (2), $x \in C(X_i)$, for $i \geqslant 1$, contradicting the choice of $\{X_i\}$.

COROLLARY Given a space (S,ρ), an enumerable subset A of S cannot be both complete and dense-in-itself.

PROOF Suppose A were enumerable, complete, and dense-in-itself (that is, $A'^A = A$). There is no loss of generality in taking $A = S$. If $S = \bigcup_{i \geqslant 1} (x_i)$ it is clear from Theorem 2.5 that $x_i \in (S - (x_i))'$ for each i; that is, (x_i) is not open, and hence $\left(\overline{(x_i)}\right)^\circ = (x_i)^\circ = \varnothing$, contradicting Theorem 3.33.

Example 3.3.6 $(S,\rho) = (R)_1$; $A = Q$ in the Corollary. Since $Q \subset R = Q'$, it follows that A is not complete. More generally, if ρ' is *any* metric on Q such that Q is dense-in-itself w.r.t.ρ', (Q,ρ') is not complete.

Example 3.3.7 $S = \bigcup_{n \geqslant 1} (n^{-1})$; $\rho(x,y) = |x - y|$ for x,y in S. For each $n \geqslant 1$, $(n^{-1}) = N_{\varepsilon_n}(n^{-1})$ for $\varepsilon_n = 1/n(n + 1)$; that is, (S,ρ) is discrete and hence clearly of the Second Category. However it is not complete.

From Theorems 3.27 and 3.33, any complete space satisfies the requirements of:

°DEFINITION 15* A space (S,ρ) is said to be **totally of the Second Category** if every non-null closed subset is of the Second Category.

Since, for any space, $\mathscr{F}_\rho \subseteq (\mathscr{G}_\rho)_\delta$ (by Theorem 2.16), the next theorem shows that the requirements of Definition 15 could be considerably strengthened.

°THEOREM 3.34* If (S,ρ) is totally of the Second Category, and X is any non-null G_δ-subset of S, then X is totally of the Second Category.

PROOF If not, $\exists$ a sequence $\{G_i\}$, $i \geqslant 1$, of members of $\mathscr{G}$ such that, if $X = \bigcap_{i \geqslant 1} G_i$, $\exists$ a member F of $\mathscr{F}_X$ (that is, a subset F of X, closed relative to X) and a sequence $\{X_i\}$, $i \geqslant 1$, of subsets of F, each nowhere-dense in F, with

$$F = \bigcup_{i \geqslant 1} X_i. \tag{1}$$

Now, since $F \in \mathscr{F}_X$, $F = {}^{\rho}\bar{F} \cap X$, and so:

$$\bar{F} - F = \bar{F} \cap C_S(X) = \bar{F} \cap (\bigcup_{i \geqslant 1} C_S(G_i)) = \bigcup_{i \geqslant 1} Y_i,$$

where

$$Y_i = \bar{F} \cap C_S(G_i) \quad \text{for } i \geqslant 1. \tag{2}$$

But each Y_i is nowhere-dense in $\bar{F}$, for, if not, $\exists$ i such that $Y_i^{\circ \bar{F}} \neq \varnothing$, since Y_i is, *a fortiori*, closed relative to $\bar{F}$; that is, $\exists$ a member H_i of $\mathscr{G}$ such that $\varnothing \subset \bar{F} \cap H_i \subseteq Y_i$. But $F \cap H_i \neq \varnothing$ (otherwise $F \subseteq C(H_i)$, implying: $\bar{F} \subseteq C(H_i)$); hence clearly $F \cap Y_i \neq \varnothing$, contradicting the inequality: $F \subseteq G_i$. Now (by Ex. 5, Section 2.5) each X_i in (1) is also nowhere-dense *in* $\bar{F}$; hence (1), (2) together would imply that $\bar{F}$ is of the First Category, contradicting the requirements of Definition 15.

°COROLLARY I If (S,ρ) is complete, and X a non-null G_δ-subset of S, X is totally of the Second Category.

COROLLARY II If ρ_1 is the usual metric on R, Q is *not* a G_δ-subset of R (w.r.t.ρ_1).

Worked Exercises

1. If (S,ρ) is complete, and G is a proper non-null *open* subset of S, show that $\exists$ a metric ρ'' on G such that (G,ρ'') is a complete subspace of (S,ρ).

Solution: From Worked Ex. 2, Section 2.1, it is seen that the function: $f(x) \equiv (\rho(x,C(G)))^{-1}$ is (ρ_G,ρ_1)-continuous from G into R. If ρ' is the metric on $G \times R$ obtained from ρ_G, ρ_1 as in Note 4 of Chapter 2, and if T is the graph of f on G, it follows from Theorem 2.45 that (in the usual notation) g is a homeomorphism of (G,ρ_G) onto (T,ρ'_T). Since completeness is an isometric property of a space, it suffices by Ex. 9, Section 2.6, to show that (T,ρ'_T) is complete. If $\{g(x_i)\}$, $i \geqslant 1$, is a given ρ'_T-fundamental sequence of elements of T, then it is clear from the choice of the metric ρ' that $\{x_i\}$ will be a ρ-fundamental sequence of elements of S, and $\{f(x_i)\}$ a ρ_1-fundamental sequence of elements of R. But (S,ρ) and $(R)_1$ are both complete; hence $\exists x$ in S and y in R such that:

(a): $x_i \underset{\rho}{\rightarrow} x$, (b): $f(x_i) \underset{\rho_1}{\rightarrow} y$. Now $x \in G$, for, if not, it would follow from (a) that $\rho(x_i,C(G)) \underset{\rho_1}{\rightarrow} 0$, contradicting (b). Hence (by the continuity of g) $g(x_i) \underset{\rho'_T}{\rightarrow} g(x)$, and result is established.

2. Given a space (S,ρ) and a completion (T,ρ') of (S,ρ), show that:

(a) (S,ρ) is separable if and only if (T,ρ') is separable;

(b) (S,ρ) is totally-bounded if and only if (T,ρ') is compact.

Solution:

(a) If X is an enumerable subset of S which is dense in S, then, since S is dense in T, it follows from Theorem 2.31, that (T,ρ') is separable. The converse is immediate from Theorem 3.5 Corollary.

(b) If (S,ρ) is given to be totally-bounded, it suffices by Theorem 3.26 to show that (T,ρ') is totally-bounded. Given $\varepsilon > 0$, $\exists$ a finite sequence $x_1, \ldots, x_n$ of elements of S such that, for each y in S, $\exists\, i$ (dependent on y) such that

$$\rho(y,x_i) < \varepsilon/2. \tag{1}$$

If now x is an arbitrary element of T, $x \in {}^{\rho'}\bar{S}$; hence $\exists\, y$ in S such that $\rho'(x,y) < \varepsilon/2$. Then if i is chosen as in (1), it is easy to see (since $\rho = \rho'_S$) that $\rho'(x,x_i) < \varepsilon$. If, conversely, (S,ρ) were *not* totally-bounded, it would follow (Cf. argument of Theorem 3.10) that (T,ρ') could not be (countably) compact.

Exercises for Solution

1. Show that the space (S',ρ') of Ex. 6, Section 2.1, is complete.

2. Show that the space (S,ρ) of part (c) of Ex. 3, Section 2.1, is complete.

3. If (S,ρ) is any space, G,f,T are as in the Worked Ex. 1 above, and (S',ρ') is a product space of (S,ρ) and $(R)_1$, show that $T \in \mathscr{F}_{\rho'}$; hence supply an alternative treatment of the Worked Ex. 1.

4. If (S,ρ) is any space, $\{G_i\}$, $i \geqslant 1$, a sequence of proper non-null open subsets of S, and $(S'\rho')$ is the space of Ex. 1 above, show that the function: $f(x) \equiv \{(\rho(x,C(G_i)))^{-1}\}$, $i \geqslant 1$, is (ρ_X,ρ')-continuous from $X(=\bigcap_i G_i)$ into S'. Hence (by an argument analogous to Ex. 3, or otherwise) establish a generalization (from open sets to G_δ-sets) of the result of the Worked Ex. 1.

5. Find a set S, and two discrete metrics ρ,ρ' on S such that just one of the spaces (S,ρ), (S,ρ') is complete.

6. Given a space (S,ρ), show that (see Worked Ex. 1, Section 3.2):
   (a) (S,ρ) is complete if and only if every totally bounded subset of S is relatively compact
   (b) (S,ρ) is totally bounded if and only if $\exists$ a complete space (S',ρ') in which (S,ρ) can be isometrically imbedded in such a way that S is relatively compact (as a subset of S').

7.* Show that:
   (a) a space (S,ρ) is of the Second Category if and only if for any sequence $\{G_i\}$, $i \geqslant 1$, of dense open subsets of S, $\bigcap_{i \geqslant 1} G_i \neq \varnothing$;
   (b) if (S,ρ) is of the Second Category, and A is the union of a sequence of subsets of S, each nowhere-dense *in* S, then $C(A)$ is of the Second Category;

(c) if (S,ρ) is of the First Category, and G is a non-null open subset of S, then G is of the First Category;
(d) the proviso in (c) that G be *open* is essential, (by considering the subset S of R^2 of all points $\{x_1,x_2\}$ satisfying at least one of the two conditions: (i): x_1 and x_2 are rational, (ii): $x_2 = 0$).

3.4 Connected Spaces

DEFINITION 16* A space (S,ρ) is said to be **separated** if there exist non-null members X_i, $i = 1,2$, of $\mathscr{G}$ such that $X_1 \cap X_2 = \varnothing$ and $X_1 \cup X_2 = S$.

Clearly '$\mathscr{G}$' can be replaced here by '$\mathscr{F}$'. Such a pair (X_1,X_2) is called a **partition** of S (w.r.t.ρ).

DEFINITION 17* A space (S,ρ) is said to be **connected** when it is *not* separated.

These two properties of separatedness and connectedness are extended as usual to apply to a non-null subset of a space, and are clearly homeomorphic. Thus, a non-null subset A of S is connected if and only if $\mathscr{G}_A \cap \mathscr{F}_A$ contains A, $\varnothing$ as its *only* members.

Example 3.4.1 Any one-element subset of a space is connected.

Example 3.4.2 $(R)_1$ is connected. If not, let (X_1,X_2) be a partition of R. Choose x_i in X_i, for $i = 1,2$; if $x_1 < x_2$, let $Y_i = [x_1,x_2] \cap X_i$ for $i = 1,2$. Since each Y_i is non-null, bounded, and closed, it is compact (by Theorem 3.16); hence, by Theorem 3.21, $\exists$ a member y_i of Y_i with $|y_1 - y_2| = \rho(Y_1,Y_2)$. Then if $z = \frac{1}{2}(y_1 + y_2)$, it is clear that, for each i, and $j \neq i$: $|y_i - z| < \rho(Y_i,Y_j)$; that is, z belongs to neither of Y_1, or Y_2. But $Y_1 \cup Y_2 = [x_1,x_2]$, yielding a contradiction.

Example 3.4.3 If ρ is a discrete metric on a set S, containing more than one member, then, for each x in S, the subsets $((x),S - (x))$ form a partition of S; that is (S,ρ) is separated.

Example 3.4.4 If ρ is the restriction to Q of the usual metric ρ_1 on R, (Q,ρ) is separated. For if $a \in R - Q$, the subsets $X_1 \equiv \,]\leftarrow,a[\, \cap Q$ and $X_2 \equiv \,]a,\rightarrow[\, \cap Q$ clearly form a partition of Q (w.r.t.ρ).

Note 7 From Definition 16, a given non-null *subset* A of a space (S,ρ) is separated if and only if $\exists$ non-null subsets X_1,X_2 of A with:
(i) $A = X_1 \cup X_2$; (ii) $X_1 \cap X_2 = \varnothing$; (iii) $X_i \in \mathscr{F}_A$ for $i = 1,2$.

It is convenient to replace conditions (ii), (iii) together by a single condition on X_1, X_2 which is expressed in terms of their closures *w.r.t.*ρ; that is, where they are regarded as subsets of the original space (S,ρ) rather than as subsets of a subspace (A,ρ'). To do so, we require:

DEFINITION 18* Given a space (S,ρ), two non-null subsets X_1, X_2 of S are said to be **mutually separated** (w.r.t.ρ) if:

$$(X_1 \cap {}^{\rho}\overline{X}_2) \cup (X_2 \cap {}^{\rho}\overline{X}_1) = \varnothing. \tag{1}$$

THEOREM 3.35* Given a space (S,ρ), a non-null subset A of S is separated if and only if A contains two subsets X_1, X_2, mutually separated (w.r.t.ρ), such that $A = X_1 \cup X_2$.

PROOF It suffices to show that, if X_1, X_2 are any non-null subsets of S such that $A = X_1 \cup X_2$, then

$$X_1 \cap X_2 = \varnothing \quad \textit{and} \quad X_i \in \mathscr{F}_A, \qquad i = 1,2 \tag{2}$$

if and only if (1) (of Definition 18) holds.

Now $X_1 \in \mathscr{F}_A$ if and only if

$$X_1 \supseteq \overline{X}_1 \cap A = X_1 \cup (\overline{X}_1 \cap X_2)$$

that is:

$$\overline{X}_1 \cap X_2 \subseteq X_1 \quad \textit{or (equivalently)}: \overline{X}_1 \cap X_2 \subseteq X_1 \cap X_2.$$

Since a similar criterion holds for X_2 to belong to $\mathscr{F}_A$, it is clear that:

$$X_i \in \mathscr{F}_A, \qquad i = 1,2$$

if and only if $X_1 \cap X_2$ contains the left-hand side expression in (1) above. Since on the other hand the latter contains $X_1 \cap X_2$ in any case, the required result is immediately evident.

THEOREM 3.36* Given a space (S,ρ), a non-null subset A of S, and mutually-separated subsets X_i of S such that $X_i \cap A \neq \varnothing$, $i = 1,2$, then $X_1 \cap A$ and $X_2 \cap A$ are mutually-separated.

The proof is left to the reader.

COROLLARY* If A is connected and $A \subseteq X_1 \cup X_2$, (where X_1, X_2 are mutually-separated) then $A \subseteq X_i$ for some $i = 1,2$.

THEOREM 3.37* Given a space (S,ρ), and a connected subset A of S, then if $A \subseteq X \subseteq \overline{A}$, X is connected.

PROOF If X is not connected, then (by Theorem 3.35) $\exists$ mutually-separate subsets X_i of S with $X = X_1 \cup X_2$; hence (by the above Corollary) $\exists\ i$ (= 1 or 2) such that $A \subseteq X_i$. If $i = 1$, say, then $X \subseteq \bar{A} \subseteq \overline{X_1}$, implying: $X_2 \subseteq \overline{X_1}$, contradicting Definition 18.

Note 8 Since connectedness is a homeomorphic property of a subset of a space, it follows from Example 3.4.2 above and Example 2.6.10 that any (finite or infinite) open interval of R is connected; hence, by Theorem 3.37 (and Example 2.3.12) also any (finite or infinite) half-closed or closed interval of R is connected. We now show that, conversely, any connected subset X of R is either R itself or an interval of some form. Consider the following cases:

(a) X bounded. If X contains more than one element, and if $a = \inf X$, $b = \sup X$, it suffices to show that $]a,b[\subseteq X$. If not, $\exists\ x_1$ with $a < x_1 < b$ and $x_1\ \omega\ X$. If X_1,X_2 are respectively the subsets of X of those members which are less than, greater than x_1, then $X_1 \neq \varnothing$ (otherwise a would not be the greatest of the lower bounds of X), and similarly for X_2. Since, further, $X_i = I_i \cap X$, where I_1,I_2 are respectively the closed intervals $[a,x_1]$, $[x_1,b]$, each $X_i \in \mathscr{F}_X$, giving a contradiction.

(b) X bounded below, but not above. If $a = \inf X$, and $]a,\rightarrow[$ were *not* a subset of X, $\exists\ x_1 > a$ with $x_1\ \omega\ X$; if subsets X_1,X_2 of X are defined as in (a), they will again form a partition of X.

(c) X bounded above, but not below. This is treated similarly to (b).

(d) X bounded neither above nor below. If $X \subset R$, let $x_1 \in C_R(X)$, and proceed as before.

The next theorem, on two arbitrary mutually-separate subsets of any space, is a generalization of Theorem 2.17:

THEOREM 3.38 Given a space (S,ρ) and two mutually-separated subsets X_1,X_2 of S, there exist open subsets G_1,G_2 of S such that $G_1 \cap G_2 = \varnothing$, and $X_i \subseteq G_i$, for $i = 1,2$.

PROOF Let G_1 be the set of those elements x of S such that $\rho(x,X_1) < \rho(x,X_2)$, and define G_2 by interchanging X_1,X_2. For each element x of X_1, $x\ \omega\ \overline{X}_2$, that is: $\rho(x,X_2) > 0 = \rho(x,X_1)$, so that $X_1 \subseteq G_1$; similarly $X_2 \subseteq G_2$. Since evidently $G_1 \cap G_2 = \varnothing$, it remains to verify that G_1,G_2 belong to $\mathscr{G}$. But (as seen immediately from Worked Ex. 2, Section 2.1) for each $i = 1,2$, the function f_i from S into R such that $f_i(x) = \rho(x,X_i)$ is (ρ,ρ_1)-continuous (where ρ_1 is the usual metric on R). Hence clearly $f \equiv f_2 - f_1$ is

(ρ,ρ_1)-continuous, so that (as pointed out in Example 2.6.3) $f^{-1}\{]0,\rightarrow[\} \in \mathscr{G}$; that is, $G_1 \in \mathscr{G}$. Similarly $G_2 = f^{-1}\{]\leftarrow,0[\}$.

COROLLARY If F_1,F_2 are disjoint closed subsets of S, there exist open subsets G_1,G_2 of S with $G_1 \cap G_2 = \varnothing$ and $F_i \subseteq G_i$ for $i = 1,2$.

This corollary can actually be strengthened to read as follows:

THEOREM 3.39 Given a space (S,ρ), and two disjoint closed subsets F_1,F_2 of S, there exist open subsets G_1,G_2 of S with $\bar{G}_1 \cap \bar{G}_2 = \varnothing$ and $F_i \subseteq G_i$ for $i = 1,2$.

PROOF By the above Corollary, $\exists$ disjoint open sets G',G_2 with $F_1 \subseteq G'$, $F_2 \subseteq G_2$. Since $C(G')$, F_1 are then disjoint and closed, $\exists$ again disjoint open sets G_1,G'' with $F_1 \subseteq G_1$, $C(G') \subseteq G''$. (1)

Since $G_1 \cap G'' = \varnothing$, and $C(G'')$ is closed, clearly $\bar{G}_1 \subseteq C(G'')$; secondly, $G' \cap G_2 = \varnothing$ similarly implies: $\bar{G}_2 \subseteq C(G') \subseteq G''$, by (1).

THEOREM 3.40* Given spaces (S,ρ), (S',ρ') and a connected subset A of S, let f be a (ρ,ρ')-continuous function from A into S; then $f(A)$ is connected.

PROOF There is no loss in generality in taking $A = S$ and supposing that $f(S) = S'$. If S' is not connected, $\exists$ non-empty disjoint members G_i' of $\mathscr{G}_{\rho'}$ such that $S' = G_1' \cup G_2'$. By the continuity of f, $G_i \equiv f^{-1}(G_i') \in \mathscr{G}_\rho$ for $i = 1,2$, and clearly (G_1,G_2) forms a partition of S (w.r.t.ρ).

A well-known theorem in analysis is generalized in:

THEOREM 3.41* Given a space (S,ρ), a connected subset A of S, and a (ρ,ρ_1)-continuous function f from A into R, if a,b are members of A with $f(a) < f(b)$ and $f(a) < \eta < f(b)$, then there exists an element x of A with $f(x) = \eta$.

PROOF By the previous theorem, $f(A)$ is connected; hence, by Note 8, $f(A)$ is either R itself or some interval.

The condition introduced in the next theorem is used by some authors (e.g., HALL and SPENCER, Reference [2] p. 78) to *define* the concept of connectedness:

THEOREM 3.42* Given a space (S,ρ), a subset A of S is connected if and only if there does *not* exist a (ρ,ρ_1)-continuous function f from A into R such that $f(A)$ contains exactly two points.

PROOF In view of the previous theorem, only the sufficiency of the condition need be considered. If A is *not* connected, $\exists$ a subset H of A with $\varnothing \subset H \subset A$ and H in $\mathscr{G}_A \cap \mathscr{F}_A$. Define a function f from A into R where:

$$f(x) = 1 \quad \text{for } x \text{ in } H, \qquad f(x) = 0 \quad \text{for } x \text{ in } C_A(H).$$

For any open subset G' of R, (that is, if $G' \in \mathscr{G}_{\rho_1}$) $\exists$ just four possibilities for $f^{-1}(G')$; that is, $\varnothing$, H, $C_A(H)$, A, each of which belongs to $\mathscr{G}_A$. Hence f is (ρ,ρ_1)-continuous, and a contradiction is obtained.

THEOREM 3.43 Given a space (S,ρ), let A be a connected subset of S with more than one member; then A is non-enumerable.

PROOF Given two distinct members a,b of A define a function f from A into R by writing: $f(x) = \rho(x,a)$ for each x in A. Then (from Worked Ex. 2, Section 2.1) f is (ρ,ρ_1)-continuous and $f(a) = 0 < f(b)$; it follows by Theorem 3.41 that $f(A)$, and hence A itself, is non-enumerable.

DEFINITION 19* Given a space (S,ρ) and a non-null subset A of S, two elements x,y of A are said to be **Connected in** A if there exists a connected subset B of A such that x and y are members of B.

THEOREM 3.44* Given a space (S,ρ), let $\{A_i\}$, $i \in I$, be a family of connected subsets of S such that $A_i \cap A_j \neq \varnothing$ for any i,j in I. Then $A \equiv \bigcup_i A_i$ is connected.

PROOF If not, $\exists$ (by Theorem 3.35) mutually-separate sets X_1,X_2 with $A = X_1 \cup X_2$. Let $x_k \in X_k$ for $k = 1,2$; then $\exists\, i,j$ in I such that $x_1 \in A_i$, $x_2 \in A_j$. But, by Theorem 3.36, Corollary, $A_i \subseteq X_1$, and $A_j \subseteq X_2$; hence $X_1 \cap X_2 \neq \varnothing$, contradictory to Definition 18.

COROLLARY I* If A is connected, and $\{A_i\}$, $i \in I$, is a family of connected sets with $A \cap A_i \neq \varnothing$, for each i in I, then $A \cup (\bigcup_i A_i)$ is connected.

PROOF For each i in I, let $B_i = A \cup A_i$; an application of the Theorem to A,A_i *only*, shows that B_i is connected. Since $A \subseteq B_i \cap B_j$ for each i,j in I, a second application of the Theorem, now to the family $\{B_i\}$, gives the desired result.

COROLLARY II* If A is a set such that any pair of its members is connected in A, then A itself is connected.

PROOF Given an element x of A, there corresponds to each element y of A a connected subset X_y of A such that x,y both belong to X_y. Clearly $A = \bigcup_{y \in A} X_y$, which is connected by the Theorem.

THEOREM 3.45* A product space (S,ρ) of a finite sequence of spaces $\{(S_i,\rho_i)\}$, $1 \leqslant i \leqslant n$, is connected if and only if each space (S_i,ρ_i) is connected.

PROOF For each i, the projection π_i of S onto S_i is (ρ,ρ_i)-continuous; hence (by Theorem 3.40) the connectedness of (S,ρ) would imply that of each space (S_i,ρ_i).

To prove the converse, suppose that each (S_i,ρ_i) is connected. Then, if (S,ρ) is *not* connected, $\exists$ (by Theorem 3.42) a (ρ,ρ')-continuous function f from S into R such that $f(S) = (0,1)$ (where ρ' denotes the usual metric on R). Then, given $1 \leqslant j \leqslant n, f(x) = f(y)$ for any two elements x,y of S such that $x_i = y_i$ for each $i \neq j$. (1)

To see this, take, for example, $j = 1$ and arbitrarily choose an element $a \equiv \{a_i\}$ in S; define a function f_1 from S_1 into S by writing, for each x_1 in S_1, $f_1(x_1) = y \equiv \{y_i\}$, where $y_1 = x_1$, and $y_i = a_i$ for $2 \leqslant i \leqslant n$. It is easily seen that f_1 is (ρ_1,ρ)-continuous; hence (by Theorem 2.37) the composite function $f_1 \circ f$ is (ρ_1,ρ')-continuous from S_1 into R. Since $(f_1 \circ f)(S_1) \subseteq (0,1)$ and (S_1,ρ_1) is connected, it follows (again from Theorem 3.42) that $(f_1 \circ f)(x_1) = (f_1 \circ f)(a_1)$ for every x_1 in S_1; that is, $f(f_1(x_1)) = f(a)$, clearly implying (1). Given now two *arbitrary* elements x,y of S, $\exists$ a finite sequence $\{x^{(j)}\}$ $0 \leqslant j \leqslant n$, of elements of S such that $x^{(0)} = x$, $x^{(n)} = y$, and, for each $j \geqslant 1$, $x_i^{(j-1)} = x_i^{(j)}$ for $i \neq j$; it follows from (1) that f is constant on S, giving a contradiction with original choice of f.

Example 3.4.5 For the space $(R^n)_1$, $n \geqslant 1$, any subset of the form $\prod_{1 \leqslant i \leqslant n} X_i$, where each X_i is an interval of some form, or coincides with R itself, is connected.

DEFINITION 20* Given a space (S,ρ) and elements x,y of S, a finite sequence $\mathscr{C} \equiv \{X_i\}$, $1 \leqslant i \leqslant n$, of non-empty subsets of S, is called a **simple chain** between x, and y if:

(i) $x \in X_1$ and $y \in X_n$;

(ii) for $1 \leqslant i < j \leqslant n$, $X_i \cap X_j \begin{cases} \neq \varnothing \text{ if } j = i+1 \\ = \varnothing \text{ otherwise} \end{cases}$

Each of the sets X_i is called a **link** of $\mathscr{C}$.

THEOREM 3.46* A given space (S,ρ) is connected if and only if, given any two elements x,y of S and an open covering $\{G_i\}$, $i \in I$, of S, there exists a finite sub-collection $\mathscr{C}$ of $\{G_i\}$ (dependent on the choice of x, and y) which forms a simple chain between x, and y.

PROOF To prove first the necessity of the condition, let $x \in S$ and $\{G_i\}$, $i \in I$, be an open covering of S: let A denote the set of those elements y of S such that $\exists$ a finite sub-collection $\mathscr{C}_y$ of $\{G_i\}$ (dependent on the choice of y) forming a simple chain between x and y. Clearly $x \in A$; we show now that:

(i) $A \in \mathscr{G}$. Given y in A, $\exists$ a simple chain $\mathscr{C}_y \equiv \{G_{i_r}\}$, $1 \leqslant r \leqslant n$, (where $i_r \in I$) between x and y; then $y \in G_{i_n} \subseteq A$ (since $\mathscr{C}_y$ is also a chain between x and any element z of G_{i_n}).

(ii) $A \in \mathscr{F}$. Given y in $\bar{A}$, $\exists\, i'$ in I such that $y \in G_{i'}$; since $G_{i'} \in \mathscr{N}(y)$, $\exists$ a member z of A belonging to $G_{i'}$. If $\mathscr{C}_z \equiv \{G_{i_r}\}$, $1 \leqslant r \leqslant n$, is a simple chain between x and z, $z \in G_{i'} \cap G_{i_n}$; hence $\exists$ a least integer $r'(1 \leqslant r' \leqslant n)$ such that $G_{i'} \cap G_{i_{r'}} \neq \varnothing$. Then $G_{i_1}, \ldots, G_{i_{r'}}, G_{i'}$ form a simple chain between x, and y; that is, $y \in A$.

Since (S,ρ) is connected, it follows that $A = S$.

Conversely, if S were *not* connected, then $\exists$ a partition (G_1,G_2) of S. If $x \in G_1$, $y \in G_2$, it is clear that *no* sub-collection $\mathscr{C}$ exists of the open covering $\{G_i\}$, $i = 1,2$, of S such that $\mathscr{C}$ is a chain between x, and y.

COROLLARY If (S,ρ) is connected, and $x,y \in S$, then, given $\varepsilon > 0$, there exists a finite sequence $\{x_i\}$, $0 \leqslant i \leqslant n+1$, of elements of S such that:

(a) $x = x_0$; $y = x_{n+1}$; (b) for $0 \leqslant i \leqslant n$, $\rho(x_i,x_{i+1}) < \varepsilon$.

Such a set of elements is called an 'ε-chain' between x, and y. A space (S,ρ) is said to be **ε-connected** if any two elements of S can be joined by an ε-chain of members of S.

Note 9 The converse of the above Corollary does not hold.

Example 3.4.6 $S = R - (0)$; $\rho(x,y) = |x - y|$. If $X_1 =]\leftarrow,0[$, $X_2 =]0,\rightarrow[$, the sets (X_1,X_2) form a partition of S; that is, S is not connected. However, given $\varepsilon > 0$, any two points of S can clearly be joined by an ε-chain in S.

Thus the condition of the *compactness* of (S,ρ) cannot be omitted from:

THEOREM 3.47 A compact space (S,ρ) is connected if it is ε-connected for any $\varepsilon > 0$.

PROOF If (X_1,X_2) were a partition of S, then each $X_i \in \mathscr{F}$; hence, by Theorems 3.12, and 3.21, $\rho(X_1,X_2) = \varepsilon$, where $\varepsilon > 0$. Thus, for *any* elements x,y in X_1,X_2 respectively, $\rho(x,y) \geqslant \varepsilon$, and so clearly $\exists$ *no* ε-chain joining x, and y.

DEFINITION 21* Given a space (S,ρ), and a connected subset of A, then:

(i) A is said to be a **continuum** if A is compact and has at least two members;

(ii) A is said to be a **domain** if it is open.

By Note 8, the only domains in $(R)_1$ are the (finite or infinite) open intervals and R itself, while the only continua there are the finite closed intervals $[a,b]$ with $a < b$. Indeed, for any space (S,ρ), Theorem 3.43 shows that a continuum cannot be enumerable.

Example 3.4.7 For any normed (vector) space $[S,v]$, and x in S, and $\varepsilon > 0$, $N_\varepsilon(x)$ is a domain; in particular, in $(R^n)_1$, $\overline{N_\varepsilon(x)}$ is a continuum. For it follows from Note 8 and Theorem 2.47 that any segment $\langle y,z \rangle$ is connected, so that any two elements of a *convex* subset X of S are connected in X; hence, by Theorem 3.44, Corollary II, X and so, in particular, $N_\varepsilon(x)$ and $\overline{N_\varepsilon(x)}$, are connected. The rest follows from Theorem 3.16.

Given a space (S,ρ) and a non-null subset A of S, the binary relation $\mathscr{R}_A$ defined on A, where: $x\mathscr{R}_A y$ if and only if x,y are connected in A, is immediately seen to be reflexive and symmetric. To show that $\mathscr{R}_A$ is also transitive, let x,y,z be elements of A such that (x,y) and (y,z) are pairs of elements connected in A; that is, $\exists$ connected subsets B,C of A such that $x \in B$, $y \in B \cap C$, $z \in C$. By Theorem 3.44, $B \cup C$ is a connected subset of A. The corresponding $\mathscr{R}_A$ classes are called the **components** of A (w.r.t.ρ).

THEOREM 3.48* Given a space (S,ρ), and a non-null subset A of S:

(a) if $x \in A$, that component C of A which contains x is the *maximum* connected subset of A which contains x;

(b) if C is a component of A, and X is a connected subset of A such that $X \cap C \neq \varnothing$, then $X \subseteq C$;

(c) a given subset C of A is a component of A if and only if C is a *maximal* connected subset of A;

(d) if C is a component of A, it is closed relative to A.

PROOF (a) If X is a connected subset of A containing x, it is immediate from the definition of the component C that $X \subseteq C$; hence, if y is any member of C, it follows that x,y are connected *in* C (and not only in A). By Theorem 3.44, Corollary II, C is therefore connected.

(b) This is immediate from (a).

(c) The necessity of the condition is immediate from (a), (b). Conversely, given that C is a maximal connected subset of A, let $x \in C$ and $y \in A$. If $y \in C$, clearly $x\mathscr{R}_A y$; if, on the other hand, $x\mathscr{R}_A y$, $\exists$ a connected subset B of A containing x and y. Hence, clearly from Theorem 3.44, $X \equiv C \cup B$ is connected; since $C \subseteq X \subseteq A$, it follows by assumption that $X = C$ and hence that $y \in C$.

(d) By (a) and the relations: $C \subseteq \bar{C}^A \subseteq \bar{C}$, it follows from Theorem 3.37, that $\bar{C}^A$ is connected; hence, from (b), $\bar{C}^A = C$.

DEFINITION 22* Given a space (S,ρ), a subset A of S is said to be **totally-disconnected** if, for each member x of A, the corresponding component of A contains x only.

Example 3.4.8 By Theorems 3.43, and 3.48 (a), any enumerable subset A of a space (S,ρ) is totally-disconnected.

Example 3.4.9 Any isolated subset of a space is totally-disconnected. By Note 25, (II) of Chapter 2, it suffices to remark that if (S,ρ) is *discrete*, then S is totally-disconnected (the only connected subsets of S being the one-element subsets).

That, however, a totally-disconnected set need not be isolated is shown by Example 3.4.8, taking (S,ρ) to be $(R)_1$, and A to be Q.

THEOREM 3.49* Given a finite sequence $\{(S_i,\rho_i)\}$, $1 \leqslant i \leqslant n$, of spaces, and an element x_i of S_i, for $1 \leqslant i \leqslant n$, let C_i be the component of S_i which contains x_i; if (S,ρ) is a product space of $\{(S_i,\rho_i)\}$, and $x = \{x_1, \ldots, x_n\}$, then the component C of S which contains x is $\prod_{1 \leqslant i \leqslant n} C_i$.

PROOF By Theorem 3.45, $X \equiv \prod_{1 \leqslant i \leqslant n} C_i$ is connected. If Y is any connected subset of S containing x, $x_i \in \pi_i(Y)$, where $\pi_i(Y)$ is a connected subset of S_i, by Theorem 3.40; hence, by Theorem 3.48 (a), $\pi_i(Y) \subseteq C_i$. It follows by Theorem 1.4 that: $Y \subseteq X$; that is, $X = C$.

Note 10 It is clear from Theorem 3.48 (d) that, for any space (S,ρ), any component of a non-null *closed* subset A of S is again *closed* (w.r.t.ρ). However this is not necessarily true when 'closed' is replaced by 'open'; in particular, the components of S itself need not be open.

Example 3.4.10 $S = \bigcup_{i \geqslant 1} (i^{-1}) \bigcup (0)$; $\rho(x,y) = |x - y|$. By Example 3.4.8, (0) is a component of S; however clearly it is not open.

In Theorem 3.50 below, it will indeed be seen that a space (S,ρ) has the property 'any component of a non-null *open* subset of S is *open*' if and only if it possesses the property defined in:

DEFINITION 23* A space (S,ρ) is said to be **locally-connected** when, for each element x in S and member X of $\mathcal{N}(x)$, there exists a connected member Y of $\mathcal{N}(x)$ such that $Y \subseteq X$.

This property extends as usual to apply to a non-null subset of a space, and is homeomorphic.

Example 3.4.11 By Example 3.4.7 above, any normed vector space is locally connected.

Example 3.4.12 A locally-connected space is not necessarily connected, e.g., where $S = R - (0)$, $\rho(x,y) = |x - y|$, or any discrete space (with more than one element).

Example 3.4.13 A connected space is not necessarily locally connected. Let f be the function from $A \equiv]0,1[$ into R, where: $f(x) = \sin \pi x^{-1}$ for $0 < x \leqslant 1$. If T is the graph of f on A, let $S = T \cup \{0,0\}$, and ρ be the restriction to S of the usual metric on R^2.

Then, first, (S,ρ) is connected. For, since f is clearly $((\rho_1)_A,\rho_1)$-continuous, it follows from Theorem 2.45 that g (where $g(x) = \{x,f(x)\}$, for x in A) is $((\rho_1)_A,\rho)$-continuous; hence, since A is clearly connected, $T(= g(A))$ is connected. But $S = {}^{\rho}\overline{T}$ (since for each $\varepsilon > 0$ and integer $n > \varepsilon^{-1}$, $x_n \equiv \{n^{-1},0\} \in N_{\varepsilon}^{\rho}((0,0)) \cap T$); so, by Theorem 3.37, S is connected.

Secondly, (S,ρ) is *not* locally-connected; that is, it will be shown that the member $N_{\frac{1}{2}}^{\rho}((0,0))$ of $\mathcal{N}_{\rho}((0,0))$ contains no connected member Y. If such a set Y existed, and π' denoted the restriction to S of the projection of R^2 onto R, clearly $\pi'(Y)$ would be connected, and so, by Note 8, it would consist of some interval in R. Now, if $x_n = \{n^{-1},0\}$, for $n \geqslant 1$, it is clear from above that $\{x_n\} \underset{\rho}{\rightarrow} \{0,0\}$; hence $\exists\, n_0$ such that $x_n \in Y$ for $n \geqslant n_0$, implying that: $n^{-1} \in \pi'(Y)$ for $n \geqslant n_0$. In particular, $\pi'(Y)$ contains n_0^{-1}, $(n_0 + 1)^{-1}$ and so would contain any point between them, for example: $y \equiv 2(2n_0 + 1)^{-1}$. Since, however, y can only belong to $\pi'(Y)$ if $|f(y)| < \frac{1}{2}$, this is impossible.

The following theorem shows, in particular, that Definition 23 is consistent with those occurring in HOCKING and YOUNG, Reference [4] p. 105, and NEWMAN, Reference [8] p. 84.

THEOREM 3.50 For any space (S,ρ), the following five statements are equivalent:

(a) (S,ρ) is locally-connected;
(b) for each element x of S and open subset G of S containing x, there exists a connected open set G' such that $x \in G' \subseteq G$;
(c) for each element x of S and positive ε, there exists positive δ (depending on the choice of x, and ε) such that any two members of $N_\delta(x)$ are connected in $N_\varepsilon(x)$;
(d) any component of a non-null open subset of S is open;
(e) the subset $\mathscr{G}'$ of $\mathscr{G}$ of all its connected members forms a base for $\mathscr{G}$.

PROOF This divides into two parts:
(I) (Equivalence of (a), (b), (d) and (e)).*

First, (a) implies (d). Given G in $\mathscr{G}$, and a component C of G, let $x \in C$; then, since $G \in \mathscr{N}(x)$, it follows by (a) that $\exists$ a connected member Y of $\mathscr{N}(x)$ such that $Y \subseteq G$; but (by Theorem 3.48) $Y \subseteq C$. Thus $C \in \mathscr{N}(x)$.

Secondly, it is immediate that (d) implies (b) and that (b) implies (a), while the equivalence of (b) and (e) follows from Theorem 2.4.
(II) (Equivalence of (a) and (c)).

First, (a) implies (c). Given x in S and $\varepsilon > 0$, $N_\varepsilon(x) \in \mathscr{N}(x)$, and so $\exists$ a connected member Y of $\mathscr{N}(x)$ such that $Y \subseteq N_\varepsilon(x)$; further, $\exists\, \delta > 0$ such that $N_\delta(x) \subseteq Y$. Then any two members of $N_\delta(x)$ lie in the connected subset Y of $N_\varepsilon(x)$.

Secondly, (c) implies (a). Given x in S and X in $\mathscr{N}(x)$, $\exists\, \varepsilon > 0$ such that $N_\varepsilon(x) \subseteq X$; if δ is chosen as in (c), it is clear that $N_\delta(x)$ is a subset of that component C of $N_\varepsilon(x)$ which contains x. Thus C is a connected member of $\mathscr{N}(x)$, and $C \subseteq X$.

COROLLARY* If (S,ρ) is locally connected, and G is a non-null open set, G is locally connected.

(Since (S,ρ) is a subspace of the locally-connected space $(R^2)_1$), Example 3.4.13 shows that the condition '$G \in \mathscr{G}$' cannot be omitted from the above Corollary; that is, local connectedness is *not* hereditary property of a space.

THEOREM 3.51* A product space (S,ρ) of a finite sequence of spaces $\{(S_i,\rho_i)\}$, $1 \leqslant i \leqslant n$, is locally-connected if and only if each space (S_i,ρ_i) is locally-connected.

The proof is left to the reader.

The next theorem could be compared with Theorem 3.24 on local compactness:

THEOREM 3.52* Given spaces (S,ρ), (S',ρ'), and a locally connected subset A of S, let f be a (ρ,ρ')-continuous and (ρ,ρ')-closed function from A into S'; then $f(A)$ is locally connected.

PROOF As in the Theorem 3.24, there is no loss of generality in taking $A = S$ and f onto S'. Given $\varnothing \subset G' \in \mathscr{G}_{\rho'}$, and a component C' of G', it suffices by Theorem 3.50 to show that $C' \in \mathscr{G}_{\rho'}$. Corresponding to each member x of $f^{-1}(C')$, let C_x denote that component of $f^{-1}(G')$ which contains x; since $f(C_x)$ is a connected subset of G' it follows from Theorem 3.48 that $f(C_x) \subseteq C'$; that is $C_x \subseteq f^{-1}(C')$. Thus:

$$f^{-1}(C') = \bigcup_{x \in f^{-1}(C')} C_x. \qquad (1)$$

Since the continuity of f implies that $f^{-1}(G') \in \mathscr{G}_\rho$, $C_x \in \mathscr{G}_\rho$ (by hypothesis and Theorem 3.50). Hence, by (1), $f^{-1}(C') \in \mathscr{G}_\rho$, and so $f^{-1}(C_{S'}(C')) = C_S(f^{-1}(C')) \in \mathscr{F}_\rho$. Since f is closed, $f(f^{-1}(C_{S'}(C')))$ $\in \mathscr{F}_{\rho'}$, that is, (since f is *onto* S') $C_{S'}(C') \in \mathscr{F}_{\rho'}$.

COROLLARY Given spaces (S,ρ), (S',ρ'), let A be a locally connected and compact subset of S; if f is (ρ,ρ')-continuous from A into S, $f(A)$ is locally connected (and compact).

Note 11 The condition that f be closed is essential in Theorem 3.52.

Example 3.4.14 $A = S = \bigcup_{i \geqslant 1} (i) \cup (0)$, $S' = \bigcup_{i \geqslant 1} (i^{-1}) \cup (0)$, ρ,ρ' the usual metrics. For x in S, let $f(x) = x^{-1}$ if $x \neq 0$, and 0 if $x = 0$; then $f(A) = S'$. Since (S,ρ) is discrete, it is locally-connected and f is (ρ,ρ')-continuous; however (S',ρ') is not locally connected for it is easily seen that no member of $\mathscr{N}_{\rho'}(0)$ can be connected.

°*Note 12* Even in a space (S,ρ) which is both connected and locally connected, it is not necessarily true that *every* ε-neighbourhood of each element is connected (w.r.t. ρ).

Example 3.4.15 $S = A_1 \cup A_2 \cup A_3 \cup A_4$, where the A_i, $1 \leqslant i \leqslant 4$, are subsets of R defined as follows:

$$A_1 = [0,1] \times (0), \qquad A_2 = (1) \times [0,1], \qquad A_3 = [0,1] \times (1),$$
$$A_4 = (0) \times [0,1].$$

If ρ is the usual metric:

(I) (S,ρ) is connected. Successive applications of Theorem 3.44 to A_1,A_2, then to $A_1 \cup A_2,A_3$, and finally to $A_1 \cup A_2 \cup A_3,A_4$ show that this is so.

(II) (S,ρ) is locally connected. For each x in S and $0 < \varepsilon \leqslant 1$, $N_\varepsilon(x)$ consists either of one open interval or a connected union of intervals.

(III) For $x = \{\frac{1}{2},0\}$ and $1 < \varepsilon < \frac{1}{2}5^{\frac{1}{2}}$, $N_\varepsilon(x)$ is *not* connected. For $N_\varepsilon(x) = (A_1 \cup B_2 \cup B_4) \cup B_3$, where $B_2 = (1) \times [0,\frac{1}{2}(4\varepsilon^2 - 1)^{\frac{1}{2}}[$, $B_3 =]\frac{1}{2} - (\varepsilon^2 - 1)^{\frac{1}{2}}, \frac{1}{2} + (\varepsilon^2 - 1)^{\frac{1}{2}}[\times (1)$, $B_4 = (0) \times [0,\frac{1}{2}\sqrt{(4\varepsilon^2 - 1)}[$. Clearly $A_1 \cup B_2 \cup B_4$ and B_3 form a partition of $N_\varepsilon(x)$. (See Figure 1.)

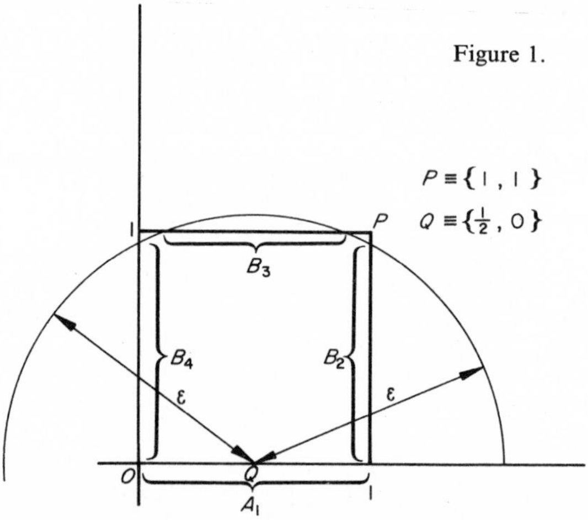

Figure 1.

If, however, ρ is here replaced by the equivalent metric: $\rho'(x,y) = \min(1,\rho(x,y))$, $N_\varepsilon^{\rho'}(x)$ is connected w.r.t. ρ' for each x in S and $\varepsilon > 0$, thus providing an illustration of the following general result:

°THEOREM 3.53 Given a space (S,ρ), a metric ρ' can be defined on S such that (a) $\rho \equiv \rho'$ and (b) $N_\varepsilon^{\rho'}(x)$ is connected w.r.t. ρ' for each x in S, and $\varepsilon > 0$, if and only if (S,ρ) is both connected and locally connected.

PROOF If such a metric ρ' can be defined on S, (S,ρ') is clearly locally connected. Also, given x in S, it is clear from Theorem 3.44 that $\bigcup_{\varepsilon>0} N_\varepsilon^{\rho'}(x)$ is connected; that is, (S,ρ') is connected. Since $\rho \equiv \rho'$ and the properties of connectedness and local connectedness are homeomorphic, the necessity of the condition is proved.

Conversely, if (S,ρ) is given to be connected and locally connected, we can suppose that ρ is *bounded* (for otherwise it can be replaced by an equivalent bounded metric). Then, given any two elements x, y of S, the subset $A(x,y)$ of $P(S)$ containing all connected subsets X of S such that $x,y \in X$, is non-null (since $S \in A(x,y)$) and the diameter $D(X)$ of each of its members is defined. If $\rho'(x,y) = \inf D(X)$ for $X \in A(x,y)$, clearly $\rho(x,y) \leqslant \rho'(x,y)$. Further:

(I) ρ' is a metric on S. Clearly conditions M1, M2 are satisfied, and also M4, for $x = y$ implies $(x) \in A(x,y)$, and hence $\rho'(x,y) = 0$. To verify M3, let x,y,z be elements of S and $\varepsilon > 0$; $\exists X_1$ in $A(x,y)$ such that $D(X_1) < \rho'(x,y) + \varepsilon/2$ and $\exists X_2$ in $A(y,z)$ such that $D(X_2) < \rho'(y,z) + \varepsilon/2$. Since $y \in X_1 \cap X_2$ it follows that $X_1 \cup X_2 \in A(x,z)$. Hence, from Ex. 5, Section 2.1:

$$\rho'(x,z) \leqslant D(X_1 \cup X_2) \leqslant D(X_1) + D(X_2) < (\rho'(x,y) + \rho'(y,z)) + \varepsilon.$$

(II) $\rho' \equiv \rho$. Since $\rho(x,y) \leqslant \rho'(x,y)$ for all x,y in S, it is immediate that $\rho \leqslant \rho'$; it remains to show that $\rho' \leqslant \rho$. Given x in S, $\varepsilon > 0$, then (since (S,ρ) is locally connected) $\exists$ a connected member X of $\mathcal{N}_\rho(x)$ such that $X \subseteq N_{\varepsilon/3}^\rho(x)$; choose $\delta > 0$ such that $N_\delta^\rho(x) \subseteq X$. Since $D(X) \leqslant 2\varepsilon/3 < \varepsilon$, it follows from the construction of ρ' that $\rho'(x,y) < \varepsilon$ for any y such that $\rho(x,y) < \delta$; result follows then from Theorem 2.23.

(III) $N_\varepsilon^{\rho'}(x)$ is connected (w.r.t. ρ'). Given x in S, $\varepsilon > 0$, and y in $N_\varepsilon^{\rho'}(x)$, $\rho'(x,y) < \varepsilon$; that is, $\exists$ a connected set X_y (dependent on the choice of y) containing x,y and with $D(X_y) < \varepsilon$. If z is any member of X_y it is clear, again from the construction of ρ', that $\rho'(x,z) < \varepsilon$; that is, each $X_y \subseteq N_\varepsilon^{\rho'}(x)$. Thus, x,y are connected in $N_\varepsilon^{\rho'}(x)$; that is, that component C of $N_\varepsilon^{\rho'}(x)$ which contains x coincides with $N_\varepsilon^{\rho'}(x)$ itself; that is, $N_\varepsilon^{\rho'}(x)$ is connected (w.r.t. ρ).

The equivalence of ρ,ρ' then gives the desired result.

Worked Exercises

1. If S denotes the subset of R^2 containing the points $a \equiv \{0,1\}$, $b = \{0,-1\}$, and all points of the form $\{n^{-1},y\}$, where n is a positive integer and $-1 \leqslant y \leqslant 1$, and if ρ denotes the restriction to S of the usual metric on R^2:
   (a) determine the components of S (w.r.t.ρ);
   (b) show that, although a,b are not connected in S, the latter cannot be expressed as the union of two mutually-separated subsets X_1, X_2 such that $a \in X_1$, $b \in X_2$.

Solution: For $n = 1,2,\ldots,$ denote the set of points $\{n^{-1},y\}$, where $-1 \leqslant y \leqslant 1$, by A_n. Then

$$S = (a) \cup (b) \cup (\bigcup_{n \geqslant 1} A_n). \tag{1}$$

(a) The components of S are: (a),(b), and each A_n, $n \geqslant 1$. For, first, (a) is connected, while if A were a connected subset of S such that $(a) \subset A$, A must contain some point of S *not* on the y-axis (otherwise $A = (a) \cup (b)$, clearly not connected). Hence if π' denotes the restriction to S of the projection of R^2 onto the x-axis, $\pi'(A)$ must contain more than one point and so, since it is enumerable, it follows by Theorem 3.43 that it cannot be connected. Thus (by Theorem 3.40) A itself cannot be connected and hence, by Theorem 3.48(c), (a) is a component of S; similarly, (b) is a component. Secondly, for each n, A_n is an interval and therefore is connected. If A were a connected subset of S properly containing A_n, it is clear that, as before, $\pi'(A)$ would contain more than one point and so could not be connected. Thus each A_n is a component of S, and it is clear from (1) that *all* the components have thus been determined.

(b) It is clear, from the definition of component, that a,b are not connected in S. Suppose $\exists$ mutually-separated subsets X_1, X_2 of S such that $S = X_1 \cup X_2$, $a \in X_1$, $b \in X_2$. Then by Ex. 6 below, $\exists$ subsets J_1, J_2 of J^+ (set of all positive integers) such that $J_1 \cap J_2 = \emptyset$, $J_1 \cup J_2 = J^+$ and

$$X_1 = (a) \cup (\bigcup_{n \in J_1} A_n), \qquad X_2 = (b) \cup (\bigcup_{n \in J_2} A_n). \tag{2}$$

If J_1, say, were infinite, then

$$b \in \overline{\bigcup_{n \in J_1} A_n}. \tag{3}$$

For, if, given $\varepsilon > 0$, n_0 is chosen in J_1 such that $n_0 > \varepsilon^{-1}$, then $x' \equiv \{n_0^{-1},-1\} \in A_{n_0} \subset \bigcup_{n \in J_1} A_n$, and $\rho(x',b) < \varepsilon$. But (3) would imply: $\overline{X}_1 \cap X_2 \neq \emptyset$, contrary to assumption on X_1,X_2.

2.* If (S,ρ) is locally-connected, A a non-null subset of S, and B a connected subset of A, open relative to A, show that $\exists$ an open connected subset G of S such that $B = A \cap G$.

Solution: Choose a member G' of $\mathscr{G}$ such that $B = A \cap G'$. If G is a component of G' such that $B \cap G \neq \varnothing$, it follows from Theorem 3.48 both that G is connected and that it contains B. Hence $B \subseteq A \cap G \subseteq A \cap G' = B$. By Theorem 3.50, $G \in \mathscr{G}$.

Exercises for Solution

1.* Given a space (S,ρ) and non-null subsets A,B of S, show that:

(a) if each is closed relative to $A \cup B$, which is connected, and $A \cap B$ contains at most two elements, then at least one of A,B must be connected.

(b) If each is connected and A,B are not mutually-separated, then $A \cup B$ is connected.

2. Given a space (S,ρ) show that:

(a) if X_1,X_2 are any non-null closed subsets of S, then $\exists$ closed subsets F_1,F_2 of S such that $F_1 \cup F_2 = S$ and $F_i \cap (X_1 \cup X_2) = X_i$ for $i = 1,2$;

(b) if H_1,H_2 are open subsets of S such that $H_1 \cup H_2 = S$, $\exists$ closed subsets F_1F_2 of S such that $F_1 \cup F_2 = S$ and $F_i \subseteq H_i$ for $i = 1,2$.

3. Given a space (S,ρ) and $\varepsilon > 0$, show that the subset $A_{x,\varepsilon}$ of S containing those elements which can be joined to a given element x by an ε-chain in S is closed. If (S,ρ) is compact, show further that if $y \,\omega\, A_{x,\varepsilon}$ then $\exists$ an element z' in $A_{x,\varepsilon}$ such that $\rho(y,z) \geqslant \rho(y,z') > 0$ for each z in $A_{x,\varepsilon}$; deduce that if $\overline{N_r(y)} = S_r(y)$ for each y in S and $r > 0$, then (S,ρ) is connected.

4.* Show that a space (S,ρ) is connected if and only if, given a discrete space (S',ρ') and a (ρ,ρ')-continuous function f from S into S', then $f(S)$ contains one element only.

5.* Given a space (S,ρ), let $\{A_i\}$, $i \geqslant 1$, be a sequence of connected subsets of S such that corresponding to each $i > 1$, $\exists j < i$ (dependent on i) such that $A_i \cap A_j \neq \varnothing$; show that $\bigcup_{i\geqslant 1} A_i$ is connected.

6.* Given a space (S,ρ), show that if X_1,X_2 are mutually-separated subsets of S such that $S = X_1 \cup X_2$, then each of X_1,X_2 is the union of a certain set of components of S; if X_1 is itself connected, deduce that it is a component of S.

7.* Given any space (S,ρ), and x in S, let A_x denote the intersection of all members of $\mathscr{N}(x) \cap \mathscr{G} \cap \mathscr{F}$. Show that $A_x = (x)$ for each x in S if and only if, given a discrete space (S',ρ') with just two elements, there exists, corresponding to each pair x,y of distinct elements of S, a (ρ,ρ')-continuous function f_{xy} from S onto S' such that $f_{xy}(x) \neq f_{xy}(y)$. Show that such a space (S,ρ) is totally disconnected.

8.* If (S,ρ) is not connected, and C is an arbitrary component of S, show that C, $C_S(C)$ are not necessarily mutually-separated. Will this be so if (S,ρ) is locally-connected?

9.* If (S,ρ) is locally-connected, show that:

(a) If A,B are non-null subsets of S such that $\exists$ *no* partition (X_1,X_2) of S with $A \subseteq X_1$, $B \subseteq X_2$, then $\exists$ a component C of S such that $C \cap A$, $C \cap B$ are both non-null;

(b) if G is a non-null open subset of S, and C a component of G, then $\mathrm{Fr}(C) \cap G = \varnothing$;

(c) if A is any non-null subset of S, and $\{C_i\}$, $i \in I$, are the components of A, then $A^\circ = \bigcup_i C_i^\circ$.

10. If (S,ρ) is locally-connected, show that:

(a) if X is a connected subset of S, and $r > 0$, then $\exists$ a connected open subset G of S such that $A \subseteq G \subseteq N_r(X)$ (in the notation of Ex. 2, Section 3.2);

(b) if (S,ρ) is also compact, and $\varepsilon > 0$, then S can be expressed as the union of a finite sequence of connected subsets, each with its diameter less than ε.

Part III
TOPOLOGICAL SPACES

CHAPTER 4

Properties of any Topological Space

4.1 First Definition and Basic Concepts

DEFINITION 1 Given a non-null set S, a **topology** τ is said to be defined on S when there is given a subset $\mathscr{G}^\tau$ of $P(S)$ such that:

(i) S, $\varnothing$ belong to $\mathscr{G}^\tau$;

(ii) the union of any family of members of $\mathscr{G}^\tau$ belongs to $\mathscr{G}^\tau$;

(iii) the intersection of any finite sequence of members of $\mathscr{G}^\tau$ belongs to $\mathscr{G}^\tau$.

The set S, together with a topology τ defined on it, is said to form a **topological space**, denoted by $|S,\tau|$; any member of $\mathscr{G}^\tau$ is said to be open w.r.t.τ, or τ-open.

Note 1 If ρ is a metric defined on a non-null set S, it was seen in Chapter 2 that the subset $\mathscr{G}_\rho$ of $P(S)$, defined as follows: 'given $X \subseteq S$, $X \in \mathscr{G}_\rho$ if and only if for each member x of X, $\exists\, \varepsilon > 0$ (dependent on choice of x) such that

$$N_\varepsilon^\rho(x) \subseteq X\text{'} \tag{1}$$

satisfies conditions (i)–(iii) of Definition 1; that is, ρ gives rise to the definition of a (unique) topology τ^ρ on S such that the set $\mathscr{G}^{\tau^\rho}$ of τ^ρ-open subsets of S coincides with $\mathscr{G}_\rho$ defined in (1). From Note 2 below, it will be seen however that if, on the other hand, τ is an arbitrary topology defined on S, then it is not necessarily possible to define a metric ρ such that $\mathscr{G}^\tau = \mathscr{G}_\rho$.

DEFINITION 2 A topological space $|S,\tau|$ is said to be **metrizable** if a metric ρ can be defined on S such that $\mathscr{G}^\tau = \mathscr{G}_\rho$.

If $|S,\tau|$ is metrizable, a metric ρ defined on S such that $\mathscr{G}^\tau = \mathscr{G}_\rho$ is called a τ-metric on S. Clearly any other metric ρ' is then a τ-metric on S if and only if ρ,ρ' are equivalent.

DEFINITION 3 Given a topological space $|S,\tau|$ and an element x of S, a subset X of S is said to be a neighbourhood of x w.r.t.τ

(or a τ-neighbourhood of x) if there exists a member G of $\mathscr{G}^\tau$ such that $x \in G \subseteq X$.

For any x in S, the set of all τ-neighbourhoods of x is denoted by $\mathscr{N}^\tau(x)$; clearly $S \in \mathscr{N}^\tau(x)$. If, now, in the proof of Theorem 2.3 each reference to 'Theorem 2.1' is replaced by a reference to Definition 3 (above) and each reference to a part of 'Theorem 2.2' by the corresponding part of Definition 1 (above), there is proved:

THEOREM 4.1 For a topological space $|S,\tau|$, x in S and $X,Y \subseteq S$:
(a) $X \in \mathscr{G}^\tau$ if and only if $X \in \mathscr{N}^\tau(x)$ for each x in X.
(b) If $X \in \mathscr{N}^\tau(x)$ and $X \subseteq Y$, then $Y \in \mathscr{N}^\tau(x)$.
(c) The intersection of any finite sequence of members of $\mathscr{N}^\tau(x)$ belongs to $\mathscr{N}^\tau(x)$.
(d) If $X \in \mathscr{N}^\tau(x)$, there exists a member Z of $\mathscr{N}^\tau(x)$ (dependent on the choice of X) such that $X \in \mathscr{N}^\tau(y)$ for each y in Z.

For a subset X of S, a cluster point of X (w.r.t.τ) (or 'τ-cluster point of X'), its derived set X'^τ and its τ-closure $\overline{X}^\tau$ are defined as in Part II. If, in the proof of Theorem 2.7, each reference to 'Theorem 2.3' is replaced by a reference to Theorem 4.1 (above), there is proved:

THEOREM 4.2 For a topological space $|S,\tau|$ and $X,Y \subseteq S$:
(a) The τ-closure of the null set is the null set.
(b) $X \subseteq \overline{X}^\tau$.
(c) $\overline{\overline{X}^\tau} = \overline{X}^\tau$.
(d) $\overline{X \cup Y}^\tau = \overline{X}^\tau \cup \overline{Y}^\tau$.

For $X \subseteq S$, the τ-interior of X is denoted by $X^{\circ\tau}$; X is said to be τ-closed when $X = \overline{X}^\tau$. If the set of τ-closed subsets of S is denoted by $\mathscr{F}^\tau$, two of its properties are noted particularly in:

THEOREM 4.3 For a topological space $|S,\tau|$ and $X \subseteq S$:
(a) $X \in \mathscr{G}^\tau$ if and only if $C(X) \in \mathscr{F}^\tau$.
(b) $\overline{X}^\tau$ is the minimum member of $\mathscr{F}^\tau$ which contains X as a subset.

For $X \subseteq S$, its τ-exterior $E^\tau(X)$, τ-frontier $\mathrm{Fr}^\tau(X)$, as well as the notions of τ-isolated points and sets, and τ-discrete sets, are defined as in Part II, together with the notion of the 'τ-convergence' of a sequence $\{x_i\}$, $i \geqslant 1$, of elements of S; the notation '$x_i \underset{\tau}{\rightarrow} x$' is used to denote that $\{x_i\}$ τ-converges to the element x of S.

Note 2 (As already indicated in the Introduction) any property of a metric space presented in a 'starred' theorem of Part II will be valid for any topological space $|S,\tau|$; if, in particular, $|S,\tau|$ is metrizable, it will in addition possess any 'unstarred' properties in Part II which would have a sense for $|S,\tau|$, that is, expressible ultimately in terms of $\mathscr{G}^\tau$. For each of the spaces introduced in the following examples there are one or more properties of the latter type which it lacks; it is consequently not metrizable.

Example 4.1.1 Given an arbitrary non-null set S, $\mathscr{G}_0 \equiv (S,\varnothing)$ satisfies the conditions of Definition 1 and so defines a topology τ_0 on S, called the **trivial** topology on S. If $X = (x)$, and S has more than one member, clearly $X'^{\tau_0} = S - (x)$, which is *neither* empty *nor* τ_0-closed; that is, neither Theorem 2.5, Corollary (hence nor Theorem 2.5 itself) nor Theorem 2.11 holds.

Example 4.1.2 Given an infinite set S, it is easily verified that the subset $\mathscr{G}$ of $P(S)$ containing those subsets X of S such that $C(X) = S$ or is finite, satisfies the conditions of Definition 1, and so defines a topology τ on S. If G_1,G_2 are any two non-null τ-open subsets, clearly $G_1 \cap G_2 \neq \varnothing$ (being, indeed, infinite); hence Theorem 2.17 (or its Corollary), does not hold. Secondly, since for each $x \in S$ and each member X of $\mathscr{N}^\tau(x)$, X contains all but a finite number of the elements of S, any sequence $\{x_i\}$, $i \geqslant 1$, of distinct elements of S τ-converges to *every* element x of S; that is, Theorem 2.19(c) does not hold. Finally, if S is non-enumerable, and G a non-null τ-open subset, G is non-enumerable, while any τ-closed proper subset of S is finite; hence, if $G \subset S$, G is *not* a member of $(\mathscr{F}^\tau)_\sigma$, that is, G is not expressible as the union of a sequence of members of $\mathscr{F}^\tau$, so that Theorem 2.16 fails.

Example 4.1.3 Given a non-enumerable set S, the subset $\mathscr{G}$ of $P(S)$ containing those subsets X of S such that $C(X) = S$ or is enumerable, again defines a topology τ on S. Here, a sequence $\{x_i\}$, $i \geqslant 1$, of elements of S τ-converges to an element x of S only if $\exists\, i_0$ such that $x_i = x$ for $i \geqslant i_0$. For, by definition, corresponding to each X in $\mathscr{N}^\tau(x)$,

$$\exists\, i_0, \text{ dependent on } X, \text{ such that } x_i \in X \text{ for } i \geqslant i_0 \tag{1}$$

But $X \equiv C(\bigcup_{i \geqslant 1} (x_i)) \cup (x)$ contains x and belongs to $\mathscr{G}^\tau$, since $C(X)$ is contained in the enumerable set $\bigcup_{i \geqslant 1} (x_i)$; that is, $X \in \mathscr{N}^\tau(x)$. It follows from (1) that $\exists\, i_0$ such that $x_i = x$ for $i \geqslant i_0$. If A is then an arbitrary non-null subset of S, containing a given element x, and $\{x_i\}$, $i \geqslant 1$, τ-converges to x, $x_i \in A$ for $i \geqslant$ some integer i_0; however A need not be τ-open; that is, Theorem 2.21 (b) (and hence part (a)) fails here.

Example 4.1.4 Given an arbitrary non-null set S, $\mathscr{G}_I \equiv P(S)$ defines a topology τ_I on S which is easily seen to be the only topology τ on S such that S is τ-discrete (that is, $S'^{\tau} = \varnothing$); τ_I is accordingly called the **discrete** topology on S. $|S,\tau_I|$ is metrizable, and a metric ρ defined on S is a τ_I-metric if and only if ρ is discrete.

4.2 Alternative Methods of Definition

In Section 4.1, a topology was defined on S by postulating the existence of a certain system $\mathscr{G}^{\tau}$ of subsets of S satisfying axioms suggested by properties of the system $\mathscr{G}_{\rho}$ of open subsets of a metric space (S,ρ). Two alternative procedures of definition are now considered, based respectively on the properties of the neighbourhood systems $\mathscr{N}_{\rho}(x)$ and subsets ${}^{\rho}\overline{X}$ for (S,ρ).

In the first of these, the existence is postulated of a certain function $\sigma(x)$ from S into $P(P(S))$ where the systems $\sigma(x)$ satisfy axioms founded on properties of the systems $\mathscr{N}_{\rho}(x)$; in the second, a function χ from $P(S)$ into $P(S)$ is postulated where the subsets $\chi(X)$ of S have just those properties of the subsets ${}^{\rho}\overline{X}$ which are set out in Theorem 2.7. Before the equivalence of the three procedures is established, the following result is required:

THEOREM 4.4 Given a non-empty set S:

(I) If there is given a function σ from S into $P(P(S))$ such that:

(a) for each x in S, $\sigma(x)$ is non-null;

(b) for each x in S, and X in $\sigma(x)$, $x \in X$;

(c) if $X \in \sigma(x)$, and $X \subseteq Y \subseteq S$, then $Y \in \sigma(x)$;

(d) the intersection of any finite sequence of members of $\sigma(x)$ belongs to $\sigma(x)$;

(e) if $X \in \sigma(x)$, there exists a member Y of $\sigma(x)$ (dependent on the choice of X) such that $X \in \sigma(y)$ for each y in Y,

then a topology τ is defined on S such that, for each x in S, $\sigma(x) = \mathscr{N}^{\tau}(x)$.

(II) If there is given a function χ from $P(S)$ into $P(S)$ such that:

(a) $\chi(\varnothing) = \varnothing$;

(b) for each $X \subseteq S$, $X \subseteq \chi(X)$;

(c) for each $X \subseteq S$, $\chi(\chi(X)) \subseteq \chi(X)$;

(d) for $X,Y \subseteq S$, $\chi(X \cup Y) = \chi(X) \cup \chi(Y)$, then a topology τ is defined on S such that, for each $X \subseteq S$, $\chi(X) = \overline{X}^{\tau}$.

Proof (I) Define a subset $\mathscr{G}$ of $P(S)$ as follows:

given $X \subseteq S$, $X \in \mathscr{G}$ if and only if $X \in \sigma(x)$ for each x in X. (1)

Then, first, $S, \varnothing$ belong to $\mathscr{G}$. For it is immediate from (a), (c) that $S \in \mathscr{G}$. Further, writing (1) in the 'negative form':

$$X \in \mathscr{G} \text{ if and only if } X\,\omega\,\sigma(x) \text{ implies } x\omega X \qquad (1)$$

shows that $\varnothing \in \mathscr{G}$.

Secondly, it is clear from (c) that the union of an arbitrary family of members of $\mathscr{G}$ belongs to $\mathscr{G}$, and, thirdly, it is clear from (d) that the same holds for the intersection of a finite sequence of members of $\mathscr{G}$. That is, $\mathscr{G}$ satisfies the conditions of Definition 1, so that a topology τ is defined on S such that $\mathscr{G}^{\tau} = \mathscr{G}$.

Now, for each element x in S, and X in $\mathscr{N}^{\tau}(x)$, there exists (by Definition 3) a member Y of $\mathscr{G}^{\tau}(= \mathscr{G})$ such that $x \in Y \subseteq X$. By (1), $Y \in \sigma(x)$; hence, by (c), $X \in \sigma(x)$; that is, $\mathscr{N}^{\tau}(x) \subseteq \sigma(x)$. Conversely, given X in $\sigma(x)$, let Y denote the set of those elements y in S where $X \in \sigma(y)$. Clearly $x \in Y \subseteq X$, using (b); further, $Y \in \mathscr{G}^{\tau}(= \mathscr{G})$. For, if $y \in Y$, then, by (e), there exists (since $X \in \sigma(y)$) a member Z of $\sigma(y)$ such that $X \in \sigma(z)$ for each member z of Z; that is, $Z \subseteq Y$ where $Z \in \sigma(y)$. Hence, by (c), $Y \in \sigma(y)$, and so $Y \in \mathscr{G}$, by (1); thus, by Definition 3, $X \in \mathscr{N}^{\tau}(x)$.

Proof (II) Define a subset $\mathscr{G}$ of $P(S)$:

$$\text{given } X \subseteq S,\ X \in \mathscr{G} \text{ if and only if } \chi(C(X)) \subseteq C(X). \qquad (2)$$

It is immediate from (a) that $S \in \mathscr{G}$; also, $\chi(C(\varnothing)) \subseteq S$, that is, $\varnothing \in \mathscr{G}$. If, secondly, $\{X_i\}$, $i \in I$, is an arbitrary family of members of $\mathscr{G}$, and $X = \bigcup_i X_i$, denote each $C(X_i)$ by Y_i. Then, from (d):

$$\chi(\bigcap_i Y_i) \subseteq \chi(Y_i) \subseteq Y_i, \quad \text{by (2)}$$

and:

$$\chi(C(X)) = \chi(\bigcap_i Y_i) \subseteq \bigcap_i Y_i = C(X).$$

To prove, thirdly, that the intersection of a finite sequence $\{X_i\}$, $i \leqslant i \leqslant n$, of members of $\mathscr{G}$ belongs to $\mathscr{G}$, it suffices to consider the case where $n = 2$. If $X = X_1 \cap X_2$, and Y_i is as above, then:

$$\chi(C(X)) = \chi(Y_1 \cup Y_2) = \chi(Y_1) \cup \chi(Y_2) \subseteq Y_1 \cup Y_2 = C(X).$$

Again, a topology τ is defined on S with $\mathscr{G}^{\tau} = \mathscr{G}$.

By Theorem 4.3, it remains to verify that, for each subset X of S, $\chi(X)$ is the minimum member of $\mathscr{F}^\tau$ containing X. To see this, note first that, for arbitrary $Y \subseteq S$, it is clear from Theorem 4.3 and (2) that:

$$Y \in \mathscr{F}^\tau \text{ if and only if } \chi(Y) \subseteq Y. \tag{3}$$

Hence, from (c), $\chi(X) \in \mathscr{F}^\tau$; also, $X \subseteq \chi(X)$, by (b). On the other hand, if Z is any member of $\mathscr{F}^\tau$ such that $X \subseteq Z$, then, by (d) and (3): $\chi(X) \subseteq \chi(Z) \subseteq Z$.

Given now an arbitrary non-null set S, let G_S, Σ_S, and X_S denote the collections respectively of all subsets $\mathscr{G}^\tau$ of $P(S)$ satisfying the conditions of Definition 1, of all functions σ from S into $P(P(S))$ satisfying the conditions of Theorem 4.4(I) and of all functions χ from $P(S)$ into $P(S)$ satisfying the conditions of Theorem 4.4(II).

A function Φ can be defined from G_S into Σ_S by letting $\Phi(\mathscr{G}^\tau)$ (for each $\mathscr{G}^\tau$ in G_S) denote the function from S into $P(P(S))$ such that, for each x in S, $(\Phi(\mathscr{G}^\tau))(x) = \mathscr{N}^\tau(x)$, for, by Theorem 4.1, $\Phi(\mathscr{G}^\tau) \in \Sigma_S$. Again, a function Ψ can be defined from Σ_S into G_S by letting $\Psi(\sigma)$ (for each σ in Σ_S) denote the subset $\mathscr{G}$ of $P(S)$ defined in (1) of proof of Theorem 4.4(I); for, in the proof of that theorem, it was seen that $\mathscr{G} \in G_S$. If, in particular, given any $\mathscr{G}^\tau$ in G_S, σ is taken in (1) to be $\Phi(\mathscr{G}^\tau)$, then, for $X \subseteq S$: $X \in \Psi(\Phi(\mathscr{G}^\tau))$ if and only if $X \in (\Phi(\mathscr{G}^\tau))(x)$, for each x in X; that is, if and only if $X \in \mathscr{N}^\tau(x)$ for each x in X; or, equivalently, (by Theorem 4.1) $X \in \mathscr{G}^\tau$. Thus, for any $\mathscr{G}^\tau$ in G_S,

$$\Psi(\Phi(\mathscr{G}^\tau)) = \mathscr{G}^\tau. \tag{4}$$

On the other hand, given any σ in Σ_S, it is proved in Theorem 4.4(I) that the topology τ defined on S by its image $\Psi(\sigma)$ is such that $\sigma(x) = \mathscr{N}^\tau(x)$ for each x in S; that is, (taking $\mathscr{G}^\tau = \Psi(\sigma)$ in the definition of Φ) $\sigma(x) = (\Phi(\Psi(\sigma)))(x)$, so that: for any σ in Σ_S,

$$\Phi(\Psi(\sigma)) = \sigma. \tag{5}$$

From (4), (5) and Theorem 1.3, it follows that Φ is a (1,1) function onto Σ_S, and Φ,Ψ are mutually inverse. That is, a (1,1) correspondence between G_S and Σ_S has been set up in such a way that, for any pair $(\mathscr{G}^\tau,\sigma)$ of corresponding members, σ gives the 'neighbourhood systems' corresponding to $\mathscr{G}^\tau$ (as in Definition 3) while, reciprocally, $\mathscr{G}^\tau$ can be obtained from σ by (1), Theorem 4.4.(I). Exactly the same amount of generality is thus achieved by replacing Definition 1 by the following alternative definition:

DEFINITION 1′ Given a non-null set S, a topology τ is said to be defined on S when there is given a function σ^τ from S into $P(P(S))$ satisfying conditions (a)–(e) of Theorem 4.4(I).

Secondly, a function Φ' can be defined from G_S into X_S by letting $\Phi'(\mathscr{G}^\tau)$ (for each $\mathscr{G}^\tau$ in G_S) denote the function from $P(S)$ into $P(S)$ such that, for each $X \subseteq S$, $(\Phi'(\mathscr{G}^\tau))(X) = \overline{X}^\tau$, for, by Theorem 4.2, $\Phi'(\mathscr{G}^\tau) \in X_S$. Again, a function Ψ' can be defined from X_S into G_S by letting $\Psi'(\chi)$ (for each χ in X_S) denote the subset $\mathscr{G}$ of $P(S)$ defined in (2), proof of Theorem 4.4(II); for it is proved there that $\mathscr{G} \in G_S$. If, in particular, given any $\mathscr{G}^\tau$ in G_S, χ is taken in (2) to be $\Phi'(\mathscr{G}^\tau)$, then, for $X \subseteq S$: $X \in \Psi'(\Phi'(\mathscr{G}^\tau))$ if and only if $(\Phi'(\mathscr{G}^\tau))(C(X)) \subseteq C(X)$; that is, if and only if $\overline{C(X)}^\tau \subseteq C(X)$; or equivalently (by Theorem 4.3) $X \in \mathscr{G}^\tau$. Thus, for any $\mathscr{G}^\tau$ in G_S,

$$\Psi'(\Phi'(\mathscr{G}^\tau)) = \mathscr{G}^\tau. \tag{4'}$$

On the other hand, given any χ in X_S, it is proved in Theorem 4.4(II) that the topology τ defined on S by $\Psi'(\chi)$ is such that $\chi(X) = \overline{X}^\tau$ for all $X \subseteq S$; that is, (taking $\mathscr{G}^\tau = \Psi'(\chi)$ in the definition of Φ') $\chi(X) = (\Phi'(\Psi'(\chi)))(X)$, so that for any χ in X_S,

$$\Phi'(\Psi'(\chi)) = \chi. \tag{5'}$$

From (4′), (5′) it follows as before that Φ' is a (1,1) function onto X_S, and Φ',Ψ' are mutually inverse. For any pair $(\mathscr{G}^\tau;\chi)$ of corresponding members, χ is the 'closure operation' corresponding to $\mathscr{G}^\tau$ while, reciprocally, $\mathscr{G}^\tau$ can be obtained from χ as in (2), Theorem 4.4(II). A second alternative to Definition 1 is thus:

DEFINITION 1″ Given a non-null set S, a topology τ is said to be defined on S when there is given a function χ^τ from $P(S)$ into $P(S)$ satisfying conditions (a)–(d) of Theorem 4.4(II).

Example 4.2.1 Given any poset $(E, \leqslant)$, let σ^τ (respectively $\sigma^{\tau'}$) denote the function from E into $P(P(E))$ defined as follows: for x in E, and $X \subseteq E$, $X \in \sigma^\tau(x)$ (respectively $\sigma^{\tau'}(x)$) if and only if $M(x) \subseteq X$ (respectively $L(x) \subseteq X$).

It is immediately seen that conditions (a)–(e) of Theorem 4.4(I) are satisfied by $\sigma^\tau,\sigma^{\tau'}$; to see that σ^τ, for example, satisfies (e), note that, given X in $\sigma^\tau(x)$, Y can be taken to be $M(x)$ itself; then, for y in Y, $M(y) \subseteq M(x) \subseteq X$; that is, $X \in \sigma^\tau(y)$.

The topologies τ,τ' thus defined on E can be seen to have the following properties (actually, characteristic properties, as seen from Ex. 5.1):

(a) Intersection of an arbitrary family of members of $\mathscr{G}^\tau$ (or $\mathscr{G}^{\tau'}$) is a member of $\mathscr{G}^\tau$ (or $\mathscr{G}^{\tau'}$).

(b) If x,y are members of E such that $\overline{(x)}^\tau = \overline{(y)}^\tau$ (or $\overline{(x)}^{\tau'} = \overline{(y)}^{\tau'}$), then x,y coincide.

Property (b) is a consequence of the equalities: $\overline{(x)}^\tau = L(x)$, $\overline{(x)}^{\tau'} = M(x)$, which show, incidentally, that, in general, (x) is not τ-closed or τ'-closed.

Example 4.2.2 If $S = J^+$, let σ^τ denote the function from S into $P(P(S))$ defined as follows: given $X \subseteq S$ and $x \neq 1$, $X \in \sigma^\tau(x)$ if and only if $x \in X$, while, $X \in \sigma^\tau(1)$ if and only if: $1 \in X$ *and* $\exists$ an infinite sequence $\{n_i\}$, $i \geqslant 1$, of members of S such that X contains all members of S of the form $2^i(2j - 1)$ where $i \in S$, and $j > n_i$. Conditions (a)–(c) of Theorem 4.4(I) are clearly satisfied by σ^τ; if, further, $\{X_r\}$, $1 \leqslant r \leqslant n$, is any finite sequence of members of $\sigma^\tau(1)$, and $\{n_i^{(r)}\}$, $i \geqslant 1$, is a sequence of members of S corresponding as above to X_r $(1 \leqslant r \leqslant n)$, then $X \equiv \bigcap_{1 \leqslant r \leqslant n} X_r$ contains all numbers $2^i(2j - 1)$ where $j > n_i = \max(n_i^{(1)}, \ldots, n_i^{(n)})$ and $i \in S$; that is, $X \in \sigma^\tau(1)$. Clearly condition (e) is satisfied by taking $Y = (x)$ if $x \neq 1$, and $Y = X$ if $x = 1$.

Example 4.2.3 Given an arbitrary topological space $|S,\tau|$ and an arbitrary non-null set N such that $S \cap N = \varnothing$, write $T = S \cup N$, and define a function $\chi^{\tau'}$ from $P(T)$ into $P(T)$ as follows: for $X \subseteq T$

$$\chi^{\tau'}(X) = \begin{cases} \overline{X \cap S}^\tau \cup (X \cap N) & \text{if } X \cap N \text{ is finite} \\ T & \text{otherwise.} \end{cases}$$

Then:

(a) $\chi^{\tau'}(\varnothing) = \overline{\varnothing}^\tau = \varnothing$.

(b) $X = (X \cap S) \cup (X \cap N) \subseteq \chi^{\tau'}(X)$.

(c) If $X \cap N$ is finite, it is easily verified that $\chi^{\tau'}(X) \cap N = X \cap N$, and so:

$$\chi^{\tau'}(\chi^{\tau'}(X)) = \overline{\chi^{\tau'}(X) \cap S}^\tau \cup (X \cap N)$$
$$= \overline{\overline{X \cap S}^\tau} \cup (X \cap N) = \chi^{\tau'}(X).$$

(d) If, first, $X \cap N$, $Y \cap N$ are both finite, then so is $(X \cup Y) \cap N$ and:

$$\chi^{\tau'}(X \cup Y) = \overline{(X \cup Y) \cap S}^\tau \cup ((X \cup Y) \cap N)$$

$$= \overline{X \cap S}^{\tau} \cup \overline{Y \cap S}^{\tau} \cup (X \cap N) \cup (Y \cap N)$$

$$= \chi^{\tau'}(X) \cup \chi^{\tau'}(Y).$$

If otherwise, clearly $\chi^{\tau'}(X) \cup \chi^{\tau'}(Y) = T = \chi^{\tau'}(X \cup Y)$.

It is worth remarking that if S is finite, τ is the discrete topology on S, and N is infinite, then the topology τ' thus defined on T (as in Definition 1″) has the property that $X \in \mathscr{G}^{\tau'}$ if and only if $C(X) = S$ or is finite; that is, it coincides with that defined in Example 4.1.2.

It may appear disconcerting (or perverse!) that no attempt has been made here to define the notion of a *topology* itself. It is certainly a common and straightforward practice, (e.g., MENDELSON, Reference [7], p. 84) to define a topology on a set S simply as a subset $P(S)$ which satisfies the conditions of Definition 1; this would of course amount, in our notation, to an actual *identification* of τ with $\mathscr{G}^{\tau}$. It was felt here, however, that this treatment would give undue priority to the approach through open sets, at the expense of the two alternative procedures dealt with in the present section.

4.3 Comparison of Topologies: Subspaces

Given an arbitrary non-null set S, let T_S denote the collection of all topologies τ which can be defined on S. It is clear from (the proof of) Theorem 2.22 that, given members τ,τ' of T_S, the three statements: (a) '$\mathscr{G}^{\tau} \subseteq \mathscr{G}^{\tau'}$', (b) '$\mathscr{N}^{\tau}(x) \subseteq \mathscr{N}^{\tau'}(x)$ for each x in S', (c) '$\overline{X}^{\tau'} \subseteq \overline{X}^{\tau}$ for each $X \subseteq S$' are *equivalent*, and so a partial order can be unambiguously defined on T_S by writing $\tau \leqslant \tau'$ if and only if one of (a), (b), (c) holds; then, τ' is said to be **finer** than τ, and τ **coarser** then τ'. If ρ,ρ' are two *metrics* on S, then $\rho \leqslant \rho'$ (in the quasi-ordering of Definition 20, Chapter 2) if and only if $\tau^{\rho} \leqslant \tau^{\rho'}$ in the sense just introduced.

THEOREM 4.5 For any non-null set S, $(T_S, \leqslant)$ is a complete lattice.

PROOF By Theorem 1.8, it is only necessary to show that: (i) T_S has a maximum element, and: (ii) for each non-null subset A of T_S, the infimum $\bigwedge A$ of A exists. Clearly the discrete topology τ_I gives (i); secondly, let $\mathscr{G}$ be the intersection of all the sets $\mathscr{G}^{\tau}$, where $\tau \in A$. It is clear that $\mathscr{G}$ satisfies the conditions of Definition 1, so that $\exists$ a member τ' of T_S such that $\mathscr{G} = \mathscr{G}^{\tau'}$. Then $\tau' = \bigwedge A$, for, clearly $\tau' \leqslant \tau$, for each τ in A while, on the other hand, if

τ'' is an arbitrary member of T_S such that $\tau'' \leqslant \tau$, for each τ in A, then, by construction of τ', it is clear that $\mathscr{G}^{\tau''} \subseteq \mathscr{G}^{\tau'}$; that is, τ' is the maximum lower bound of A in T_S.

The trivial topology τ_0 (of Example 4.1.1) is clearly the minimum member of T_S.

Definition 23 of Chapter 2 suggests the following result for topological spaces:

THEOREM 4.6 Given a topological space $|S,\tau|$, and a non-null subset A of S, the subset $\mathscr{G}_A^\tau$ of all members of $P(A)$ of the form $G \cap A$, where G belongs to $\mathscr{G}^\tau$, defines a topology τ_A on A.
PROOF $\mathscr{G}_A^\tau$ satisfies the conditions of Definition 1; so that a topology τ_A is defined on A such that $\mathscr{G}^{\tau_A} = \mathscr{G}_A^\tau$. To verify, for example, that condition (ii) holds, let $\{G_i'\}$, $i \in I$, be an arbitrary family of members of $\mathscr{G}_A^\tau$; if $G_i \in \mathscr{G}^\tau$ and $G_i \cap A = G_i'$, then $\bigcup_i G_i' = (\bigcup_i G_i) \cap A$, where $\bigcup_i G_i \in \mathscr{G}^\tau$.

The topology τ_A is called the **relativization** of τ to A or the **relative topology** on A; it is said to be **induced** on A by τ. The space $|A,\tau_A|$ is said to be a **subspace** of $|S,\tau|$. The consistency of this conception with that introduced in Chapter 2 is clear, for if (S,ρ) is a *metric* space, A is a non-null subset of S, and ρ' a metric on A, then (A,ρ') is a subspace of (S,ρ) (in the sense of the Definition 23, cited above) if and only if $\mathscr{G}_{\rho'} = \mathscr{G}_A^{\tau^\rho}$ (notation of Theorem 4.6) where τ^ρ as usual denotes the topology on S arising from the metric ρ; that is, if and only if $|A,\tau^{\rho'}|$ is a subspace (in the sense just introduced) of $|S,\tau^\rho|$. Since, for any non-null subset A of S, (A,ρ_A) is, in particular, a subspace of (S,ρ), it follows that any subspace $|A,\tau_A|$ of a metrizable space is again metrizable (since if ρ is a τ-metric on S, it is clear from above that $\tau_A = \tau^{\rho_A}$); that is, metrizability is a hereditary property of a space.

For any space $|S,\tau|$, notions as τ-dense, and so on, are defined as in Chapter 2.

Example 4.3.1 In Example 4.2.3, $|S,\tau|$ is a subspace of the space $|T,\tau'|$ constructed there. For, given $X \subseteq S$, $\overline{X}^{\tau'} = \chi^{\tau'}(X) = \overline{X}^\tau$, so that $\overline{X}^\tau = \overline{X}^{\tau'} \cap S = \overline{X}^{\tau'_S}$, where τ'_S is the topology induced on S by τ'; that is, $\tau = \tau'_S$.

4.4 Bases; Product Spaces

DEFINITION 4 Given a space $|S,\tau|$, a subset $\mathscr{G}'$ of $P(S)$ is said to form a **τ-base on S** if:

(i) $\mathscr{G}' \subseteq \mathscr{G}^\tau$;

(ii) each non-null member of $\mathscr{G}^\tau$ is the union of some family of members of $\mathscr{G}'$.

It should be noted that if $\mathscr{G}'$ is a τ-base on S, then $\mathscr{G}^\tau$ (with the exception of $\varnothing$) is seen to *coincide* with the set of all subsets of S expressible as the union of members of $\mathscr{G}'$; consequently, $\mathscr{G}'$ cannot be a τ-base for more than one topology τ on S.

THEOREM 4.7 Given a space $|S,\tau|$, a subset $\mathscr{G}'$ of $P(S)$ is a τ-base on S if and only if:

(a) $\mathscr{G}' \subseteq \mathscr{G}^\tau$;

(b) for each x in S, and X in $\mathscr{N}^\tau(x)$, there exists a member G of $\mathscr{G}'$ (dependent on the choice of x, X) such that $x \in G \subseteq X$.

The proof follows that of Theorem 2.4.

THEOREM 4.8 Given a non-null set S, and a subset $\mathscr{G}'$ of $P(S)$, a topology τ can be defined on S such that $\mathscr{G}'$ is a τ-base on S if and only if:

(a) S coincides with the union of the members of $\mathscr{G}'$;

(b) for each x in S, and members G, G' of $\mathscr{G}'$ each containing x, there exists a member H of $\mathscr{G}'$ such that $x \in H \subseteq G \cap G'$.

PROOF The necessity of the conditions (a), (b) is almost immediate from Theorem 4.7. Conversely, if $\mathscr{G}'$ satisfies (a), (b), let $\mathscr{G}$ denote the subset of $P(S)$ containing, together with $\varnothing$, all sets expressible as the union of members of $\mathscr{G}'$. Then $\mathscr{G}$ satisfies the conditions (i)–(iii) of Definition 1. For example, in order to verify condition (iii), it will suffice to consider two members G_1, G_2 of $\mathscr{G}$ with $G_1 \cap G_2 \neq \varnothing$; the rest follows by induction. If $x \in G_1 \cap G_2$, then (by construction of $\mathscr{G}$) $\exists\, G_i'$ in $\mathscr{G}'$ $(i = 1,2)$ such that $x \in G_i' \subseteq G_i$; then, by assumption, $\exists\, H'$ in $\mathscr{G}'$ such that $x \in H' \subseteq G_1' \cap G_2'$; that is, corresponding to each member x of $G_1 \cap G_2$, $\exists$ a member H_x' of $\mathscr{G}'$ such that $x \in H_x' \subseteq G_1 \cap G_2$. Thus $G_1 \cap G_2 = \bigcup H_x$ for x in $G_1 \cap G_2$, and so belongs to $\mathscr{G}$.

A subset $\mathscr{G}'$ of $P(S)$ which is a τ-base on S for some topology which can be defined on S, is called a **base on S**.

DEFINITION 5 Of two bases $\mathscr{G}_i'$, $i = 1,2$ on a non-null set S, $\mathscr{G}_2'$ is said to be **finer** than $\mathscr{G}_1'$ (and $\mathscr{G}_1'$ **coarser** than $\mathscr{G}_2'$) when $\tau_1 \leqslant \tau_2$, where $\mathscr{G}_i'$ is a τ_i-base on S.

If the above relation is written: $\mathscr{G}_1' \leqslant \mathscr{G}_2'$, a *quasi-ordering* is defined on the set of all bases on S. If $\mathscr{G}_1' \leqslant \mathscr{G}_2'$ *and* $\mathscr{G}_2' \leqslant \mathscr{G}_1'$ the bases are said to be **equivalent**.

THEOREM 4.9 If $\mathscr{G}_i'$, $i = 1,2$, are bases on a non-null set S, then $\mathscr{G}_1' \leqslant \mathscr{G}_2'$ if and only if for each x in S, and member G' of $\mathscr{G}_1'$ containing x, there exists a member G'' of $\mathscr{G}_2'$ such that $x \in G'' \subseteq G'$.

The proof (which depends on Theorem 4.7) is left to the reader.

Definition 22 (with succeeding remarks) of Chapter 2 suggests the following result for topological spaces:

THEOREM 4.10 For each of the spaces $|S_i,\tau_i|$, $1 \leqslant i \leqslant n$, let $\mathscr{G}_i'$ be a τ_i-base on S_i; if $S = \prod_{1 \leqslant i \leqslant n} S_i$, and $\mathscr{G}'$ denotes the subset of $P(S)$ of all sets of the form $\prod_{1 \leqslant i \leqslant n} G_i'$, where G_i' belongs to $\mathscr{G}_i'$, then:

(a) $\mathscr{G}'$ is a base on S;
(b) for any two choices $\{\mathscr{G}_i'\}$, $\{\mathscr{G}_i''\}$ of τ_i-bases on S_i, the corresponding bases $\mathscr{G}'$, $\mathscr{G}''$ so formed on S are equivalent.

PROOF The proof of (a) is almost immediate from Theorem 4.8, while that of (b) follows readily from Theorem 4.9.

That is, a topology τ can be defined on S such that, for any choice of τ_i-bases $\mathscr{G}_i'$ on S_i, $\mathscr{G}'$ is a τ-base on S. τ is called the **product topology** of the topologies τ_i, and $|S,\tau|$ the **product space** of the spaces $|S_i,\tau_i|$. It is clear again that if (S_i,ρ_i) are *metric* spaces, and ρ is a metric on S, then (S,ρ) is a product space of (S_i,ρ_i) (in the sense of the Definition 22 cited above) if and only if $|S,\tau^\rho|$ is the product space (in the sense just introduced) of $|S_i,\tau^{\rho_i}|$, $1 \leqslant i \leqslant n$. It is evident that the product space of metrizable spaces is again metrizable.

If $|S,\tau|$ is any space, A a non-null subset of S, and $\mathscr{G}'$ a τ-base on S, it is clear that the subset $\mathscr{G}_A'$ of all members of $P(A)$ of the form $G' \cap A$, where G' belongs to $\mathscr{G}'$, forms a τ_A-base on A.

DEFINITION 6 Given a space $|S,\tau|$, a subset $\mathscr{G}''$ of $P(S)$ is said to form a **τ-subbase on S** if:

(i) $\mathscr{G}'' \subseteq \mathscr{G}^\tau$;
(ii) the set $\mathscr{G}'$ of all subsets of S which are expressible as the intersection of a finite sequence of members of $\mathscr{G}''$ forms a τ-base on S.

THEOREM 4.11 Given a non-null set S, and a subset $\mathscr{G}''$ of $P(S)$, a topology τ can be defined on S such that $\mathscr{G}''$ is a τ-subbase on S if and only if S coincides with the union of the members of $\mathscr{G}''$.

The proof is immediate from Theorem 4.8.

A subset $\mathscr{G}''$ of $P(S)$ with the property described in Theorem 4.11 is called a **subbase on S**.

If $\mathscr{A}$ is an *arbitrary* non-null subset of $P(S)$, the subset A of T_S of those members τ' of T_S such that $\mathscr{A} \subseteq \mathscr{G}^{\tau'}$ is non-null (the discrete topology τ_I belongs to A); if $\mathscr{G}$ denotes the intersection of the sets $\mathscr{G}^{\tau'}$, for $\tau' \in A$, there exists (as in the proof of Theorem 4.5) clearly a member τ of A such that $\mathscr{G} = \mathscr{G}^{\tau}$; that is, A has a *least* member τ, which is called the topology on S **generated** by the subset $\mathscr{A}$ of $P(S)$. The following result shows in particular that a subbase $\mathscr{G}''$ on S cannot be a τ-subbase for more than one topology τ on S:

THEOREM 4.12 Given a space $|S,\tau|$, and a τ-subbase $\mathscr{G}''$ on S, τ is the topology on S generated by $\mathscr{G}''$.

PROOF It is only necessary to note that if τ' is any topology on S, such that $\mathscr{G}'' \subseteq \mathscr{G}^{\tau'}$, then, in the notation of Definition 6, $\mathscr{G}' \subseteq \mathscr{G}^{\tau'}$; for, since $\mathscr{G}'$ is a τ-base on S, it will in turn follow that $\mathscr{G}^{\tau} \subseteq \mathscr{G}^{\tau'}$.

Example 4.4.1 Given any *chain* $(E, \leqslant)$, an 'open interval' of E is defined just as for the chain of real numbers and, with an obvious notation, will have any of the forms: $]a,b[$, $]a,\rightarrow[$ and $]\leftarrow,b[$. It is easily seen that the subset $\mathscr{G}'$ of $P(E)$ containing, together with E itself, all such open intervals of E satisfies the conditions of Theorem 4.8 and so a topology τ^E can be defined on E such that $\mathscr{G}'$ is a τ^E-base on E. τ^E is called the **intrinsic** topology on E.

Example 4.4.2 Given an *arbitrary* poset $(E, \leqslant)$, let $\mathscr{G}'$ denote that subset of $P(E)$ containing all subsets G of E which satisfy the two conditions:

(α) if C is a *maximal* chain in E, then (in the notation of the previous example) $G \cap C \in \mathscr{G}^{\tau^C}$;

(β) G is convex in E.

It is again evident that a topology τ' can be defined on E such that $\mathscr{G}'$ is a τ'-base on E. This topology is mainly of interest where $(E, \leqslant)$ is a lattice (Cf. the discussion immediately following Example 4.4.4) for which case it was originally defined by Rennie (Reference [9]) and called the **L-topology** on E. It is worth noting that Theorem 1.10, Corollary ensures that condition (α) is never merely satisfied vacuously.

Example 4.4.3 If $S = J^+$, and $G_i = (2i - 1, 2i)$ for each i in J^+, it is immediate from Theorem 4.8 that $\mathscr{G}' \equiv \{G_i\}$, $i \geqslant 1$, forms a τ-base for some topology τ on S. *Any* non-null subset X of S possesses a τ-cluster point, for if X contains an odd integer

$2j - 1$, clearly every τ-neighbourhood of $2j$ contains G_j and so meets X; that is, $2j \in X'^{\tau}$. Analogously, if $2j \in X$, $2j - 1 \in X'^{\tau}$. It follows that if $x_i = i$, $i \geqslant 1$, Theorem 2.21(c) does *not* hold for $\{x_i\}$.

If the notion of '$\mathscr{F}^{\tau}$-base' or 'base for the τ-closed sets' on S is defined as in Definition 16, of Chapter 2, then, as before, a subset $\mathscr{F}'$ of $P(S)$ is a $\mathscr{F}^{\tau}$-base on S if and only if the subset $\mathscr{G}'$ of $P(S)$ containing the complements of the members of $\mathscr{F}'$ is a τ-base on S. A subset $\mathscr{F}'$ of $P(S)$ which is a $\mathscr{F}^{\tau}$-base on S for some topology τ definable on S is called an $\mathscr{F}$-base on S. If the further notions of '$\mathscr{F}^{\tau}$-subbase on S' and '$\mathscr{F}$-subbase on S' are defined in an obvious way, there follows immediately from Theorem 4.11:

THEOREM 4.13 Given a non-null set S, a subset $\mathscr{F}''$ of $P(S)$ is a $\mathscr{F}$-subbase on S if and only if the intersection of the members of $\mathscr{F}''$ is null.

An analogue of Theorem 4.12 would be:

THEOREM 4.14 Given a space $|S,\tau|$ and a $\mathscr{F}^{\tau}$-subbase $\mathscr{F}''$ on S, τ is the coarsest topology τ' definable on S such that $\mathscr{F}'' \subseteq \mathscr{F}^{\tau'}$.

Example 4.4.4 Given a poset $(E, \leqslant)$ (with more than one element), the subset $\mathscr{F}''$ of $P(E)$ containing all subsets of E of either of the forms $M(a)$, $L(a)$ (where $a \in E$) satisfies the condition of Theorem 4.13; in fact, if a,b are two distinct elements of E, $M(a) \cap L(a) \cap M(b) \cap L(b)$ is null. Thus, $\mathscr{F}''$ is a $\mathscr{F}^{\tau}$-subbase for a topology τ on E known as the **interval** topology; when, in particular, $(E, \leqslant)$ is a chain, it is easily seen that $\tau = \tau^E$ (the intrinsic topology on E).

°If $(E, \leqslant)$ is a lattice, τ is related to the L-topology τ' on E by: $\tau \leqslant \tau'$. To see this, note first that, by Theorem 4.14, it will suffice to verify that $\mathscr{F}'' \subseteq \mathscr{F}^{\tau'}$. Given $F \equiv M(a)$ in $\mathscr{F}''$, we show that $G \equiv C_E(F)$ satisfies conditions (α), (β) of Example 4.4.2.

(α) If C is a maximal chain in E, suppose $\varnothing \subset G \cap C \subset C$; then if x_1,x_2 are any members of $C_1 \equiv G \cap C$ and $C_2 \equiv F \cap C$ respectively,

$$x_1 < x_2 \tag{1}$$

(for, otherwise, $x_1 \geqslant x_2 \geqslant a$, giving x_1 in F). Consider the following two cases:

(1) C_1 has *no* greatest member. If $x \in C_1$ and y is a member of C_1 with $x < y$, then, by remark (1) above, $x \in]\leftarrow, y[\subset C_1$, where $]\leftarrow, y[$ denotes an open interval *in* C. Since $]\leftarrow, y[\in \mathscr{G}^{\tau^C}$, it is clear that $C_1 \in \mathscr{G}^{\tau^C}$.

(2) C_1 has a greatest member k ($k \ngeqslant a$, otherwise $k \in C_2$). Then, for each member x_2 in C_2: $x_2 \geqslant a$ *and* $x_2 > k$ (by (1) above); thus:

$$x_2 \geqslant k \vee a > k \geqslant x_1, \quad \text{for each } x_1 \text{ in } C_1. \tag{2}$$

That is, $k \vee a$ is commensurable with each member of C; that is, the subset $C' \equiv C \cup (k \vee a)$ of E is a chain. It follows by the maximality of C that $k \vee a \in C$, hence (from (2)) $k \vee a$ is the least member of C_2, and so C_1 coincides with the open interval $]\leftarrow, k \vee a[$ of C, and is again a member of $\mathscr{G}^{\tau C}$.

(β) It is immediate that G is convex.

Similarly $G' \equiv C_E(L(a))$ satisfies (α), (β) and the result required follows.

A consequence of the inequality '$\mathscr{F}^{\tau} \subseteq \mathscr{F}^{\tau'}$' is that each maximal chain C of E is τ'-closed; for the maximality of C implies that it can be put in the form:

$$C = \bigcap_{c \in C} (M(c) \cup L(c)), \quad \text{a member of } \mathscr{F}^{\tau}.$$

Definition 7 Given a space $|S,\tau|$, and x in S, a family $\mathscr{B}(x) \equiv \{X_i\}$, $i \in I$, of members of $P(S)$ is said to form a **local τ-base at x** if:

(i) $\mathscr{B}(x) \subseteq \mathscr{N}^{\tau}(x)$;

(ii) for each X in $\mathscr{N}^{\tau}(x)$, $X_i \subseteq X$ for some i in I.

Further, a subset $\mathscr{D}(x)$ of $\mathscr{N}^{\tau}(x)$ is said to form a **local τ-subbase at x** if the subsets of S expressible as the intersection of a finite sequence of members of $\mathscr{D}(x)$ form a local τ-base at x.

From Theorem 4.7 it is clear that if $\mathscr{G}'$ is a τ-base on S, then, for each x in S, the subset $\mathscr{B}(x)$ of $\mathscr{G}'$ of those members of $\mathscr{G}'$ to which x belongs, forms a local τ-base at x.

Definition 8 A topological space $|S,\tau|$ is said to satisfy the **first axiom** (of countability) if, for each x in S, there exists an enumerable local τ-base $\mathscr{B}(x)$ at x.

It should be noted that, in Definition 8, it can without loss of generality be assumed that the members of $\mathscr{B}(x)$ are so enumerated that: $X_{i+1} \subseteq X_i$ for each $i \geqslant 1$, for, if not, the sets $Y_i \equiv \bigcap_{1 \leqslant j \leqslant i} X_j$ form, for $i \geqslant 1$, again a local τ-base at x.

Example 4.4.5 Any metrizable space $|S,\tau|$ satisfies the first axiom. For if ρ is a τ-metric on S, and $X_i = N^{\rho}_{i^{-1}}(x)$, for $i \geqslant 1$, $\mathscr{B}(x) \equiv \{X_i\}$, $i \geqslant 1$, forms a local τ-base at x.

Example 4.4.6 The space $|S,\tau|$ defined in Example 4.1.3 does not satisfy the first axiom. For, given x in S, let $\{G_i\}$, $i \geqslant 1$, be an arbitrary sequence of members of $\mathscr{G}^\tau$ each containing x. If $G = \bigcap_{i \geqslant 1} G_i$, then $C(G) = \bigcup_{i \geqslant 1} C(G_i)$, so that $C(G)$ is enumerable; that is, $G \in \mathscr{N}^\tau(x)$. If, then, y is a member of G distinct from x, it is clear that $G' \equiv G - (y) \in \mathscr{N}^\tau(x)$, but $\exists$ no i such that $G_i \subseteq G'$.

Example 4.4.7 (Although S is itself enumerable) the space $|S,\tau|$ of Example 4.2.2 does not satisfy the first axiom. For, let $\{Y_i\}$, $i \geqslant 1$, be an arbitrary sequence of members of $\mathscr{N}^\tau(1)$; then, for each i, the element 1 of S is a τ-cluster point of the set Z_i of elements of S of the form $2^i(2j - 1)$, $j \geqslant 1$ (since, by construction, each member of $\mathscr{N}^\tau(1)$ contains (an infinity of) members of Z_i); hence, in particular, $Y_i \cap Z_i$ is non-null, so that $\exists$ an element x_i of S such that $2^i(2x_i - 1) \in Y_i$. If Y denotes that subset of S which contains 1 and all elements of S of the form $2^i(2j - 1)$ where $i \geqslant 1$ and $j > x_i$, then $Y \in \mathscr{N}^\tau(1)$ but clearly $\exists$ no i such that $Y_i \subseteq Y$.

Theorem 2.21 holds in the following form:

THEOREM 4.15 If $|S,\tau|$ satisfies the first axiom, $A \subseteq S$, and x is a member of S, then:

(a) $x \in A'^\tau$ if and only if there exists a sequence $\{x_i\}$ of members of $A - (x)$ such that $x_i \underset{\tau}{\rightarrow} x$.

(b) A is τ-open if and only if for each x in A and sequence $\{x_i\}$ such that $x_i \underset{\tau}{\rightarrow} x$, there exists i_0 such that x_i belongs to A for $i \geqslant i_0$.

(c) If $A_n = \bigcup_{i \geqslant n} (x_i)$ and x belongs to $\bar{A}_n^\tau$ for each $n \geqslant 1$, then $\{x_i\}$ contains a subsequence $\{x_{i_r}\}$ such that $x_{i_r} \underset{\tau}{\rightarrow} x$.

Clearly the property of satisfying the first axiom is hereditary.

4.5 Functions on a Topological Space

Given two topological spaces $|S,\tau|$, $|S',\tau'|$, and a subset A of S, a function f from A into S' is said to be (for example) **(τ,τ')-continuous on A** when, for each element x in A, and member Y of $\mathscr{N}^{\tau'}(f(x))$, $f^{-1}(Y) \in \mathscr{N}^{\tau_A}(x)$. Although other concepts introduced in Section 2.6 can be similarly defined for topological spaces, the following important divergences from the situation for metric spaces should be noted:

(I) Theorem 2.38 takes the more concise form:

THEOREM 4.16 If $|S,\tau|$ is the product space of the spaces $|S_i,\tau_i|$,

$1 \leqslant i \leqslant n$, then τ is the coarsest topology τ' on S such that π_i is (τ',τ_i)-continuous for each i.

(II) Part of Theorem 2.39 takes the form:

THEOREM 4.17 Given spaces $|S,\tau|$, $|S',\tau'|$, with $|S,\tau|$ satisfying the first axiom (of countability), and $A \subseteq S$, a function f from A into S' is (τ,τ')-continuous on A if (and only if) for x in A and a sequence $\{x_i\}$ of members of A such that $x_i \underset{\tau}{\to} x$, then $f(x_i) \underset{\tau'}{\to} f(x)$.

That the condition that $|S,\tau|$ should satisfy the first axiom cannot be omitted, is shown by:

Example 4.5.1 If S is a non-enumerable set, let τ be defined on S as in Example 4.1.3; take $A = S = S'$, and τ' as the discrete topology. If f is the identity function, then if $x_i \underset{\tau}{\to} x, f(x_i) = f(x)$ for i sufficiently large, so that $f(x_i) \underset{\tau'}{\to} f(x)$; however, if A' is any enumerable subset of S', $A' \in \mathscr{G}^{\tau'}$, but $f^{-1}(A') = A' \,\omega\, \mathscr{G}^{\tau}$, so that f is *not* (τ,τ')-continuous.

(III) If two topological spaces $|S,\tau|$, $|S',\tau'|$ are homeomorphic (that is, if $\exists$ a (1,1) function f from S onto S' such that f is (τ,τ')-continuous and f^{-1} is (τ',τ)-continuous) then, on the identification of each element x of S with the corresponding element $f(x)$ of S', $\mathscr{G}^{\tau}$ becomes coincidental with $\mathscr{G}^{\tau'}$; that is, τ,τ' coincide and the *topological* spaces here become *identical*. If $|S',\tau'|$ is a subspace of a third space $|S'',\tau''|$; that is, if $S' \subseteq S''$ and $\tau' = \tau''_{S'}$ (the topology induced on S' by τ''), then under the above identification $|S,\tau|$ becomes itself a subspace of $|S'',\tau''|$, and is said again to be homeomorphically (or 'topologically') imbedded in $|S'',\tau''|$.

THEOREM 4.18 If $|S,\tau|$, $|S',\tau'|$ are homeomorphic and one of them is metrizable, so is the other.

That is, metrizability is a homeomorphic (or 'topological') property of a space.

(IV) Neither Theorem 2.46, nor either of its Corollaries holds for an arbitrary topological space. It is clearly sufficient to show that Theorem 2.46 does not hold.

Example 4.5.2 Let $|S,\tau|$ be defined as in Example 4.1.2; if $|S',\tau'|$ is the product space of $|S,\tau|$, $|S,\tau|$, $\Delta_S \,\omega\, \mathscr{F}^{\tau'}$. For, otherwise, there would exist non-null members G,G' of $\mathscr{G}^{\tau}$ such that $G \times G' \subseteq C_{S'}(\Delta_S)$; that is, such that $G \cap G'$ is null.

°*Note 3* Theorem 4.16 suggests a procedure for extending the notion of product space to an *arbitrary* family $\{|S_i,\tau_i|\}$, $i \in I$, of spaces. If $S = \prod_i S_i$, let T' denote the subset of T_S (in the notation of Section 4.3) containing all members τ' such that, for each i in I, the projection π_i is (τ',τ_i)-continuous. Here T' is non-null (it contains the discrete topology on S) and it is easily seen that T' contains its infimum τ in T_S^*. τ is called the **product topology** on S of the family $\{\tau_i\}$, and $|S,\tau|$ the **product space** of the family $\{|S_i,\tau_i|\}$. If, for each i in I, $\mathscr{G}_i'$ denotes a given τ_i-base on S_i, then, in view of Theorem 4.12, τ could alternatively be described as the topology on S defined by the subbase $\mathscr{G}''$ on S containing all subsets of S of the form: $\pi_i^{-1}(G_i')$, where $G_i' \in \mathscr{G}_i'$. It follows (see Ex. 7 of § 1.2) that a τ-base on S will be formed by the set $\mathscr{G}'$ of all subsets G of S of the form: $\prod_i B_i$, where $B_i \in \mathscr{G}_i'$ for all i in some *finite* subset I' of I (where I' depends on G), and B_i equals S_i otherwise. Such results in Part I as Theorems 2.25 and 2.40, and Theorems 3.15 and 3.45 generalize here with little modification to their proofs. (As regards Theorem 3.45, see Ex. (13) below.)

Worked Exercises (on Sections 4.1–4.5)

1. If, given a non-null set S, the subset of T_S containing those topologies τ on S such that S is τ-dense-in-itself is denoted by D_S, show that a given member τ of D_S is maximal in D_S if and only if: every subset X of S, which is τ-dense-in-itself, is τ-open. (1)

Solution: It is clear, first of all, that D_S is non-null (it contains the trivial topology τ_0 on S); let $\tau \in D_S$. Suppose that τ satisfies condition (1) and that τ' is a member of T_S such that $\tau < \tau'$. Then, if $G \in \mathscr{G}^{\tau'} - \mathscr{G}^{\tau}$, it follows from (1) that $G \nsubseteq G'^{\tau}$; that is, $\exists$ a member x of G and a member G'' of $\mathscr{G}^{\tau}$ such that $G \cap G'' = (x)$. But, since clearly $G \cap G'' \in \mathscr{G}^{\tau'}$, this means that x is *not* a τ'-cluster point of S. Thus, $\tau' \,\omega\, D_S$. Conversely, suppose that τ does *not* satisfy (1); that is, $\exists$ a subset X of S such that $X \subseteq X'^{\tau}$ and $X \,\omega\, \mathscr{G}^{\tau}$. By Theorem 4.11, the subset $\mathscr{G}^{\tau} \cup (X)$ of $P(S)$ is a τ'-subbase for some topology τ' on S. Here $\tau < \tau'$, and the members of $\mathscr{G}^{\tau}$, together with all sets of the form $G \cap X$, where $G \in \mathscr{G}^{\tau}$, clearly form a τ'-base. Then $\tau' \in D_S$; for, *if not*, $\exists$ an element x of S and a member G_1 of $\mathscr{G}^{\tau}$ such that $(x) = G_1 \cap X$ (since $\tau \in A$, $(x) \,\omega\, \mathscr{G}^{\tau}$). Since, however, $x \in X'^{\tau}$, a contradiction is obtained.

2. If E is an arbitrary infinite set, show that a partial order $\leqslant$ can be defined on E such that:
   (a) $(E, \leqslant)$ is a complete lattice;
   (b) the *interval* topology τ' on E coincides with the topology τ defined in Example 4.1.2.

Solution: $\mathscr{F}^{\tau}$ is the subset of $P(S)$ which contains, together with S, all finite subsets of S. Hence, since $(a) = M(a) \cap L(a) \in \mathscr{F}^{\tau'}$ for each element a of S, it suffices to show that a partial order $\leqslant$ can be defined on S which, together with condition (a) above, satisfies the condition that all sets of the form $M(x)$, $L(x)$, (which form a $\mathscr{F}^{\tau'}$-subbase $\mathscr{F}''$ on S) are *finite*. To do this, choose two distinct elements x_0, x_1 from S. Then, given any two elements x,y of S, write $x < y$ if and only if *either* $x = x_0$ and $y \neq x_0$ *or* $y = x_1$ and $x \neq x_1$ (or both). It will be seen that a partial order $\leqslant$ is thereby defined on S such that, first, $(E,\leqslant)$ is a complete lattice (with $x_0 < x < x_1$ for $x \in S - (x_0,x_1)$ and any two distinct members of $S - (x_0,x_1)$ incommensurable), and, secondly, each member of the $\mathscr{F}^{\tau'}$-subbase $\mathscr{F}''$ has, at most, two members.

Exercises for Solution (on Sections 4.1–4.5)

1. Define a topological space S, such that:
(a) each non-enumerable subset of S possesses a non-enumerable set of τ-condensation points;
(b) *no* enumerable subset of S possesses a cluster point.

2. If $S = J$, and q a given integer ($\neq 0,1$), define a function from S into $P(P(S))$ as follows: given x in S, and $X \subseteq S$, then $X \in \sigma^\tau(x)$ if and only if $\exists$ an integer $r \geqslant 0$ (dependent on X) such that $x + mq^r \in X$ for all m in S. Verify that σ^τ satisfies conditions (a)–(e) of Theorem 4.4(I) and so defines a topology on S.

3. Given a topological space $|S,\tau'|$ and a τ'-dense subset A of S, let T denote the subset of T_S containing those topologies τ on S such that:

$$(a):\ \tau' \leqslant \tau, \quad (b):\ A \text{ is } \tau\text{-dense}, \quad (c):\ \tau_A = \tau'_A.$$

Show that
(a) the set M of *maximal* elements of T is non-null;
(b) given τ in T_S, $\tau \in M$ if and only if each subset X of S, such that $A \cap X$ is τ_X-dense and τ_A-open, belongs to $\mathscr{G}^\tau$;
(c) if $\tau \in M$, then $C(A) \in \mathscr{F}^\tau$ and $|C(A),\tau_{C(A)}|$ is discrete;
(d) if $\tau \in M$, and τ_A is maximal in D_A (in the notation of Worked Ex. 2) then τ is maximal in D_S.

4. Given a poset $(E,\leqslant)$, let τ,τ' denote the topologies defined on E as in Example 4.2.1. If A is a non-null subset of E and τ_1,τ'_1 denote the topologies defined *on* A by the same procedure (i.e. replacing $(E,\leqslant)$ by the poset $(A,\leqslant)$), show that, in the notation of Section 4.3, $\tau_1 = \tau_A$ and $\tau'_1 = \tau'_A$.

5. Given a totally-ordered set $(E,\leqslant)$, and a non-null subset A of E, let τ^E denote the intrinsic topology on E, and τ^A that on A (i.e. replacing $(E,\leqslant)$ by $(A,\leqslant)$ in Example 4.4.1). Show that:
(a) for any $A \subseteq E$: $\tau^A \leqslant \tau^E_A$ (in the notation of Section 4.3);
(b) if A is any *interval* of E, $\tau^A = \tau^E_A$.
If, in particular, $E \equiv Q \times J$ is (totally)-ordered, by writing $\{r,n\} \leqslant \{r',n'\}$

when *either* $r < r$ *or* $r = r'$, and $n \leqslant n'$, and if $A = Q \times (0)$, show that equality does *not* hold in (a).

6. Give an example to show that it is not always possible to select a sequence of *distinct* elements x_i in Theorem 4.15(a).

7. Given a sequence (S_i,ρ_i), $i \geqslant 1$, of metric spaces, let $|S,\tau|$ be the product space, as defined in Note 3, of the topological spaces: $|S_i,\tau^{\rho_i}|$. Show that the function:

$$\rho(x,y) = \sum_{i=1}^{\infty} 2^{-i}\{\max(1,\rho_i(x_i,y_i))\}$$

is a τ-metric on S.

8. Given posets $(E,\leqslant)$, $(E',\leqslant')$, let τ (resp. τ') denote the topology defined on E (resp. E') by the *first* procedure given in Example 4.2.1. If f is a function from E into E', establish a simple necessary and sufficient condition on f that it be (τ,τ')-continuous.

9. If $S = S' = [0,1]$, τ is the usual topology on S, and τ' the topology on S' of Example 4.1.2, show that $|S,\tau|$ and $|S',\tau'|$ are *not* homeomorphic.

10. Find spaces $|S,\tau|$, $|S',\tau'|$ and two (τ,τ')-continuous functions f,g such that the set of x in S with $f(x) = g(x)$ is *not* τ-closed. (Cf. Example 4.5.2.)

11. Given a topological space $|S,\tau|$, and a non-null subset A of S, let g_A be the restriction to A of the identity function on S. Show that τ_A is, *first*, the *coarsest* topology τ_1 on A such that, for any space $|S',\tau'|$ and a (τ',τ_1)-continuous function f from S' into A, the composite $f \circ g_A$ is (τ',τ)-continuous from S' in S, and, *secondly*, the *finest* topology τ_1 on A such that, for any space $|S',\tau'|$ and function f from S' into A such that $f \circ g_A$ is (τ',τ)-continuous, then f is (τ',τ_1)-continuous.

12. If $|S,\tau|$, $|S',\tau'|$ both satisfy the first axiom of countability, f is a function from S into S', and x,x' are elements of S,S' respectively such that $x' \in \overline{f(X)}^{\tau'}$ for every τ-neighbourhood X of x, show that $\exists$ a sequence $\{x_i\}$ of elements of S such that $x_i \underset{\tau}{\rightarrow} x$ and $f(x_i) \underset{\tau'}{\rightarrow} x'$.

13. Given an arbitrary family $\{|S_i,\tau_i|\}$, $i \in I$, of spaces, let $|S,\tau|$ denote their product space, as defined in Note 3, and $a \equiv \{a_i\}$ a given element of S. If X denotes the subset of S of all elements $x \equiv \{x_i\}$ with $x_i = a_i$ for all but a *finite* set of members i of I, show that X is τ-dense and hence that, if f is a (τ,τ^{ρ_1})-continuous function from S into R with $f(x) = f(a)$ for all x in X, then f is constant throughout S. Thus show how the proof of Theorem 3.45 can be modified to apply to an arbitrary family of spaces.

4.6 Separable and Completely Separable Spaces

THEOREM 4.19 If a topological space $|S,\tau|$ is completely separable, then:

(a) it satisfies the first axiom (of countability);
(b) it is separable;
(c) it is a Lindelöf-space.

The proof (partially as for Theorem 3.5) is left to the reader.

In contrast with Theorem 3.5 just cited, a topological space possessing one of the properties (b) and (c) need not possess the other, as shown by:

Example 4.6.1 If $|S,\tau|$ is as defined in Example 4.1.3, every non-null subset A of S has the Lindelöf property. For, given an arbitrary τ-open covering $\{G_i\}$, $i \in I$, of A, choose i_0 in I; if $A \nsubseteq G_{i_0}$, it is clear that $B \equiv A - G_{i_0}$ is enumerable. If, for each member x of B, i_x is chosen in I so that $x \in G_{i_x}$, the sets G_{i_0}, $G_{i_x}(x \in B)$ form an enumerable sub-covering of A. However, if X is an arbitrarily chosen enumerable subset of S, $X \in \mathscr{F}^\tau$, so that X cannot be τ-dense; that is, $|S,\tau|$ is not separable.

Example 4.6.2 It is easily verified that the subset $\mathscr{G}'$ of $P(R)$ of all intervals of the form $[a,b[$ forms a τ-base for some topology τ on R; clearly Q is τ-dense, so that $|R,\tau|$ is separable. It follows that the product space $|S,\tau'|$ of $|R,\tau|$ by $|R,\tau|$ is separable. However $|S,\tau'|$ does not possess the Lindelöf property, for, if it did, it could be shown (by an argument analogous to that of Theorem 3.12) that each τ'-*closed* non-null subset F of S must be a Lindelöf set. Now the set F_1 of all elements $\{x_1,x_2\}$ of S such that $x_1 + x_2 = 1$ is τ^{ρ_1}-closed (where ρ_1 is the usual metric on S) and it is clear, from Theorem 4.9, that $\tau^{\rho_1} \leqslant \tau'$. However, F_1 is *not* a Lindelöf set, since if, for each $x \in R$, G_x denotes the subset: $[x,x + 1[\times [1 - x, 2 - x[$ of S, the family $\{G_x\}$, for $x \in R$, forms a non-enumerable τ'-open covering of F_1 containing *no* proper sub-cover.

The next example shows further that a topological space which possesses both (b), (c) above need not be completely separable:

Example 4.6.3 If S is an arbitrary non-enumerable set, and τ is the topology defined in Example 4.1.2, an argument analogous to that in Example 4.6.1 above shows that every non-null subset is actually *compact*; further, it is clear that every infinitely enumerable subset is τ-dense. However $|S,\tau|$ is not completely separable. If $\mathscr{G}' \equiv \{G_i\}$, $i \geqslant 1$, is an arbitrary enumerable subset of $\mathscr{G}^\tau$, it is clear that, for each i, the subset $\mathscr{G}_i$ of $\mathscr{G}^\tau$ of those members G such that $G_i \subseteq G$, is finite; it follows that the subset $\mathscr{G}$ of $\mathscr{G}^\tau$ of all members expressible as the union of members of $\mathscr{G}'$ is enumerable.

Since $\mathscr{G}^\tau$ is not enumerable (for each x in S, $S - (x) \in \mathscr{G}^\tau$), $\mathscr{G}'$ cannot be a τ-base.

The following result shows that separability is *not* a hereditary property of topological space:

THEOREM 4.20 Given an *arbitrary* topological space $|S,\tau|$, a separable space $|T,\tau'|$ exists of which $|S,\tau|$ is a subspace.

PROOF In Section 4.3 it was noted that $|S,\tau|$ was a subspace of the space $|T,\tau'|$ constructed in Example 4.2.3. If N is taken to be infinitely enumerable, clearly N is a τ'-dense subset of T.

A final remark in this section is that a continuous image of a completely separable topological space need not be completely separable:

Example 4.6.4 Take $S = S' = J^+$; if τ is the discrete topology on S, τ' is the topology of Example 4.2.2, and f the identity function, f is (τ,τ')-continuous and $|S,\tau|$ is completely separable. However, as seen in Section 4.4, $|S',\tau'|$ does not even satisfy the first axiom (of countability). That is, the condition 'f is (τ,τ')-open' cannot be omitted from:

THEOREM 4.21 Let spaces $|S,\tau|$, $|S',\tau'|$ be such that there exists a (τ,τ')-continuous and open function f from S onto S'; then if $|S,\tau|$ is completely separable, so is $|S',\tau'|$.

The proof is left to the reader.

4.7 Compact and Countably Compact Spaces

The principal properties of a metric space established in Section 3.2 which do *not* carry over to an arbitrary topological space are, first, that a countably compact space (or set) need not be compact, and, secondly, that a compact set need not be closed. (With regard to sequential compactness, see Ex. 5.3) In order that a given space $|S,\tau|$ be compact, it is necessary and sufficient that:

(a) $|S,\tau|$ should be a Lindelöf-space;

(b) each enumerable τ-open covering of S should contain a finite subcovering.

In the section just referred to, Theorems 3.10 and 3.9 respectively, established that any countably compact *metric* space satisfies (a) and (b). The following examples show that a countably compact *topological* space may fail to satisfy (a) or (b) (so that, in particular, the condition (b) is only a *sufficient* condition for countable compactness of a topological space):

Example 4.7.1 If S, I denote respectively the intervals $]1,4]$ and $]1,2]$ of R, then for each x in I, let G_x denote the subset $(x,2x)$ of S. Since any two distinct members of the family $\mathscr{G}' \equiv \{G_x\}$, $x \in I$, are disjoint, it is immediate that a topology τ can be defined on S such that $\mathscr{G}'$ is a τ-base and so is a non-enumerable τ-open covering of S containing no proper subcovering; that is, (a) is not satisfied. However (by an argument analogous to that for the example cited below) $|S,\tau|$ is countably compact.

Example 4.7.2 For the space $|S,\tau|$ of Example 4.4.3, it was shown that any non-null subset X of S possesses a τ-cluster point, so that $|S,\tau|$ is countably compact; however the τ-base $\mathscr{G}'$ is an enumerable τ-open covering of S containing no proper subcovering.

Example 4.7.2, above, can also serve to show that a continuous image of a countably compact space need not be countably compact. For, if $S' = S$ and τ' denotes the discrete topology on S', then the function f from S *onto* S' obtained by writing, for each x in S, $f(x)$ equal to the least integer not less than $\frac{1}{2}x$, is (τ,τ')-continuous.

To illustrate the second main point of the present section (that a compact subset of a topological space $|S,\tau|$ is not necessarily τ-closed) it is necessary only to recall that in Example 4.6.3 it was pointed out that in the case of the space defined in Example 4.1.2, *every* non-null subset A is compact; but if A is an infinite proper subset, A is not τ-closed. A consequence of this second point is that a continuous function f defined on a compact space need not be closed; if, in particular, f is (1,1), it need not be a homeomorphism:

Example 4.7.3 The space $|S,\tau|$ of Example 4.1.2 is compact, and if $S' = S$ and τ' is the trivial topology on S', the identity function f is (τ,τ')-continuous (from S onto S').

A final example in the present set shows that only part of Theorem 3.17 is valid for a topological space; indeed for the space $|S,\tau|$ of Example 4.7.4, below, *no* infinite subset of S is countably compact, despite the fact that every (τ,τ^{ρ_1})-continuous function from S into R is actually constant:

Example 4.7.4 If $|S,\tau|$ is the space of Example 4.1.3, and A an infinite subset of S, let X be an enumerably infinite subset of A. Then if $x \in A$ and $G = C(X) \cup (x)$, $G \in \mathscr{N}^{\tau}(x)$, but $G \cap X$ contains *x at most*; that is, $x \,\omega\, X'^{\tau}$. Secondly, suppose $\exists$ a (τ, τ^{ρ_1})-continuous function f from S into R such that $f(S)$ contains (at least) the two distinct members a,b. Then, if $a < c < b$, $\emptyset \subset f^{-1}\{]\leftarrow, c[\} \subseteq f^{-1}\{]\leftarrow, c]\} \subset S$. But since clearly the τ-open set $f^{-1}\{]\leftarrow, c[\}$ is non-enumerable, while the τ-closed set $f^{-1}\{]\leftarrow, c]\}$ is enumerable, a contradiction hereby results.

The next result could be compared with Theorem 4.20:

THEOREM 4.22 Given an arbitrary topological space $|S,\tau|$, there exists a compact space $|S',\tau'|$ of which $|S,\tau|$ is a subspace and such that $S' - S$ has one member only.

PROOF If $x_0 \,\omega\, S$, and $S' = S \cup (x_0)$, define a subset $\mathscr{G}'$ of $P(S')$ as follows:

Given $X \subseteq S'$, then;

(a) if $X \subseteq S$, $X \in \mathscr{G}'$ if and only if $X \in \mathscr{G}^{\tau}$;

(b) otherwise, $X \in \mathscr{G}'$ if and only if $C_S(X \cap S)$ is τ-closed *and* (if non-null) is compact.

Clearly S', $\emptyset \in \mathscr{G}'$; secondly, if $\{X_i\}$, $i \in I$, is any family of members of $\mathscr{G}'$, and $X = \bigcup_i X_i$, it is only necessary to consider case where $x_0 \in X$, that is, $x_0 \in X_{i'}$ for some i' in I. Then:

$$C_S(X \cap S) = C_S(\bigcup_i (X_i \cap S)) = \bigcap_i C_S(X_i \cap S) \in \mathscr{F}^{\tau};$$

hence $C_S(X \cap S)$ is, *a fortiori*, closed relative to the compact subset $C_S(X_{i'} \cap S)$ of S, and so satisfies (b) above; that is, $X \in \mathscr{G}'$. Thirdly, if $\{X_i\}$, $1 \leqslant i \leqslant n$, is a finite sequence of members of $\mathscr{G}'$, consider case where $x_0 \in Y \equiv \bigcap_{1 \leqslant i \leqslant n} X_i$; then $C_S(Y \cap S) = \bigcup_{1 \leqslant i \leqslant n} C_S(X_i \cap S)$, and so again (b) is satisfied, and $Y \in \mathscr{G}'$.

Thus, (by Definition 1) $\mathscr{G}'$ defines a topology τ' on S. Since clearly a given subset X of S belongs to $\mathscr{G}^{\tau}$ if and only if $X = X' \cap S$ for some member X' of $\mathscr{G}'(= \mathscr{G}^{\tau'})$, $\tau = \tau'_S$; that is, $|S,\tau|$ is a subspace of $|S',\tau'|$.

Finally, given an arbitrary τ'-open covering $\{G_i\}$, $i \in I$, of S', $\exists\, i'$ in I such that $x_0 \in G_{i'}$. Since $\{G_i\}$ covers the compact set $C_S(G_{i'} \cap S)$, there exists a finite sequence $\{i_1, \ldots, i_r\}$ of members of I such that $C_S(G_{i'} \cap S) \subseteq \bigcup_{1 \leqslant s \leqslant r} G_{i_s}$; the sets G_{i_s}, $1 \leqslant s \leqslant r$, together with $G_{i'}$, constitute a covering of S', and so $|S',\tau'|$ is compact.

Note 4 A space $|S^{*},\tau'|$ constructed as in the proof of Theorem

4.22 is said to be a **one-point compactification** of $|S,\tau|$. That a space $|S',\tau'|$ satisfying the requirements of the enunciation of this theorem need *not* however be a one-point compactification of $|S,\tau|$ in this special sense is shown by:

Example 4.7.5 Given distinct elements x,y,z,w, let $S = (x,y,z)$, $S' = (x,y,z,w)$; clearly topologies τ,τ' can be defined on S,S' respectively such that $\mathscr{G}^{\tau} = (\varnothing,S,(x),(y,z))$, $\mathscr{G}^{\tau'} = (\varnothing,S',(x),(y,z,w))$. It is easily verified that $|S,\tau|$ is a subspace of the (compact) space $|S',\tau'|$; however, the subset $\mathscr{G}'$ of $P(S')$ constructed in the proof of Theorem 4.22 would contain (y,z), *not* a member of $\mathscr{G}^{\tau'}$, so that $|S',\tau'|$ is not a one-point compactification of $|S,\tau|$.

Example 4.7.6 The metric space $(R)_1$ gives rise to the topological space $|R,\tau|$, where $\mathscr{G}^{\tau}$ contains, together with the null set, all subsets of R expressible as the union of some family of open intervals. The construction of a one-point compactification of $|R,\tau|$ then amounts to the adjunction of an element 'ω' to R, yielding a space $|R \cup (\omega),\tau'|$ where the τ'-open subsets X of $R \cup (\omega)$ are either (a) as in $\mathscr{G}^{\tau}$ if $X \subseteq R$ or (b) of the form $X_1 \cup (\omega)$ where $X_1 \in \mathscr{G}^{\tau}$ and $C_R(X_1)$ is *bounded.* (Theorem 3.13, Corollary and Theorem 3.16.) It follows from (b) that, given X such that $\omega \in X \subseteq R \cup (\omega)$, then X is a τ'-neighbourhood of ω if and only if $\exists\, a,b$ in R (with $a > b$) such that $]a, \rightarrow [\, \cup\,]\leftarrow, b[\subseteq X$. Hence a given sequence $\{x_i\}$, $i \geqslant 1$, of real numbers τ'-converges to ω if and only if given $N > 0$, $\exists$ an integer i_0 (dependent on choice of N) such that $|x_i| > N$ for $i \geqslant i_0$; that is, if and only if '$|x_i| \rightarrow \infty$'. Thus, ω acts as a 'point at infinity'.

°*Note 5* It is sometimes convenient to replace the criterion (1) for compactness in Theorem 3.8, (that is, that for an *arbitrary* family $\{F_i\}$, $i \in I$, of members of $\mathscr{F}^{\tau}$ having the finite intersection property, $\bigcap_i F_i \neq \varnothing$) by a weaker form:

†°THEOREM 4.23 A space $|S,\tau|$ is compact if and only if there exists a $\mathscr{F}^{\tau}$-subbase $\mathscr{F}''$ such that, for any family $\{F_i''\}$, $i \in I$, of members of $\mathscr{F}''$ having the finite intersection property,

$$\bigcap_i F_i'' \neq \varnothing. \tag{1'}$$

PROOF Let $\mathscr{X}_0 \equiv \{F_i\}$, $i \in I$, be an *arbitrary* family of members of $\mathscr{F}^{\tau}$ having the finite intersection property. If $\mathscr{S}$ denotes the subset of $P(\mathscr{F}^{\tau})$ of all families $\mathscr{X}$ of members of $\mathscr{F}^{\tau}$ with the finite intersection property, Tukey's Lemma (Cf. proof of Theorem 3.15)

† Theorem 4.23 provides a short proof of Theorem 3.15 (see Kelley, p. 143, Reference [6]).

can be applied to show that $\mathscr{S}$ has a maximal member $\mathscr{X}_1$ such that $\mathscr{X}_0 \subseteq \mathscr{X}_1$; that is, the members of $\mathscr{X}_1$ could be indexed in the form: $\{F_j\}, j \in K$, where $I \subseteq K$. Then:

(a) if F is a member of $\mathscr{F}^\tau$ such that $F_j \subseteq F$ for some j in K, then $F \in \mathscr{X}_1$;

(b) if $\{F^{(1)}, \ldots, F^{(n)}\}$ is a finite sequence of members of $\mathscr{F}^\tau$ such that $F^{(1)} \cup \ldots \cup F^{(n)} \in \mathscr{X}_1$, then $F^{(r)} \in \mathscr{X}_1$, for some r with $1 \leqslant r \leqslant n$.

To prove (b), it is sufficient to take $n = 2$. If neither of $F^{(1)}, F^{(2)}$ belonged to $\mathscr{X}_1$, then, by maximality of $\mathscr{X}_1$, neither of the families $\mathscr{X}_1 \cup (F^{(1)})$, $\mathscr{X}_1 \cup (F^{(2)})$ would belong to $\mathscr{S}$; it would clearly follow that there would exist a finite subfamily $\{F_{j_1}, \ldots, F_{j_r}\}$ of $\mathscr{X}_1$ such that:

$$\Big(\bigcap_{1 \leqslant s \leqslant r} F_{j_r}\Big) \cap F^{(1)} = \varnothing = \Big(\bigcap_{1 \leqslant s \leqslant r} F_{j_r}\Big) \cap F^{(2)},$$

implying evidently that $F^{(1)} \cup F^{(2)} \,\omega\, \mathscr{X}_1$.

If $x \,\omega \bigcap_{j \in K} F_j$, $\exists j'$ in K such that $x \,\omega\, F_{j'}$. If $\mathscr{F}''$ is a $\mathscr{F}^\tau$-subbase satisfying (1′), the collection $\mathscr{F}'$ of all finite unions of members of $\mathscr{F}''$ forms a $\mathscr{F}^\tau$-base on S; since $F_{j'}$ is the intersection of some family of members of $\mathscr{F}'$, $\exists$ a member F' of $\mathscr{F}'$ such that $F_{j'} \subseteq F'$, but $x \,\omega\, F'$. Now, by (a), $F' \in \mathscr{X}_1$; hence if $F' = \bigcup_{1 \leqslant i \leqslant n} F_i''$, where each $F_i'' \in \mathscr{F}''$, it follows from (b) that $F_i'' \in \mathscr{X}_1$ for some i such that $1 \leqslant i \leqslant n$; that is (writing $F_i'' = F_{j''}$) $\exists j''$ in K such that $F_{j''} \in \mathscr{F}''$ and $x \,\omega\, F_{j''}$. Hence, if K' denotes that subset of K which contains those members j such that $F_j \in \mathscr{F}''$, then K' is non-null and:

$$\bigcap_{K'} F_j \subseteq \bigcap_{K} F_j. \tag{2}$$

But on the one hand, since $K' \subseteq K$, the family $\{F_j\}, j \in K'$, has the finite intersection property; hence, by condition (1′), $\bigcap_{K'} F_j \neq \varnothing$; since, on the other hand, $\bigcap_{K} F_j \subseteq \bigcap_{I} F_i$, it follows from (2) that $\bigcap_{I} F_i \neq \varnothing$.

°**Example 4.7.7** If $(E, \leqslant)$ is a complete lattice and τ the interval topology (of Example 4.4.4), then E has least and greatest elements O,I respectively, say, and the subset $\mathscr{F}''$ of $P(E)$ containing all 'closed intervals' of the form $[O,b]$, $[a,I]$ (with an obvious notation) forms a $\mathscr{F}^\tau$-subbase on E. If $\{[a_i,b_i]\}, i \in I$, is any family of members of $\mathscr{F}''$ having the finite intersection property, then, in particular, $[a_i,b_i] \cap [a_j,b_j] \neq \varnothing$ for i,j in I; hence: $a_i \leqslant b_j$. Hence, if a

denotes $\bigvee a_i$ (the supremum of the family $\{a_i\}$), $a \in [a_i,b_i]$ for each i in I. It follows immediately from Theorem 4.23 that $|E,\tau|$ is compact. (Cf. Worked Ex. 2 on Section 4.4 and Example 4.6.3.)

°*Note 6* Provided that $(E, \leqslant)$ is given to be a lattice, it is worth remarking that the converse of the result of Example 4.7.7 above holds also; that is, on the assumption that $|E,\tau|$ is compact, it will be shown that each non-null subset X of E has a supremum and infimum. First, the family $\{M(x)\}$, $x \in X$, of members of $\mathscr{F}^\tau$ clearly possesses the finite intersection property, so that the intersection of its members is non-null; that is, $M(X) \neq \varnothing$. Then, the family $\{[x,y]\}$, where $x \in X$ and $y \in M(X)$, also possesses the finite intersection property; hence their intersection contains an element of E which is easily verified to be the supremum of X. The existence of the infimum of X is established similarly.

Note 7 Condition (a) of Theorem 3.22, (that each element x of S possess at least one compact τ-neighbourhood X) is *not* sufficient that a topological space $|S,\tau|$ be locally compact, since the argument in that theorem depends on the assumption that if G is a member of $\mathscr{G}^\tau$ such that $x \in G \subseteq X$ (where X is compact) then $X \in \mathscr{F}^\tau$, so that $\bar{G}^\tau \subseteq X$. An immediate consequence of this is the failure also of Theorem 3.24.

Example 4.7.8 In Example 4.2.3, take $|S,\tau|$ to be an infinite discrete space, and N infinite. Then a non-null subset X of T belongs to $\mathscr{G}^{\tau'}$ if and only if $N - X$ is finite. For each x in T, $G_x \equiv N \cup (x) \in \mathscr{G}^{\tau'}$ and is clearly compact. However, the infinite covering of T constituted by the family: $\{G_x\}$, $x \in S$, contains no proper sub-covering of T; consequently, T is not itself compact. Since the τ'-closure of any non-null τ'-open set G coincides with T, it follows that $|T,\tau'|$ is *not* locally compact.

4.8 Connected and Locally-Connected Spaces

The following results of Section 3.4 are not valid for topological spaces:

(I) Theorem 3.38, its Corollary, and Theorem 3.39. (Cf. Example 4.1.2.)

(II) Theorem 3.43. Indeed, a connected subset of a topological space can have any finite number of elements or be enumerably infinite.

Example 4.8.1 If S is an arbitrary enumerable set, and τ the trivial topology τ_0 on S, $|S,\tau|$ is connected.

Example 4.8.2 If S is an enumerably infinite set, and τ the topology defined in Example 4.1.2, $\mathscr{G}^\tau, \mathscr{F}^\tau$ have in common only $S, \varnothing$, so that $|S,\tau|$ is connected.

It follows that an enumerable set need not be totally disconnected.

(III) Part of Theorem 3.52, Corollary; that is, that a continuous image of a locally-connected and compact set is locally connected. For the proof depends on the assumption that a continuous function defined on a compact space is closed.

Exercises for Solution (on Sections 4.6–4.8)

1. If $|S,\tau|$ is completely separable, and $\mathscr{G}'$ is an arbitrarily chosen τ-base on S, show that $\mathscr{G}'$ contains an enumerable subset, which constitutes a τ-base on S.
2. If $|S,\tau|$ is completely separable, show that $\mathscr{G}^\tau$ can be put in (1,1) correspondence with a subset of R.
3. If $|S,\tau|$ satisfies the first axiom of countability and S is enumerable, show that $|S,\tau|$ is completely separable.
4. Given a space $|S,\tau|$, show that the following properties are equivalent:
   (a) if $\{x_i\}$, $i \geqslant 1$, is a sequence of elements of S, and if x belongs to $\bigcap_{n\geqslant 1} (\overline{\bigcup_{i\geqslant n} (x_i)}^\tau)$, then a subsequence $\{x_{i_r}\}$, $r \geqslant 1$, exists such that: $x_{i_r} \underset{\tau}{\rightarrow} x$;
   (b) if X is an infinite subset of S such that the subspace $|X,\tau_X|$ is discrete, then $X \,\omega\, \mathscr{F}^\tau$;
   (c) each enumerable τ-open covering of S contains a *finite* subcovering;
   (d) each infinite τ-open covering of S contains a *proper* subcovering.
5. If $|S,\tau|$ is such that each non-null member G of $\mathscr{G}^\tau$ has the Lindelöf property, show that:
   (a) every non-null subset X of S has the Lindelöf property;
   (b) if X is a τ-isolated subset of S, X is enumerable.
6. If $|S,\tau|$ is completely separable, and every decreasing sequence of non-null τ-closed subsets of S has a non-null intersection, show that $|S,\tau|$ is compact.
7. Give an example of a non-lattice to show that the condition that $(E,\leqslant)$ should be a lattice is essential in Note 6. Can you find an *infinite* example?
8. Show that the space $|R,\tau|$ of Example 4.6.2 is *not* connected.
9. If $S = (x,y,z,w)$, and $\mathscr{G}^\tau = (S,\varnothing,(x,y))$, verify that $|S,\tau|$ is connected. Use a (τ,τ')-continuous function to show that if $S' = (x',y',z')$ and $\mathscr{G}^{\tau'} = (S',\varnothing,(y',z'))$, then $|S',\tau'|$ is connected.

CHAPTER 5

Separation Axioms

It has been made clear in the course of the previous chapter what a wealth of properties have been lost in the generalization from a metric space to an arbitrary topological space. With a view to recovering the more important of these, the effect is now considered of postulating a succession $P_1, \ldots, P_5$ of progressively stronger conditions on a given topological space, where each of the above conditions is satisfied by any metrizable space. These conditions $P_1, \ldots, P_5$ are called the **separation axioms**. The appropriateness of such a term will be seen from the basic form common to all of these axioms (where, for the purposes of this comparison, postulate P_1 is given the alternative formulation contained in Theorem 5.1). Two additional conditions of this type also introduced are a weaker version P_0 of P_1 (see Note 1 and Theorem 5.9) and one, lying in strength between P_3 and P_4, which appears in Ex. (20) below.

5.1 T_1-Spaces

DEFINITION 1 A topological space $|S,\tau|$ is said to be a **$\mathbf{T_1}$-space** if the following condition is satisfied:
P_1: for each x in S, (x) is τ-closed.

Example 5.1.1 If τ_0 is the trivial topology on any set S with more than one element, $|S,\tau_0|$ is *not* a T_1-space.

Example 5.1.2 If $(E,\leqslant)$ is a poset, and τ the interval topology on E, $|E,\tau|$ is a T_1-space.

THEOREM 5.1 A space $|S,\tau|$ is a T_1-space if and only if for each pair x,y of distinct elements of S, there exists a τ-open subset G of S such that $y \in G$, but $x \;\omega\; G$.

PROOF Given x,y in S, $y \in \overline{(x)}^\tau$ if and only if $G \cap (x) \neq \varnothing$ for each G with $y \in G \in \mathscr{G}^\tau$, that is, $x \in G$ for each G with $y \in G \in \mathscr{G}^\tau$. Hence $\overline{(x)}^\tau$ contains x alone if and only if for each $y \neq x$, $\exists G$ in $\mathscr{G}^\tau$ with $y \in G$, $x \,\omega\, G$.

Note 1 For any T_1-space $|S,\tau|$, Theorem 4.2 entails that every finite subset X of S is τ-closed, so that $\mathscr{G}^\tau$ must contain all subsets of the form $C(X)$, where X is finite. That is, if τ' denotes the topology on S defined in Example 4.1.2, τ' is the *coarsest* topology τ on S such that $|S,\tau|$ is a T_1-space; indeed, a given topology τ yields a T_1-space if and only if $\tau' \leqslant \tau$ in T_S (notation of Section 4.3). Such topologies τ thus form a complete sub-lattice of T_S, whose minimum member is τ', and maximum member again the discrete topology τ_I. If S is finite, τ' and τ_I coincide.

THEOREM 5.2
(a) The property of being a T_1-space is a hereditary property.
(b) The product space $|S,\tau|$ of a finite sequence $\{|S_i,\tau_i|\}$, $1 \leqslant i \leqslant n$, is a T_1-space if and only if each space $|S_i,\tau_i|$ is a T_1-space.

The proof is left to the reader.

In a T_1-space, we recover Theorem 2.5:

THEOREM 5.3 Given a T_1-space $|S,\tau|$, let x be a τ-cluster point of the subset X of S; then, for each Y in $\mathscr{N}^\tau(x)$, $Y \cap X$ is an infinite set.

PROOF If not, then $\exists\, Y$ in $\mathscr{N}^\tau(x)$ such that $Y \cap X$ is finite. If $(Y - (x)) \cap X = \varnothing$, there is nothing more to prove; if not, let $x_1, x_2, \ldots, x_n$, for some positive integer n, denote its members. By Theorem 5.1, there corresponds to each i with $1 \leqslant i \leqslant n$, a member G_i of $\mathscr{G}^\tau$ with $x \in G_i$, but $x_i \,\omega\, G_i$. If $G = \bigcap_{1 \leqslant i \leqslant n} G_i$, $Z \equiv Y \cap G \in \mathscr{N}^\tau(x)$, but $(Z - (x)) \cap X = \varnothing$.

The argument of Theorem 2.11 now yields:

THEOREM 5.4 If $|S,\tau|$ is a T_1-space, and $X \subseteq S$, X'^τ is τ-closed.

Note 2 If a space $|S,\tau|$ satisfying the first axiom (of countability) is also a T_1-space, parts (a), (c) of Theorem 4.15 can be strengthened to give:

THEOREM 5.5 If a T_1-space $|S,\tau|$ satisfies the first axiom, $A \subseteq S$ and x is a member of S, then:

(a) $x \in A'^{\tau}$ if and only if there exists a sequence $\{x_i\}$ of *distinct* members of $A - (x)$ such that $x_i \underset{\tau}{\rightarrow} x$;

(b) if $\{x_i\}$ is a sequence of elements and x is a τ-cluster point of $\bigcup_{i \geq 1} (x_i)$, then there exists a subsequence $\{x_{i_r}\}$, such that $x_{i_r} \underset{\tau}{\rightarrow} x$.

PROOF (a) If $x \in A'^{\tau}$, then, by the theorem cited, $\exists$ a sequence $\{x_i\}$ of elements of $A - (x)$ such that $x_i \underset{\tau}{\rightarrow} x$. Then $Y \equiv \bigcup_{i \geq 1} (x_i)$ is infinite, for clearly $x \in \bar{Y}^{\tau} - Y$, so that $Y \omega \mathscr{F}^{\tau}$. Hence a subsequence of distinct elements can be constructed from $\{x_i\}$.

(b) The argument is analogous to that of part (c) of Theorem 2.21, where the sets $N_{r-1}(x)$ are replaced by the members of an enumerable local τ-base at x.

Example 4.4.3 shows that the condition that $|S,\tau|$ be a T_1-space cannot be omitted from either part of Theorem 5.5.

THEOREM 5.6 Given a T_1-space $|S,\tau|$, there exists a separable T_1-space of which it is a subspace.

The above result can be readily verified from the construction given in Example 4.2.3 (and from Theorem 4.20). It is worth remarking here that a separable space $|S',\tau'|$ containing $|S,\tau|$ as a subspace could have been obtained by a simpler construction (cf. Exercise (17) below) than that given in the example cited; however this would not have yielded a T_1-space.

Theorem 5.3 above implies that part (a) (as well as part (b)) of the proof of Theorem 3.9, is valid for a T_1-space $|S,\tau|$, yielding:

THEOREM 5.7 A T_1-space $|S,\tau|$ is countably compact if *and only if* any enumerable τ-open covering of S contains a finite subcovering.

COROLLARY I A countably compact T_1-space possessing the Lindelöf property is compact.

COROLLARY II A completely separable countably compact T_1-space is compact.

Corollary II follows from Theorem 4.19.

Note 3 Neither of the conditions in Corollary II can be omitted.

Example 5.1.3 Let $(E, \leqslant)$ be a non-enumerable well-ordered set possessing a greatest element. If a is its least element, and b the least element of x of E such that $[a,x[$ is non-enumerable, denote

$[a,b[$ by S. If τ is the interval topology on S (coinciding with its intrinsic topology), $|S,\tau|$ is a T_1-space which is, further, countably compact. For if X is an arbitrarily chosen infinite subset of S, it contains, by Theorem 1.5, an infinitely enumerable subset Y. Then $M_S(Y) \neq \varnothing$; otherwise there would correspond to each member x of S a member y_x of Y such that $x < y_x$. Since however each interval $[a,y_x[$ is, by the choice of b, enumerable, it would follow again from Theorem 1.5 that S itself would be enumerable. If now the members of Y are enumerated as: x_n, $n \geqslant 1$, write $Y_n = \bigcup_{m \geqslant n} (x_m)$; if c_n denotes the least member of $M_S(Y_n)$, the elements c_n, $n \geqslant 1$, will have a least member c. It is easy to verify that $c \in Y'^{\tau} \subseteq X'^{\tau}$. However $|S,\tau|$ is not compact; otherwise, it is clear from Note 6, Chapter 4, that S itself would have to possess a greatest member. It can be verified that $|S,\tau|$ is in fact not completely separable.

Secondly, Example 4.7.2 shows that the condition that $|S,\tau|$ be a T_1-space is also essential. On the other hand, Example 4.6.3 indicates that even if a T_1-space has every non-null subset compact, it need not be completely separable.

If, again, $|S,\tau|$ is a T_1-space in the construction of the space $|S',\tau'|$ of Theorem 4.22, then there is immediately proved:

THEOREM 5.8 Any one-point compactification $|S',\tau'|$ of a T_1-space $|S,\tau|$ is a T_1-space.

Note 4 (T_0-spaces.) A weaker, less important, condition than P_1 appears in:

DEFINITION 2 A space $|S,\tau|$ is said to be a **$\mathbf{T_0}$-space** if the following condition is satisfied:

P_0: if x,y are distinct elements of S, then $\overline{(x)}^{\tau} \neq \overline{(y)}^{\tau}$

Example 5.1.4 Example 5.1.1 above is *not* a T_0-space.

Example 5.1.5 In Example 4.2.1, property (b) means that the spaces $|E,\tau|$, $|E,\tau'|$ are T_0-spaces. On the other hand, if E contains a pair of distinct commensurable elements (that is, if $\leqslant$ is not the trivial partial ordering of E) it is clear that neither is a T_1-space.

An analogue of Theorem 5.1 is given by:

THEOREM 5.9 A space $|S,\tau|$ is a T_0-space if and only if for each pair x,y of distinct elements of S, there exists a τ-open subset G of S such that $G \cap (x,y)$ contains exactly one member.

PROOF Clearly P_0 holds if and only if for each pair x,y in S with $x \neq y$, either $x \,\omega\, \overline{(y)}^\tau$ or $y \,\omega\, \overline{(x)}^\tau$; that is (Cf. the proof of Theorem 5.1) there exists a member G of $\mathscr{G}^\tau$ such that either $G \cap (x,y) = (x)$ or $G \cap (x,y) = (y)$.

The distinction between the conditions appearing in Theorems 5.1 and 5.9 is brought out by noting that (since x,y can there be interchanged) that of Theorem 5.1 could be expressed in the alternative form:

'for distinct x,y in S, $\exists$ members G,G' of $\mathscr{G}^\tau$ such that: $G \cap (x,y) = (x)$, $G' \cap (x,y) = (y)$'.

5.2 T_2-Spaces (Hausdorff)

DEFINITION 3 A topological space $|S,\tau|$ is said to be a **T_2-space** (or a **Hausdorff** space) if:

P_2: for each pair x,y of distinct elements of S, there exist τ-open subsets G,G' of S such that $G \cap G' = \varnothing$, $x \in G$, $y \in G'$.

It is clear from Theorem 5.1 that any T_2-space is a T_1-space.

Example 5.2.1 The space $|S,\tau|$ of Example 4.1.2 is a T_1-space, but is not a T_2-space.

Example 5.2.2 The space $|S,\tau|$ of Example 4.2.2 is a T_2-space. Considering only the case where $x \neq 1$, $y = 1$, let $Y = Z \cup (1)$, where Z is the set of elements of S of the form: $2^i(2j - 1)$, where $j \in S$ and $j > i + x$. If $X = (x)$, X and Y belong respectively to $\mathscr{N}^\tau(x)$, $\mathscr{N}^\tau(1)$, and are disjoint.

Example 5.2.3 Given any chain $(E, \leqslant)$, $|E,\tau^E|$ is a T_2-space. For if $x < z < y$, then $G \equiv]\leftarrow, z[$ and $G' \equiv]z, \rightarrow[$ satisfy P_2, while if no such z exists in E, take $G =]\leftarrow, y[$, $G' =]x, \rightarrow[$.

A study of the proof of Theorem 2.46 (and Corollaries) gives almost immediately:

THEOREM 5.10 If $|S',\tau'|$ is the product space of $|S,\tau|$, $|S,\tau|$, then $|S,\tau|$ is a T_2-space if and only if the diagonal Δ_S belongs to $\mathscr{F}^{\tau'}$.

COROLLARY I Given spaces $|S,\tau|$, $|S'\tau'|$, where the latter is a T_2-space, let f,g be (τ,τ')-continuous functions from S into S'; then the set of elements x of S where $f(x) = g(x)$ belongs to $\mathscr{F}^\tau$.

COROLLARY II With $|S,\tau|$, $|S',\tau'|$ and f as in Corollary I, let $|S'',\tau''|$ be the product space of $|S,\tau|$, $|S',\tau'|$; then the graph of f on S belongs to $\mathscr{F}^{\tau''}$.

If $|S,\tau|$ is a T_2-space, and τ' a topology on S which is finer than τ, clearly $|S,\tau'|$ is a T_2-space. An exact analogue of Theorem 5.2 above holds for T_2-spaces.

The most significant properties of a T_2-space appear in Theorems 5.11 and 5.13 below:

THEOREM 5.11 Given a space $|S,\tau|$, the condition: 'a sequence $\{x_i\}$, $i \geqslant 1$, of elements of S cannot τ-converge to more than one element of S' (1)

is

(a) a *necessary* condition that $|S,\tau|$ be a T_2-space

(b) a sufficient condition that $|S,\tau|$ be a T_2-space *provided that* $|S,\tau|$ satisfies the first axiom (of countability).

PROOF (a) Suppose that $|S,\tau|$ is a T_2-space and that $\exists$ distinct elements x,y such that $x_i \underset{\tau}{\rightarrow} x$, $x_i \underset{\tau}{\rightarrow} y$. If G,G' are chosen as in P_2 above (of Definition 3), $\exists$ integers i_0, i_0' such that $x_i \in G$, $x_i \in G'$ for $i \geqslant i_0, i_0'$ implying $x_i \in G \cap G'$ for i sufficiently large, and so a contradiction is obtained.

(b) If $|S,\tau|$ satisfies the first axiom, but is *not* a T_2-space, $\exists$ distinct elements x,y such that for each X in $\mathcal{N}^\tau(x)$, Y in $\mathcal{N}^\tau(y)$, $X \cap Y \neq \varnothing$. If $\{X_i\}$, $\{Y_i\}$, $i \geqslant 1$, are (enumerable) monotonic decreasing local τ-bases at x,y, respectively, and if $x_i \in X_i \cap Y_i$ for each $i \geqslant 1$, clearly $x_i \underset{\tau}{\rightarrow} x$, $x_i \underset{\tau}{\rightarrow} y$, contradicting condition (1).

Note 5 The following example shows that the proviso in Theorem 5.11(b) cannot be omitted:

Example 5.2.4 If $|S,\tau|$ is the space of Example 4.1.3 it is clear that it satisfies condition (a) of Theorem 5.11. However, for any non-null G,G' in $\mathcal{G}^\tau$, $G \cap G' \neq \varnothing$ (indeed, non-enumerable). It was pointed out in Example 4.4.5 that $|S,\tau|$ does not satisfy the first axiom.

It is also worth noting that a T_2-space (for example, that of Example 5.2.2 above and Example 5.2.5 below) need not satisfy the first axiom; that is, Theorem 5.11(b) does not yield a necessary condition.

THEOREM 5.12 If a T_2-space $|S,\tau|$ satisfies the first axiom, any countably compact subset A of S is τ-closed.

PROOF If $x \in A'^\tau$, then, by Theorem 5.5(a) $\exists$ a sequence $\{x_i\}$ of distinct members of $A - (x)$ such that $x_i \underset{\tau}{\rightarrow} x$. Now $X \equiv \bigcup_i (x_i)$ must, by assumption, have a τ-cluster point y in A. Then, by part (b) of the theorem cited, $\{x_i\}$ contains a subsequence $\{x_{i_r}\}$ such that $x_{i_r} \underset{\tau}{\rightarrow} y$. But clearly $x_{i_r} \underset{\tau}{\rightarrow} x$; hence, by Theorem 5.11(a) $x = y$, and so $x \in A$.

If A is compact, the condition on $|S,\tau|$ can be weakened to give:

THEOREM 5.13 If $|S,\tau|$ is a T_2-space, A a proper compact subset of S, and x belongs to $C(A)$, there exist τ-open subsets G,G' of S such that $G \cap G' = \varnothing$, $A \subseteq G$, and x belongs to G'.

The proof is as for Theorem 3.13.

COROLLARY For a T_2-space $|S,\tau|$, any compact subset of S is τ-closed.

°*Note 6* In the Corollary above, it is *not* sufficient merely to assume that A is countably compact; that is, the condition that $|S,\tau|$ should satisfy the first axiom is essential to Theorem 5.12.

°**Example 5.2.5** If $(E, \leqslant)$ is as in Example 5.1.3, and τ the intrinsic topology τ^E on E, then from Example 5.2.3 above, $|E,\tau|$ is a T_2-space. If A is the subset of E denoted by S in the example cited, then it is clear from Exercise 5 on Section 4.4 that A is a countably compact *subset* of $|E,\tau|$. However, A is *not* τ-closed, otherwise (since $|E,\tau|$ is compact, by Theorem 1.8, Corollary, and Example 4.7.7) A would itself be compact. It can be verified that in fact there does *not* exist an enumerable local τ-base at b.

Theorem 5.13 can be strengthened to give:

THEOREM 5.14 If $|S,\tau|$ is a T_2-space, and A_i, $i = 1,2$, are disjoint compact subsets of S, there exist τ-open subsets G_i of S such that $G_1 \cap G_2 = \varnothing$ and $A_i \subseteq G_i$ for $i = 1,2$.

PROOF Corresponding to each x in A_1, $\exists$ (by Theorem 5.13) disjoint τ-open sets G_x, G'_x such that $A_2 \subseteq G_x$, and $x \in G'_x$. Since the family $\{G'_x\}$, $x \in A_1$, covers the compact set A_1, $\exists$ a finite set $x_1, \ldots, x_n$ of elements of A_1 such that $G_1 \equiv \bigcup_{1 \leqslant i \leqslant n} G'_{x_i}$ covers A_1. If $G_2 = \bigcap_{1 \leqslant i \leqslant n} G_{x_i}$, clearly G_i satisfy the requirements stated.

Just as for Theorem 3.18 (and Corollary) there follow from the Corollary to Theorem 5.13:

THEOREM 5.15 If $|S,\tau|$ is compact, $|S',\tau'|$ is a T_2-space and f is a (τ,τ')-continuous function from S into S', f is (τ,τ')-closed.

COROLLARY If $|S,\tau|$, $|S',\tau'|$, f are as above, and, in addition, f is (1,1) onto S', then f is a (τ,τ')-homeomorphism.

If $|S',\tau'|$ is a T_2-space, the situation exemplified in Note 4, Chapter 4, cannot arise; that is:

THEOREM 5.16 If $|S',\tau'|$is a compact T_2-space, and $|S,\tau|$ a subspace of $|S',\tau'|$ such that $S' - S$ has one member only, then $|S',\tau'|$ is a one-point compactification of $|S,\tau|$.

PROOF If $S' = S \cup (x_0)$, and $\mathscr{G}'$ is defined as in Theorem 4.22, it will be shown that $\mathscr{G}' = \mathscr{G}^{\tau'}$, the set of τ'-open subsets of S'. Given $X \subseteq S'$, consider two cases:

(a) $X \subseteq S$. Since $|S',\tau'|$ is *a fortiori* a T_1-space, $x_0 \in \mathscr{F}^{\tau'}$. Hence $S \in \mathscr{G}^{\tau'}$ and so (from Theorem 2.27) $X \in \mathscr{G}^{\tau'}$ if and only if $X \in \mathscr{G}^{\tau}$.

(b) $X \nsubseteq S$. By Theorem 1.1,
$C_S(X \cap S) = S \cap C_{S'}(X) = C_{S'}(X)$, so that

$$X \in \mathscr{G}^{\tau'} \quad \text{if and only if} \quad C_S(X \cap S) \in \mathscr{F}^{\tau'}. \tag{1}$$

On the other hand, (neglecting the case: $X = S'$) it is clear from Theorem 5.13, Corollary, since $|S,\tau|$ is a subspace of the T_2-space $|S',\tau'|$, that: $X \in \mathscr{G}'$ if and only if $C_S(X \cap S)$ is compact w.r.t. the space $|S,\tau|$ *or* (clearly equivalently) w.r.t. the space $|S',\tau'|$. But, applying Theorem 5.13, Corollary, to $|S',\tau'|$ shows that the latter condition on $C_S(X \cap S)$ is equivalent to the right-hand side of (1) and the required result immediately follows.

A partial analogue of Theorem 5.8:

THEOREM 5.17 A one-point compactification $|S',\tau'|$ of a given space $|S,\tau|$ is a T_2-space if and only if $|S,\tau|$ is a *locally-compact* T_2-space.

PROOF If $|S',\tau'|$ is a T_2-space, the subspace $|S,\tau|$ is, first of all, a T_2-space. Secondly, if $x \in S$, $\exists$ disjoint τ'-open subsets G,G' of S' such that $x \in G$, $x_0 \in G'$ (where $S' = S \cup (x_0)$). By the construction of τ' on S', G is clearly a τ-open subset of S, while $C_S(G' \cap S)$ is compact and τ-closed. But, since $G \subseteq C_S(G' \cap S)$, $\bar{G}^{\tau}$ is clearly closed *relative to* $C_S(G' \cap S)$, and hence is itself compact. That is, $|S,\tau|$ is locally compact. Conversely, if $|S,\tau|$ is given to be a locally compact T_2-space, and x,y are distinct elements of S', consider only the case where $y = x_0$. By assumption, $\exists$ a τ-open subset G of S such that $x \in G$ and $\bar{G}^{\tau}$ is compact. If $G' = C_{S'}(\bar{G}^{\tau})$, then $G \cap G' = \varnothing$, $x_0 \in G'$ and $C_S(G' \cap S) = C_S(C_S(\bar{G}^{\tau})) = \bar{G}^{\tau}$, which is τ-closed and compact; that is, G', as well as G, are τ'-open subsets of S', and the proof is complete.

Theorem 5.13 is further used to prove an analogue of Theorem 3.33.

THEOREM 5.18 If $|S,\tau|$ is a compact T_2-space, it is of the Second Category.

PROOF If $|S,\tau|$ were of the First Category, $\exists$ sequence $\{X_i\}$, $i \geqslant 1$, of τ-nowhere-dense subsets of S such that $S = \bigcup_{i \geqslant 1} X_i$. Since the τ-closure of each X_i is clearly also τ-nowhere-dense, there will be no loss of generality in assuming that each $X_i \in \mathscr{F}^\tau$. Since $C(X_1)$ is τ-dense, an element x_1 can be chosen in it; since X_1 is compact, $\exists$ (by Theorem 5.13) disjoint members G_1,H_1 of $\mathscr{G}^\tau$ such that $x_1 \in G_1$ and $X_1 \subseteq H_1$. Since $C(H_1) \in \mathscr{F}^\tau$, $\bar{G}_1^\tau \subseteq C(H_1)$, giving: $\bar{G}_1^\tau \cap X_1 = \varnothing$. Secondly, $G_1 \cap C(X_2)$ is non-null (otherwise $G_1 \subseteq X_2$, implying $X_2^{\circ\tau} \neq \varnothing$) and if an element x_2 is chosen there, Theorem 5.13 can as above be used to establish the existence of a member G_2 of $\mathscr{G}^\tau$ such that $x_2 \in G_2$, but where $\bar{G}_2^\tau \cap (C(G_1) \cup X_2) = \varnothing$ (since $C(G_1) \cup X_2 = C(G_1 \cap C(X_2))$, a τ-closed, and hence compact set, not containing x_2). This process can be continued to construct recursively a sequence $\{G_i\}$, $i \geqslant 1$, of τ-open sets as follows: if, given $i > 2$, τ-open sets $G_1, \ldots, G_{i-1}$ have been constructed so that:

$$\begin{aligned} \bar{G}_1^\tau \cap X_1 &= \bar{G}_2^\tau \cap (C(G_1) \cup X_2) = \ldots \\ &= \bar{G}_{i-1}^\tau \cap (C(G_{i-2}) \cup X_{i-1}) = \varnothing \qquad \text{(A)} \end{aligned}$$

choose an element x_i in $G_{i-1} \cap C(X_i)$. Then, as above, $\exists\, G_i$ in $\mathscr{G}^\tau$ such that $x_i \in G_i$, and $\bar{G}_i^\tau \cap (C(G_{i-1}) \cup X_i) = \varnothing$; that is, (A) holds with i replaced by $i + 1$.

Now, for each $i \geqslant 2$, $\bar{G}_i^\tau \cap C(G_{i-1}) = \varnothing$, and so $\bar{G}_i^\tau \subseteq G_{i-1} \subseteq \bar{G}_{i-1}^\tau$; it follows from Theorem 3.8, Corollary, that $\exists$ an element x in $\bigcap_{i \geqslant 1} \bar{G}_i^\tau$. However if j is an integer such that $x \in X_j$, this would imply that $\bar{G}_j^\tau \cap X_j \neq \varnothing$, a contradiction.

Note 7 The condition in Theorem 5.18 that $|S,\tau|$ be a T_2-space cannot be omitted or, indeed, weakened to a requirement that it be a T_1-space.

Example 5.2.6 If S is any enumerably infinite set, and τ the topology on S defined in Example 4.1.2, then $|S,\tau|$ is a T_1-space which (as in Example 4.6.3) is compact. However if $S = \bigcup_{i \geqslant 1} (x_i)$, then each $(x_i) \in \mathscr{F}^\tau - \mathscr{G}^\tau$, so that clearly $\left(\overline{(x_i)}\right)^{\circ\tau} = \varnothing$; that is, (x_i) is τ-nowhere-dense.

Note 8 A consequence of the Corollary to Theorem 5.13 is that a T_2-space $|S,\tau|$ is locally compact *if* (as well as only if) each element of x possesses a compact τ-neighbourhood. (Cf. Note 7, Chapter 4.) Hence Theorem 3.24 will hold in the form:

THEOREM 5.19 Given a space $|S,\tau|$, a T_2-space $|S',\tau'|$, and a locally compact subset A of S, let f be a (τ,τ')-continuous and open function from A into S'; then $f(A)$ is locally compact.

A consequence of Theorem 5.15 is that Theorem 3.52, Corollary holds in the form:

THEOREM 5.20 Given a space $|S,\tau|$, and a T_2-space $|S',\tau'|$, let A be a locally connected and compact subset of S; if f is a (τ,τ')-continuous function from A into S', $f(A)$ is locally connected (and compact).

5.3 T_3-Spaces (Regular)

DEFINITION 4 A topological space $|S,\tau|$ is said to be a **T_3-space** (or a **regular** space) if:

P_3 (i) $|S,\tau|$ is a T_1-space;
(ii) if X is a non-null proper τ-closed subset of S, and x belongs to $C(X)$, there exist τ-open subsets G,G' of S such that $G \cap G' = \varnothing$, $X \subseteq G$, and $x \in G'$.

Part (i) of condition P_3 ensures that any T_3-space (or regular space) will be a T_2-space. (Cf. Example 5.3.2 below.) Some authors, however (for example, Kelley, p. 113, Reference [6] and Hall and Spencer, p. 64, Reference [2]) require of a 'regular space' *only* that it should satisfy part (ii) of condition P_3, while (as in Kelley, p. 113, Reference [6]) a 'T_3-space' is required to satisfy both parts of P_3.

Example 5.3.1 The space $|S,\tau|$ now constructed is a T_2-space which is *not* a T_3-space. If S denotes the subset of R^2 containing those points $x \equiv \{x_1,x_2\}$ such that $x_2 \geqslant 0$, and A the subset of S of those points where $x_2 = 0$, then, corresponding to each x in S, and real number $r > 0$, define a subset $X_r(x)$ of S as follows:

$$X_r(x) = \begin{cases} N_r(x) \cap S & \text{if } x \in S - A \\ [N_r(x) \cap (S - A)] \cup (x) & \text{if } x \in A \end{cases}$$

(where $N_r(x)$ has its usual meaning in $(R^2)_1$).

The collection $\mathscr{G}'$ of all sets $X_r(x)$ for x in S and $r > 0$ clearly satisfies condition (a) of Theorem 4.8. With regard to condition (b), if $x \in S$ and X,X' are members of $\mathscr{G}'$ each containing x, $\exists$ points

y,y' of S and real numbers r,r' such that $X = X_r(y)$, $X' = X_{r'}(y')$.

Suppose *first* that $x \in S - A$; then there are the following cases:

Case 1 $y,y' \in S - A$; that is, $X = N_r(y) \cap S$, $X' = N_{r'}(y') \cap S$. If $s > 0$ is chosen so that $N_s(x) \subseteq N_r(y) \cap N_{r'}(y')$ (this is possible since $N_r(y)$, $N_{r'}(y')$ are neighbourhoods of x in the *metric space* $(R^2)_1$), then $x \in X_s(x) \subseteq X \cap X'$.

Case 2 $y \in S - A$, $y' \in A$; so that $X' = [N_{r'}(y') \cap (S - A)] \cup (y')$. Since $S - A$ is clearly open in $(R^2)_1$ and $x \in N_{r'}(y') \cap (S - A)$ (since $x \neq y'$), $\exists t > 0$ with $N_t(x) \subseteq N_{r'}(y') \cap (S - A)$. Now apply Case 1 to $X_r(y)$, $X_t(x)$.

Case 3, where $y \in A$, $y' \in S - A$, is of course similar to Case 2 while, in the remaining Case 4 (where $y,y' \in A$) the argument of Case 2 could be repeated for both X and X'.

If, *secondly*, $x \in A$, four cases 1′–4′ arise as before: In Case 1′, choose s as in Case 1; then $x \in X'' \subseteq X \cap X'$, where $X'' = X_s(x)$. In Case 2′, it is clear that $X' = X_{r'}(x)$; then if r'' is chosen so that $0 < r'' \leqslant r'$ and $N_{r''}(x) \subseteq N_r(y)$, $x \in X'' \subseteq X \cap X'$ where $X'' = X_{r''}(x)$. In Case 4′, x,y,y' coincide, so that if $r'' = \min(r,r')$, $x \in X_{r''}(x) \subseteq X \cap X'$.

If τ is the topology defined on S of which $\mathscr{G}'$ is a τ-base, it is easily seen that $|S,\tau|$ is a T_2-space. On the other hand, let X denote the subset $C_A(x_0)$ of A, where $x_0 = \{0,0\}$. For each x in A and $r > 0$, $(x) = X_r(x) \cap A \in \mathscr{N}^{\tau_A}(x)$; that is, $|A,\tau_A|$ is a discrete space, so that $X \in \mathscr{F}_A$. Hence, since clearly $A \in \mathscr{F}^\tau$, $X \in \mathscr{F}^\tau$. Now let G,G' be any two members of $\mathscr{G}^\tau$ such that $X \subseteq G$, and $x_0 \in G'$. Choose $r > 0$ so that

$$N_r(x_0) \cap (S - A) \subset G'. \tag{1}$$

If $x' = \{\frac{1}{2}r,0\}$, then $x' \in G$, and so $r' > 0$ can be chosen so that:

$$N_{r'}(x') \cap (S - A) \subset G. \tag{2}$$

Now choose $0 < s < \min(\frac{1}{2}r,r')$; then if $x'' = \{\frac{1}{2}r,s\}$ it is clear that $x'' \in N_r(x_0) \cap N_{r'}(x') \cap (S - A)$; hence, from (1), (2), $x'' \in G \cap G'$, so that G,G' cannot be mutually disjoint.

Example 5.3.2 If $|S,\tau|$ is defined as in Example 4.7.5, then $\mathscr{G}^\tau$ and $\mathscr{F}^\tau$ coincide, so that clearly condition P_3 (ii) is satisfied; however, since $\overline{(y)}^\tau = (y,z) \supset (y)$, P_3 (i) is not satisfied.

Example 5.3.3 Theorem 2.17 shows that any metrizable space is regular.

THEOREM 5.21 A space $|S,\tau|$ satisfies condition P_3, part (ii) if and only if for each x in S, and τ-open subset G of S containing x, there exists a τ-open set G' containing x and such that $\bar{G}'^{\tau} \subseteq G$.

PROOF Given that $|S,\tau|$ satisfies P_3, (ii), suppose $x \in G \subset S$; then $x \,\omega\, C(G) \in \mathscr{F}^{\tau}$ so $\exists$ disjoint τ-open sets G',G'' such that $x \in G'$ and $C(G) \subseteq G''$. Then, since $C(G'') \in \mathscr{F}^{\tau}$, $\bar{G}'^{\tau} \subseteq C(G'') \subseteq G$. The converse follows just as in the first part of the theorem cited in Example 5.3.3 above.

COROLLARY A T_1-space $|S,\tau|$ is regular if and only if the condition of Theorem 5.21 is satisfied.

With the help of Theorem 5.21, condition P_3, part (ii) can be seen to be equivalent to an apparently stronger requirement:

THEOREM 5.22 If $|S,\tau|$ satisfies condition P_3, part (ii), then if X is a non-null proper τ-closed subset of S, and x belongs to $C(X)$, there exist τ-open subsets G,G' of S such that $X \subseteq G$, $x \in G'$, and $\bar{G}^{\tau} \cap \bar{G}'^{\tau} = \varnothing$.

PROOF Since $C(X) \in \mathscr{G}^{\tau}$, $\exists$ by Theorem 5.21 a τ-open set G'' such that $x \in G''$ and $\bar{G}''^{\tau} \subseteq C(X)$; a second application of that theorem yields the existence of a further member G_2 of $\mathscr{G}^{\tau}$ such that $x \in G_2$ and $\bar{G}_2^{\tau} \subseteq G''$. It can easily be verified that $G_1 \equiv C(\bar{G}''^{\tau})$ and G_2 satisfy the requirements of the enunciation.

It is easily verified that an exact analogue of Theorem 5.2 holds for T_3-spaces. It is clear from Theorem 5.13 that any compact T_2-space is regular; however, application of the idea of one-point compactification allows an almost immediate improvement of this result to:

THEOREM 5.23 A locally-compact T_2-space $|S,\tau|$ is regular.

PROOF By Theorem 5.17, a one-point compactification $|S',\tau'|$ of $|S,\tau|$ is a T_2-space; the remarks above imply that the subspace $|S,\tau|$ of $|S',\tau'|$ is regular.

5.4 T_4-Spaces (Normal)

DEFINITION 5 A topological space $|S,\tau|$ is said to be a **T_4-space** (or a **normal** space) if:

P_4
- (i) $|S,\tau|$ is a T_1-space;
- (ii) if X,Y are non-null τ-closed subsets of S such that $X \cap Y = \varnothing$, there exist τ-open subsets G,G' of S such that $G \cap G' = \varnothing$, $X \subseteq G$, $Y \subseteq G'$.

Example 5.3.2 serves to show that condition P_4, part (i) is *not* implied by part (ii) and so is required in order to ensure that any T_4-space will be a T_3-space. With regard to the term 'normal space', similar inconsistencies of usage obtain as for 'regular space'.

°**Example 5.4.1** The space $|S,\tau|$ now constructed is a T_3-space which is *not* a T_4-space. If S,A are as in Example 5.3.1, define (corresponding to each x in S and real number $r > 0$) a subset $X_r(x)$ of S:

$$X_r(x) = \begin{cases} N_r(x) \cap S & \text{if } x \in S - A \\ N_r(\{x_1,r\}) \cup (x) & \text{if } x \equiv \{x_1,0\} \in A. \end{cases}$$

Rather as in the example just cited, it could be shown that a topology τ' could be defined on S such that $\mathscr{G}' \equiv \{X_r(x)\}$, $x \in S$, $r > 0$, forms a τ'-base. $|S,\tau'|$ is clearly a T_1-space; to see that P_3(ii) is also satisfied, note first that if $x \equiv \{x_1,x_2\} \in S - A$ and $r > 0$ and if $S_r(x)$ (denoting the set of elements y *in* R^2 with $\rho_1(x,y) \leqslant r$) is *a subset of* S, then $S_r(x) \in \mathscr{F}^{\tau'}$; that is, $C_S(S_r(x)) \in \mathscr{G}^{\tau'}$. For, given $y \equiv \{y_1,y_2\}$ in $C_S(S_r(x))$, suppose first that $y_2 > 0$, so that $y \in S - A$; then clearly $\exists \varepsilon > 0$ such that $X_\varepsilon(y) \subseteq C_S(S_r(x))$. If, on the other hand, $y_2 = 0$, so that $y \in A$, then it can be verified that $N_\varepsilon(\{y_1,\varepsilon\}) \subseteq C_S(S_r(x))$ if ε is chosen so that:

$$\frac{(x_1 - y_1)^2 + (x_2^2 - r^2)}{2(r + x_2)} > \varepsilon,$$

where the left-hand expression is clearly positive. (See Figure 2.) That is, $\exists \varepsilon > 0$ such that $X_\varepsilon(y) \subseteq C_S(S_r(x))$. Given now $x \equiv \{x_1,x_2\}$ in S, and a τ'-open set G containing x, suppose first that $x_2 > 0$; then $\exists\, r > 0$ such that $N_r(x) \subseteq G$. Since $S_{r/2}(x) \in \mathscr{F}^{\tau'}$, $\overline{X_{\frac{1}{2}r}(x)}^{\tau'} \subseteq G$. If, secondly, $x_2 = 0$, choose $r > 0$ such that $X_r(x) \subseteq G$. Then: $X_{r/2}(x) \subseteq S_{r/2}(\{x_1,r/2\}) \in \mathscr{F}^{\tau'}$, implying:

$$\overline{X_{r/2}(x)}^{\tau'} \subseteq N_r(\{x_1,r\}) \cup (x) = X_r(x).$$

That is, writing $G' = X_{r/2}(x)$ in either case gives: $\bar{G}'^{\tau'} \subseteq G$; hence, by Theorem 5.21, P_3(ii) is satisfied.

On the other hand, let B denote the subset of A of those points $\{x_1,0\}$ where $x_1 \in Q$, and denote $C_A(B)$ by C. Since (as in Example 5.3.1) it is clear that $A \in \mathscr{F}^{\tau'}$ and that $|A,\tau'_A|$ is discrete, B and C both belong to $\mathscr{F}^{\tau'}$. Now let G,G' be any two members of $\mathscr{G}^{\tau'}$ such that $B \subseteq G$, $C \subseteq G'$; it is required to show that $G \cap G' \neq \varnothing$.

Figure 2.

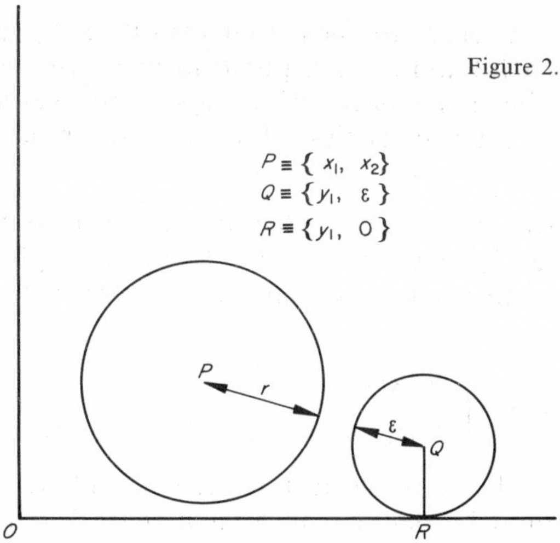

For each $n = 1,2,\ldots$, let L_n denote the set of those elements $x \equiv \{x_1,x_2\}$ of S with $x_2 = n^{-1}$; write $G_n = G \cap L_n$, $G'_n = G' \cap L_n$; let π denote the projection, restricted to S, of R^2 onto A. If $x \in B$, $x \in G \in \mathscr{G}^{\tau'}$; hence $\exists$ an integer n (depending on the choice of x) such that $X_{m^{-1}}(x) \subseteq G$ for $m \geqslant n$. In particular, $\{x,m^{-1}\} \in G_m$ for $m \geqslant n$ and hence $x \in \pi(G_m)$ for $m \geqslant n$. Thus:

$$B \subseteq \bigcup_{n\geqslant 1} \Big(\bigcap_{m\geqslant n} \pi(G_m)\Big) \subseteq \bigcap_{n\geqslant 1} \Big(\bigcup_{m\geqslant n} \pi(G_m)\Big). \tag{1}$$

Similarly

$$C \subseteq \bigcup_{n\geqslant 1} \Big(\bigcap_{m\geqslant n} \pi(G'_m)\Big). \tag{2}$$

But it is easily seen that $\pi(G_m)$ is a ρ_1-open subset of A (where ρ_1 is the usual metric on A); hence, by Theorem 3.34, Corollary II, the extreme left- and right-hand sides of (1) cannot coincide. It follows that the right-hand side of (1) must have a point in common with that of (2), so that there must exist an integer m_1 such that: $\pi(G_{m_1}) \cap \pi(G'_{m_1}) \neq \varnothing$, implying: $G \cap G' \neq \varnothing$.

Example 5.4.2 Theorem 3.38, Corollary shows that any metrizable space is normal.

The argument of Theorem 3.39 yields an exact analogue of Theorem 5.22 above:

THEOREM 5.24 If $|S,\tau|$ satisfies condition P_4, part (ii), then if X,Y are non-null τ-closed subsets of S such that $X \cap Y = \varnothing$, there exist τ-open subsets G,G' of S such that $X \subseteq G$, $Y \subseteq G'$ and $\bar{G}^{\tau} \cap \bar{G}'^{\tau} = \varnothing$.

THEOREM 5.25 A compact T_2-space $|S,\tau|$ is normal.
The proof is immediate from Theorem 5.14.

Note 9 The condition in Theorem 5.25 that $|S,\tau|$ be a T_2-space cannot be omitted, or weakened to a requirement that it be a T_1-space. Example 5.2.1 provides a compact T_1-space which is not a T_2-space. It might nevertheless be expected that, in view of the argument of Theorem 5.23, the compactness condition could here be weakened, as there, to *local* compactness. That argument however fails here since, unlike its predecessors, P_4 is *not* a hereditary property of a space. (See Example 5.4.4 below.)

That is to say, the condition P_5 now introduced is *strictly* stronger than condition P_4:

DEFINITION 6 A topological space $|S,\tau|$ is said to be a **T_5-space** (or a **completely normal** space) if:
P_5: for each non-null subset A of S, the subspace $|A,\tau_A|$ is normal.

Clearly P_5 is a hereditary property of a space.

THEOREM 5.26 A space $|S,\tau|$ is completely normal if and only if:
(a) $|S,\tau|$ is a T_1-space;
(b) given that X,Y are any two mutually τ-separated subsets of S, there exist τ-open subsets G,G' of S such that $G \cap G' = \varnothing$, $X \subseteq G$, $Y \subseteq G'$.

PROOF If $|S,\tau|$ is given to be completely normal, part (a) follows immediately from Definition 5. To prove part (b), write $A = C(\bar{X}^{\tau} \cap \bar{Y}^{\tau})$. Since X,Y are mutually τ-separated, X,Y are subsets of A, while: $\bar{X}^{\tau_A} \cap \bar{Y}^{\tau_A} = (\bar{X}^{\tau} \cap \bar{Y}^{\tau}) \cap A = \varnothing$. Hence, since $|A,\tau_A|$ is, by assumption, normal, $\exists\, G,G'$ in $\mathscr{G}_A$ such that $G \cap G' = \varnothing$, $\bar{X}^{\tau_A} \subseteq G$, $\bar{Y}^{\tau_A} \subseteq G'$. But, since $A \in \mathscr{G}^{\tau}$, G,G' both belong to $\mathscr{G}^{\tau}$ and (b) holds.

Conversely, if $|A,\tau_A|$ is any subspace of $|S,\tau|$, clearly $|A,\tau_A|$ satisfies P_4(i). Secondly, if X,Y are disjoint non-null members of $\mathscr{F}_A$, $X = \bar{X}^{\tau} \cap A$, $Y = \bar{Y}^{\tau} \cap A$ so that: $X \cap \bar{Y}^{\tau} = (X \cap A) \cap \bar{Y}^{\tau} = \varnothing = \bar{X}^{\tau} \cap Y$. Hence, immediately from condition (b) above, $\exists$ disjoint members G,G' of $\mathscr{G}^{\tau}$ such that $X \subseteq G$, $Y \subseteq G'$. Since the sets $G'' \equiv G \cap A$, $G''' \equiv G' \cap A$ are members of $\mathscr{G}_A$ with similar properties, it follows that $|A,\tau_A|$ satisfies P_4(ii).

Example 5.4.3 Theorem 3.38 and Theorem 5.26 show that any metrizable space is completely normal.

°**Example 5.4.4** Let $(E, \leqslant)$ and its elements a,b be as in Example 5.1.3. If c denotes the least member y of E such that $[a,y[$ is infinite, let τ,τ' denote the intrinsic topologies on $S \equiv [a,b]$ and $S' \equiv [a,c]$ respectively. By Theorem 1.8, Corollary and Example 4.7.7, the spaces $|S,\tau|$, $|S',\tau'|$ are compact. It is thus clear that the product space $|S'',\tau''|$ is compact, as well as T_2, and hence by Theorem 5.25 it is normal. It will however now be shown that if $A = S'' - \{b,c\}$, the subspace $|A,\tau''_A|$ is *not* normal (incidentally providing a further example of a regular non-normal space). If $X = (b) \times [a,c[$ and $Y = [a,b[\times (c)$, then X,Y are disjoint subsets of A which are τ''_A-closed (since, for example, $X = X_1 \cap A$, where $X_1 = (b) \times S' \in \mathscr{F}^{\tau''}$). Suppose that $\exists$ members G_1,G_2 of $\mathscr{G}^{\tau_A}$ such that $G_1 \cap G_2 = \varnothing$, $X \subseteq G_1$, $Y \subseteq G_2$. Then it is clear that corresponding to each member x of $[a,c[$, $\exists$ a member G'_x of $\mathscr{G}^{\tau}$ with b in G'_x and $G'_x \times (x) \subseteq G_1$; that is, $\exists$ a member z_x of $[a,b[$ such that $]z_x,b] \times (x) \subseteq G_1$. But the set of such elements z_x is enumerable and hence, as seen in the example cited at the beginning, is bounded above in $[a,b[$; it follows that $\exists$ an element d in $[a,b[$ such that: $]d,b] \times [a,c[\subseteq G_1$. Hence clearly:

$$]d,b[\times (c) \subseteq Y \cap ((\overline{]d,b]}^{\tau} \times \overline{[a,c[}^{\tau'}) \cap A) \subseteq Y \cap \overline{G_1}^{\tau''_A} .$$

Since, however, the disjointness of G_1,G_2 implies that of $\overline{G_1}^{\tau''_A}$ and G_2, a contradiction is obtained.

It is clear from Theorems 5.16 and 5.17 that $|A,\tau''_A|$ is locally compact.

It is worth remarking that the analogue of the second part also of Theorem 5.2 above fails for T_4-spaces. If $|S,\tau'|$ is the space of Example 4.6.2, then it can be shown (Kelley, pp. 133–4, Reference [6]), that although $|S,\tau'|$ is the product space of a normal space $|R,\tau|$ by itself, it is not itself normal.

THEOREM 5.27 If $|S,\tau|$ is regular and completely separable, it is completely normal.

PROOF Clearly $|S,\tau|$ satisfies condition (a) of Theorem 5.26. Secondly, if X,Y are given mutually τ-separated subsets of S, then for each x in X, $x \in C(\overline{Y}^{\tau}) \in \mathscr{G}^{\tau}$; hence (by Theorem 5.21, Corollary) $\exists$ G_x in $\mathscr{G}^{\tau}$ such that $x \in G_x$ and $\overline{G}^{\tau}_x \subseteq C(\overline{Y}^{\tau})$. Now (by Theorem 3.3) the subspace $|X,\tau_X|$ is completely separable and hence, by Theorem 4.19, it is a Lindelöf space; it follows from above that $\exists$ a sequence $\{x_i\}$ of members of X such that $\{G_{x_i}\}$,

$i \geqslant 1$, forms a τ-open covering of X. Then:

$$\overline{G}^{\tau}_{x_i} \cap \overline{Y}^{\tau} = \varnothing \quad \text{for} \quad i \geqslant 1. \tag{1}$$

Similarly $\exists$ a sequence $\{y_i\}$ of members of Y and a sequence $\{H_{y_i}\}$ of corresponding τ-open sets such that $\{H_{y_i}\}$ covers Y and:

$$\overline{H}^{\tau}_{y_i} \cap \overline{X}^{\tau} = \varnothing \quad \text{for} \quad i \geqslant 1. \tag{2}$$

If, for each $n = 1,2,\ldots$

$$U_n = G_{x_n} \cap (\bigcap_{1 \leqslant i \leqslant n} C(\overline{H}^{\tau}_{y_i})), \qquad V_n = H_{y_n} \cap (\bigcap_{1 \leqslant i \leqslant n} C(\overline{G}^{\tau}_{x_i})),$$

then clearly $U_n, V_n \in \mathscr{G}^{\tau}$ and, further:

(a) for each $n \geqslant 1$, $G_{x_n} \cap \overline{X}^{\tau} \subseteq U_n$ (from (2));

(b) for each $n \geqslant 1$, $H_{y_n} \cap \overline{Y}^{\tau} \subseteq V_n$ (from (1))

and it is easily seen that:

(c) for each $m,n \geqslant 1$, $U_m \cap V_n = \varnothing$.

Then: $$X \subseteq (\bigcup_{n \geqslant 1} G_{x_n}) \cap \overline{X}^{\tau} \subseteq \bigcup_{n \geqslant 1} U_n \equiv G_1 \in \mathscr{G}^{\tau} \quad \text{by (a).}$$

Similarly, by (b), $Y \subseteq \bigcup_{n \geqslant 1} V_n \equiv G_2 \in \mathscr{G}^{\tau}$, and, by (c), $G_1 \cap G_2 = \varnothing$.

5.5 Metrizability

The chief aim of this section is to establish conditions on a given topological space $|S,\tau|$ which will be *sufficient* (Cf. Note 12 below) to enable a metric ρ to be defined on S such that the subset $\mathscr{G}_{\rho}$ of $P(S)$ (in the notation of Note 1, Chapter 4) should coincide with $\mathscr{G}^{\tau}$. As a basis for the construction of a suitable metric, we first prove:

THEOREM 5.28 ('Urysohn's Lemma') A space $|S,\tau|$ satisfies condition P_4, part (ii) (of Definition 5) if and only if, given non-null disjoint τ-closed subsets X,Y of S, there exists a (τ,τ^{ρ_1})-continuous function f from S into R such that:

(a) $f(S) \subseteq [0,1]$ (b) $f(X) = (0)$ (c) $f(Y) = (1)$.

PROOF Given that $|S,\tau|$ satisfies condition P_4(ii), we shall associate with each number r of the form $k/2^n$ (where $k = 0,1,\ldots,2^n$; $n = 1,2,\ldots$) a τ-open subset $G(r)$ of S by the following construction: Write $G(1) = C(Y)$. If G,G' are disjoint τ-open sets such that $X \subseteq G$, $Y \subseteq G'$, write $G(0) = G$. Then $X \subseteq G(0)$ and $\overline{G(0)}^{\tau} \subseteq C(G') \subseteq C(Y) = G(1)$. Hence $X_1 \equiv \overline{G(0)}^{\tau}$, $Y_1 \equiv C(G(1))$ are disjoint

τ-closed sets, so that (again by P_4(ii)) $\exists$ disjoint τ-open sets G_1, G'_1 such that $X_1 \subseteq G_1$, $Y_1 \subseteq G'_1$. Then if $G(\frac{1}{2}) = G_1$, it follows as above that: $X \subseteq G(0) \subseteq \overline{G(0)}^\tau \subseteq G(\frac{1}{2})$ *and* $\overline{G(\frac{1}{2})}^\tau \subseteq G(1)$.

This process can be continued to construct recursively τ-open sets $G(k/2^n)$ (for $k = 0,1,\ldots,2^n$; $n = 1,2,\ldots$) as follows:

Given $n \geqslant 2$, suppose that the $2^{n-1} + 1$ τ-open sets $G(0)$, $G(1/2^{n-1}),\ldots,G(1)$, have been constructed so that $X \subseteq G(0)$ and, for $k = 0,1,2,\ldots,2^{n-1} - 1$:

$$\overline{G(k/2^{n-1})}^\tau \subseteq G((k+1)/2^{n-1}). \tag{1}$$

For each $k = 0,1,\ldots,2^{n-1} - 1$,

$$X_k \equiv \overline{G(k/2^{n-1})}^\tau, \qquad Y_k \equiv C(G((k+1)/2^{n-1}))$$

are, by (1), disjoint τ-closed sets and so by P_4(ii) $\exists$ disjoint τ-open sets G_k, G'_k with $X_k \subseteq G_k$, $Y_k \subseteq G'_k$. If $G((2k+1)/2^n)$ is set equal to G_k, it follows as before that:

$$\overline{G(k/2^{n-1})}^\tau \subseteq G((2k+1)/2^n) \subseteq \overline{G((2k+1)/2^n)}^\tau \subseteq G((k+1)/2^{n-1}).$$

If this process is carried out for each k in question, we have now obtained the $2^n + 1$ τ-open sets $G(0), G(1/2^n),\ldots,G(1)$ with $\overline{G(k/2^n)}^\tau \subseteq G((k+1)/2^n)$ for $k = 0,1,\ldots,2^{n-1}$; that is, (1) holds with $(n-1)$ replaced by n. Thus, to every number r of the form $k/2^n$ there corresponds a τ-open set $G(r)$ such that for $n = 1,2,\ldots$, $k = 0,1,2,\ldots,2^n - 1$:

$$X \subseteq G(0) \quad \text{and} \quad \overline{G(k/2^n)}^\tau \subseteq G((k+1)/2^n). \tag{2}$$

Now define a function f from S into R: given $x \in Y$, let $f(x) = 1$; if, on the other hand, $x \in C(Y)$, then $x \in G(1)$, so that the set A_x of numbers of the form $k/2^n$ ($n = 1,2,\ldots$; $k = 0,1,\ldots,2^n$) such that $x \in G(k/2^n)$, is non-empty and is bounded below (by 0); write $f(x) = \inf A_x$. Since $X \subseteq G(0)$, f clearly satisfies requirements (a)–(c) so that it remains to verify that it is continuous. Given x_0 in S and $\varepsilon > 0$, consider three cases:

Case I $f(x_0) = 0$. Choose a positive integer m such that $1/2^m < \varepsilon$. Then, since $x \in C(Y)$, $\inf A_{x_0} = 0 < 1/2^m$, so that $\exists$ integers n,k $(0 \leqslant k \leqslant 2^n)$ such that $k/2^n < 1/2^m$ and $k/2^n \in A_{x_0}$, that is, $x_0 \in G(1/2^m)$. On the other hand, if x is any member of $G(1/2^m)$, $0 \leqslant f(x) = \inf A_x \leqslant 1/2^m$; that is, $f(x) \in N_\varepsilon^{\rho_1}(f(x_0))$.

Case II $f(x_0) = 1$. Choose m as in Case I and write

$$G = C(\overline{G((2^m - 1)/2^m)^\tau}) \in \mathscr{G}^\tau.$$

Then $x_0 \in G$, since, *otherwise*, $x_0 \in G((2^{m+1} - 1)/2^{m+1})$ which, by the definition of $f(x_0)$, would imply $f(x_0) \leqslant (2^{m+1} - 1)/2^{m+1} < 1$. On the other hand, if $x \in G$, it is clear that $x \omega G(k/2^n)$ for any number $k/2^n < (2^m - 1)/2^m$, and hence: $f(x) \geqslant (2^m - 1)/2^m > 1 - \varepsilon$; that is, $f(x) \in N_\varepsilon^{\rho_1}(f(x_0))$.

Case III $0 < f(x_0) < 1$. Choose positive integers n,k such that $1/2^{n-1} < \varepsilon$ and $k/2^n < f(x_0) < (k + 1)/2^n < 1$. If $G' = G((k + 1)/2^n) \cap C(\overline{G((k - 1)/2^n)^\tau}) \in \mathscr{G}^\tau$, then $x_0 \in G'$, since $f(x_0) > k/2^n$ implies $x_0 \omega G(k/2^n)$, and hence $x_0 \omega G((k - 1)/2^n)$, while $f(x_0) < (k + 1)/2^n$ implies $x_0 \in G((k + 1)/2^n)$. On the other hand, if $x \in G'$,

$$x \in G'((k + 1)/2^n)$$

implies $f(x) \leqslant (k + 1)/2^n$, while $x \, \omega \, G((k - 1)/2^n)$ implies $f(x) \geqslant (k - 1)/2^n$; that is, $f(x) \in]f(x_0) - \varepsilon, f(x_0) + \varepsilon[= N_\varepsilon^{\rho_1}(f(x_0))$.

Conversely, if X,Y are given disjoint non-null τ-closed subsets of S, and f exists as in the enunciation of the theorem, then clearly $G \equiv f^{-1}\{]-\frac{1}{2},\frac{1}{2}[\}$ and $G' \equiv f^{-1}\{]\frac{1}{2},\frac{3}{2}[\}$ fulfil the requirements of condition P_4(ii).

THEOREM 5.29 If $|S,\tau|$ is normal and completely separable, it is metrizable.

PROOF We have to show that a metric ρ can be defined on S such that, given $X \subseteq S$:

$X \in \mathscr{G}^\tau$ if and only if for each x in X, $\exists \, \varepsilon > 0$ with $N_\varepsilon^\rho(x) \subseteq X$ (1)

If $\{G_n\}$, $n \geqslant 1$, is an (enumerable) τ-base on S, then corresponding to each n and member x of G_n, $\exists$ by Theorem 5.21, Corollary, a member G of $\mathscr{G}^\tau$ such that $x \in G$ and $\bar{G}^\tau \subseteq G_n$; further (by Theorem 4.7) $\exists$ integer m such that $x \in G_m \subseteq G$, implying: $\bar{G}_m^\tau \subseteq G_n$. It follows that if the members of the (clearly enumerable) set of all pairs $\{G_m,G_n\}$ with $\bar{G}_m^\tau \subseteq G_n$ are enumerated as: $\{G_{m_i},G_{n_i}\}$, $i \geqslant 1$, then, for each integer n and x in G_n, $\exists$ (at least one) i such that:

$$n_i = n \quad \text{and} \quad x \in G_{m_i} \tag{2}$$

For each $i \geqslant 1$, $\exists$ the two possibilities:

(a) $G_{n_i} \neq S$; (b) $G_{n_i} = S$. In the first case, since $\bar{G}_{m_i}^\tau, C(G_{n_i})$ are non-null disjoint τ-closed, $\exists$ (by Theorem 5.28) a (τ,τ^{ρ_1})-continuous function f_i from S into R such that: $f_i(S) \subseteq [0,1]$, $f_i(\bar{G}_{m_i}^\tau) = (0)$, $f_i(C(G_{n_i})) = (1)$. In the second case, let $f_i(x) = 0$ for *every* x in S;

again f_i is continuous. Then a function ρ from $S \times S$ into R can be defined by writing: for each x,y in S,

$$\rho(x,y) = \left[\sum_{i=1}^{\infty} 2^{-2i+2}(f_i(x) - f_i(y))^2 \right]^{\frac{1}{2}}$$

which clearly satisfies conditions M1–3 to be a metric on S. Further $\rho(x,y) = 0$ if $x = y$; to prove the converse of this (and thus to verify M4), suppose that x,y are distinct elements of S; then (since $|S,\tau|$ satisfies P_4(i)) $\exists\, G'$ in $\mathscr{G}^\tau$ such that $x \in G'$, $y\, \omega\, G'$. If n is chosen so that $x \in G_n \subseteq G'$, it follows from (2) that $\exists$ integer i such that $G_{n_i} \subseteq G'$ and $x \in G_{m_i}$. Since $y\, \omega\, G'$, $y \in C(G_{n_i})$ and so $f_i(x) - f_i(y) = -1$, implying $\rho(x,y) > 0$.

It remains to verify that (1) holds for the metric ρ so constructed on S. If, first, X is given in $\mathscr{G}^\tau$ and $x \in X$, then (as above) an integer i can be chosen such that $G_{n_i} \subseteq X$ and $x \in G_{m_i}$; (supposing $X \subset S$) $f_i(x) = 0$ while $f_i(y) = 1$ for each member y of $C(G_{n_i})$. Then $N^\rho_\varepsilon(x) \subseteq X$ if $\varepsilon = 2^{1-i}$; for if $y \in C(X) \subseteq C(G_{n_i})$, then:

$$\rho(x,y) \geqslant \frac{|f_i(x) - f_i(y)|}{2^{i-1}} = 2^{1-i}.$$

Suppose, *conversely*, that X is a given subset of S such that there corresponds to each member x of X a number $\varepsilon > 0$ with $N^\rho_\varepsilon(x) \subseteq X$. Given x in X and corresponding $\varepsilon > 0$, choose a positive integer r such that: $2^{-r} < \frac{1}{2}\varepsilon$. (3)

Then, given $i \geqslant 1$, the continuity of f_i implies the existence of a member Y_i of $\mathscr{N}^\tau(x)$ such that:

$$|f_i(x) - f_i(y)| < \varepsilon/2r \quad \text{for each } y \text{ in } Y_i. \tag{4}$$

If $Y = \bigcap_{1 \leqslant i \leqslant r} Y_i$, $Y \in \mathscr{N}^\tau(x)$ and, from (4):

$$|f_i(x) - f_i(y)| < \varepsilon/2r \quad \text{for } 1 \leqslant i \leqslant r \quad \text{and } y \text{ in } Y. \tag{5}$$

Then, for y in Y:

$$\begin{aligned}[\rho(x,y)]^2 &\leqslant \sum_{i=1}^{r} 2^{-2i+2}(f_i(x) - f_i(y))^2 + \sum_{i=r+1}^{\infty} 2^{-2i+2} \\ &< r(\varepsilon/2r)^2 + \tfrac{4}{3}2^{-2r} \quad \text{by (5)} \\ &< \varepsilon^2 \quad \text{by (3)}.\end{aligned}$$

Thus $Y \subseteq N^\rho_\varepsilon(x) \subseteq X$, implying $X \in \mathscr{N}^\tau(x)$. Since x is an arbitrary member of X, it follows from Theorem 4.1 that $X \in \mathscr{G}^\tau$.

By Theorem 5.27, it is immediate that the conditions in the above theorem can be weakened to give:

THEOREM 5.30 If $|S,\tau|$ is *regular* and completely separable, it is metrizable.

Note 10 A small modification of the argument of Theorem 5.29 would serve to show that, if $|S',\tau'|$ denotes the topological space to which Hilbert space H^∞ gives rise, then the function f from S into S' defined as follows: for $x \in S$, $f(x) = \{f_1(x), 2^{-1}f_2(x), 2^{-2}f_3(x), \ldots\} \in S'$, would yield a homeomorphic imbedding of $|S,\tau|$ into $|S',\tau'|$. It is easily deduced that a given *metric* space (S,ρ) is separable if and only if it can be homeomorphically imbedded in H^∞.

Note 11 In Theorem 5.30 the condition that $|S,\tau|$ be regular cannot be weakened to that that it be a T_2-space.

Example 5.5.1 If S denotes the closed interval $[0,1]$ of the real numbers, define a function σ^τ from S into $P(P(S))$ as follows: If $x \neq 0$, $X \in \sigma^\tau(x)$ if and only if $\exists\, \varepsilon > 0$ such that

$$]x - \varepsilon, x + \varepsilon[\cap S \subseteq X,$$

while $X \in \sigma^\tau(0)$ if and only if

$$[0,\varepsilon[\cap C_S(\bigcup_{i \geqslant 1} (i^{-1})) \subseteq X \quad \text{for some } \varepsilon > 0.$$

It can be verified that a topology τ is thereby defined on S such that $|S,\tau|$ is a completely separable T_2-space. However it is *not* a T_3-space for, if $C_S(\bigcup_{i \geqslant 1} (i^{-1}))$ is denoted by G, then although $G \in \mathcal{N}^\tau(0)$, $\exists$ *no* member of G' of $\mathcal{G}^\tau$ containing 0 and such that $\overline{G'}^\tau \subseteq G$. For if $0 \in G' \in \mathcal{G}^\tau$, and ε_1 is chosen so that $[0,\varepsilon_1[\cap G \subseteq G'$, write $x = i_1^{-1}$, where i_1 is a positive integer such that $i_1^{-1} < \varepsilon_1$. Then, for any $\varepsilon > 0$, the open interval $]x - \varepsilon, x + \varepsilon[$ of R contains points of G'; that is, $X \cap G' \neq \varnothing$ for each X in $\mathcal{N}^\tau(x)$. Thus although $x\, \omega\, G$, $x \in \overline{G'}^\tau$, and so $|S,\tau|$ is not regular and thus cannot be metrizable.

Note 12 As shown by Example 3.1.5 (and more trivially by any non-enumerable discrete space), the conditions given in Theorem 5.30 are *not* necessary for the metrizability of $|S,\tau|$. The solution of the problem of replacing the condition of complete separability by one which, together with that of regularity, will be both necessary and sufficient for the metrizability of $|S,\tau|$, has been but fairly recently obtained, and is outside the scope of the present work. It perhaps suffices here just to state such a suitable condition. If $|S,\tau|$ is a given topological space, a subset $\mathscr{S}$ of $P(S)$ is said to be a **locally finite** τ-system on S when, for each element x of S, there exists a τ-neighbourhood X of x such that $X \cap Y \neq \varnothing$ for only a finite set of members Y of $\mathscr{S}$. Then it can be proved (e.g., Kelley, pp. 126–9, Reference [6]) that $|S,\tau|$ is metrizable if and only if $|S,\tau|$ is regular and there exists a sequence of locally finite τ-systems on S whose union constitutes a τ-base on S.

Worked Exercises

1. Given a non-null set S, let T_S'' denote the subset of T_S containing those members τ such that $|S,\tau|$ is a T_2-space. Show that if $\exists$ a member τ' of T_S'' such that $|S,\tau'|$ is compact, then τ' is minimal in T_S''.
Solution: Suppose τ is any member of T_S'' with $\tau \leqslant \tau'$. (1)

In Theorem 3.19, take $S' = S$, and f as the identity function on S. If τ_1 denotes the product topology of τ,τ, and τ'' the product topology of τ,τ', then it follows from Theorem 5.10 that $\Delta_S \in \mathscr{F}^{\tau_1} \subseteq \mathscr{F}^{\tau''}$, by (1). Hence (by the first cited theorem) f is (τ,τ')-continuous; that is $\mathscr{G}^{\tau'} \subseteq \mathscr{G}^{\tau}$, and so $\tau = \tau'$.

2. Prove the following improvement (for T_2-spaces) on Theorem 3.23: If $|S,\tau|$ is a locally compact T_2-space, then any *locally* closed non-null subset X of S is locally compact.
Solution: Given x in X, $\exists\, Z$ in $\mathscr{N}^\tau(x)$ such that $X \cap Z \in \mathscr{F}_Z$. Then, by Theorems 5.23, 5.21, $\exists\, Y$ in $\mathscr{N}^\tau(x)$ such that $\bar{Y}^\tau \subseteq Z$. But, in turn, it follows from Theorem 3.22(c) that $\exists$ a member G of $\mathscr{G}^\tau$ such that $x \in G \subseteq Y$, and $\bar{G}^\tau$ is compact. Hence $\exists$ a *compact* member $W \equiv \bar{G}^\tau$ of $\mathscr{N}^\tau(x)$ such that $W \subseteq Z$. Then, since $X \cap Z \in \mathscr{F}_Z$, $(X \cap Z) \cap W \in \mathscr{F}_W$; that is, $W \cap X \in \mathscr{F}_W$. Thus, $\mathscr{N}_X(x)$ contains a member $W \cap X$, which is clearly compact. Since the property of being a T_2-space is hereditary, the required conclusion follows from Note 8.

Exercises for Solution

1. $|S,\tau|$ is any T_0-space such that the intersection of an arbitrary family of members of $\mathscr{G}^\tau$ is τ-open. Show that a partial order $\leqslant$ can be defined on S such that τ is identical with the first of the topologies defined in Example 4.2.1. Deduce that, for *any* T_0-space $|S,\tau|$, no finite subset of S can be τ-dense-in-itself, and hence show (using Zorn's Lemma of Part I) that if $|S,\tau|$ is any T_0-space where every non-null member G of

$\mathcal{G}^\tau$ is infinite, then $\exists$ a topology τ' on S such that:

(a) $\tau \leqslant \tau'$;

(b) τ' is maximal in D_S (see Worked Ex. 1 in Chapter 4).

2. Deduce from the second part of the above exercise that if $|S,\tau|$ is a *resolvable* T_0-space (see Worked Ex. on Section 2.5), then every non-null member of $\mathcal{G}^\tau$ is infinite.

3. Show that if a T_1-space $|S,\tau|$ satisfies the first axiom (of countability), then $|S,\tau|$ is sequentially compact if and only if it is countably compact.

4. If $|S,\tau|$ is a T_1-space and X a connected subset of S with more than one element, show that X is τ-dense-in-itself and deduce that it must therefore be infinite.

5. Let S be a non-null set such that, for some finite subset $\mathscr{A}$ of $P(S)$, the topology τ generated by $\mathscr{A}$ yields a T_1-space. Show that S itself must be finite.

6. If $|S,\tau|$ is a T_1-space such that the intersection of any family of members of $\mathcal{G}^\tau$ is τ-open, show that τ must be discrete.

7. $|S,\tau|$ is a T_2-space. If $\mathscr{H}$ is the subset of $P(S)$ containing all sets $C_S(X)$, where X is enumerable and $\overline{X}^\tau - X$ is finite, let τ' be the topology on S generated by $\mathcal{G}^\tau \cup \mathscr{H}$. Show that a τ'-convergent sequence can only contain a finite number of distinct terms and that, *unless* $|S,\tau'|$ is discrete, it does *not* satisfy the First Axiom. (Cf. Example 4.1.3.)

8. Let $|S,\tau|$ be a T_2-space such that each element x of S possesses a local τ-base, each member of which belongs to both $\mathcal{G}^\tau$ and $\mathscr{F}^\tau$. If $X \subseteq A \subseteq S$, where X is compact and belongs to $\mathcal{G}_A \cap \mathscr{F}_A$, show that $\exists$ a member B of $\mathcal{G}^\tau \cap \mathscr{F}^\tau$ such that $B \cap A = X$.

9. If $|S,\tau|$ is a T_2-space, is the same true of the space $|T,\tau'|$ constructed in Example 4.2.3?

10. Given a space $|S,\tau|$, show *directly* (that is, *without* using Theorems 5.16, 5.17) that if $\exists$ a compact T_2-space $|S',\tau'|$ such that $|S,\tau|$ is a subspace of $|S',\tau'|$ and $S' - S$ contains just one element, then $|S,\tau|$ is locally compact.

11. A T_2-space $|S,\tau|$ is said to be **semi-compact** if it possesses the (equivalent) properties given in Ex. 4 on Section 4.7. Show that:

(a) a sequence $\{x_i\}$ of a semi-compact space is τ-convergent if and only if the set $\bigcap_{n\geqslant 1} (\overline{\bigcup_{i\geqslant n} (x_i)}^\tau)$ has just one member;

(b) a semi-compact space, which satisfies the first axiom, is sequentially-compact and regular.

12. If $S = (a,b,c)$, $S' = (a',b',c')$, $\mathcal{G}^\tau = (S,\varnothing,(a,b),c)$, and τ' is the discrete topology on S', show (by considering compactness) that $\exists$ *no* (τ,τ')-continuous (1,1) function from S onto S'.

13. Show that, if a space $|S,\tau|$ satisfies condition P_3(ii), and is such that each non-null member G of $\mathcal{G}^\tau$ has the Lindelöf property, then $\mathscr{F}^\tau \subseteq (\mathcal{G}^\tau)_\delta$.

14. A (T_2-space) $|S,\tau|$ is said to be **absolutely closed** if, whenever $|S,\tau|$ is homeomorphically imbedded in a T_2-space $|S',\tau'|$, S is a τ'-closed subset of S'. For any T_2-space $|S,\tau|$, show that the following three statements are equivalent:

(a) $|S,\tau|$ is compact;
(b) $|S,\tau|$ is locally compact and absolutely closed;
(c) $|S,\tau|$ is regular, and any τ-open covering of S contains a finite sub-family, the τ-closures of whose members form a covering of S.

15. If $|S,\tau|$ is a regular space such that S can be covered by a sequence $\{A_i\}$, $i \geqslant 1$, of compact subsets of S, show that $|S,\tau|$ is completely normal.

16. Show that, for any given space $|S,\tau|$:

(a) $|S,\tau|$ satisfies condition P_3(ii) if and only if each member F of $\mathscr{F}^\tau$ coincides with the intersection of the τ-*closed* neighbourhoods of F.
(b) *if* $|S,\tau|$ satisfies condition P_4(ii), it *also* satisfies P_3(ii) if and only if each member F of $\mathscr{F}^\tau$ coincides with the intersection of *all* the neighbourhoods of F.

[A *neighbourhood* of F is a subset X of S such that $F \subseteq G \subseteq X$ for some τ-open set G.]

17. Given any topological space $|S,\tau|$, and a set T which properly contains S, show that the function χ from $P(T)$ into $P(T)$ such that $\chi(X) = \overline{X}^\tau$ for $X \subseteq S$, and $\chi(X) = T$ otherwise, defines (as in Definition 1″, Chapter 4) a topology τ' on T such that $|T,\tau'|$ is separable, but is *never* a T_1-space.

18. If $|S,\tau|$ satisfies condition P_4, part (ii), and A is a non-null member of $\mathscr{F}^\tau \cap (\mathscr{G}^\tau)_\delta$, show that $\exists$ a (τ,τ^{ρ_1})-continuous function f from S into R such that $A = f^{-1}(0)$. (ρ_1 denotes the usual metric on R.)

19. Show (conversely to Ex. 18) that if a T_2-space $|S,\tau|$ is such that, for each non-empty member A of $\mathscr{F}^\tau$, $\exists$ a function f as in Ex. 18, then $|S,\tau|$ is normal and $\mathscr{F}^\tau \subseteq (\mathscr{G}^\tau)_\delta$.

20. A T_1-space $|S,\tau|$ is said to be **completely regular** if, given x in S and a member X of $\mathscr{N}^\tau(x)$, $\exists$ a (τ,τ^{ρ_1})-continuous function f from S into R such that:

(a) $f(S) \subseteq [0,1]$; (b) $f(x) = 0$; (c) $f(C(X)) = (1)$.

Show that:

(a) any completely regular space is regular;
(b) any normal space is completely regular;
(c) if $|S,\tau|$ is completely regular, X a compact subset of S, and Y a neighbourhood of X (in the sense of Ex. 16), then $\exists$ a (τ,τ^{ρ_1})-continuous function f from S into R satisfying (a) above and such that $f(X) = (1)$, and $f(C(Y)) = (0)$.
(d) if $|S,\tau|$ is completely regular and $a \in S$, then a necessary and sufficient condition that $\exists$ a (τ,τ^{ρ_1})-continuous function f from S into R with $f(a) = 0$ and $f(x) > 0$ elsewhere, is that $\exists$ a sequence $\{X_i\}$, $i \geqslant 1$, of members of $\mathscr{N}^\tau(a)$ such that $(a) = \bigcap_{i \geqslant 1} X_i$;

(e) if $|S,\tau|$ is completely regular, and S is enumerable, then, for each element $x \in S$, $\mathcal{N}^\tau(x) \cap \mathcal{G}^\tau \cap \mathcal{F}^\tau$ constitutes a local τ-base at x.

21. If a T_2-space $|S,\tau|$ is semi-compact (in the sense of Ex. 11) and is completely separable, show that it is metrizable.

References

[1] Apostol, T. M. *Mathematical Analysis*, Addison-Wesley, Reading, U.S.A. (1957).

[2] Hall, D. W. and Spencer, G. L. *Elementary Topology*, Wiley, New York (1955).

[3] Halmos, P. R. *Naive Set Theory*, Van Nostrand, Princeton (1960).

[4] Hocking, J. G. and Young, G. S. *Topology*, Addison-Wesley, Reading, U.S.A. (1961).

[5] Jacobson, N. *Lectures in Abstract Algebra*, Vol. 1, Van Nostrand, Princeton (1951).

[6] Kelley, J. L. *General Topology*, Van Nostrand, Princeton (1955).

[7] Mendelson, B. *Introduction to Topology*, Blackie, London (1963).

[8] Newman, M. H. A. *Elements of the Topology of Plane Sets of Points* (2nd edn.), Cambridge University Press, London (1951).

[9] Rennie, B. 'Lattices', *Proc. Lond. Math. Soc.* (2) **52**, 386–400 (1951).

[10] Rudin, W. *Principles of Mathematical Analysis*, McGraw-Hill, New York (1953).

Index